MENSA PRESENTS

SECRET CODES for KIDS

THIS IS A CARLTON BOOK

This edition published by Carlton Books Limited 1995

A CIP catalogue for this book is available from the British Library

ISBN 0-7475-2678-8

Printed in Italy

MENSA PRESENTS

SECRET CODES for KIDS

Robert Allen

CARLTON

Introduction

Throughout history people have been fascinated by secret codes. The ability to send a message that can be read by your friends but not your enemies has always been highly prized. On many occasions it has been used in deadly earnest. Mary Queen of Scots, for example, lost her head largely because she put her faith in a code that her enemies were able to crack. During the Second World War the cracking of the Nazi's Enigma code by the Allies was a vital step toward victory.

But codes are also fun. In this book we have a number of codes that, at one time, would have carried life-or-death messages and we have turned them into puzzles. To help you there is a Spy School section where you can learn how the codes are constructed and how to crack them. For those who want a real challenge I suggest you try the puzzles before reading Spy School. All the codes can be cracked if you use a little ingenuity and cunning.

If you like puzzles you will like Mensa, a society that exists entirely for people who are adept at solving the knottiest problems. If you would like to take the Mensa test and meet people of like mind, then write to us at British Mensa Limited, Mensa House, St John's Square, Wolverhampton, WV2 4AH, England.

I should like to thank all those who helped with this book, including my wife Doris, and our friend Josie Fulton. Finally I must thank David Ballheimer, a puzzler who edits my outpourings without mercy and saves me from making a fool of myself in public.

R. P. Allen

Robert Allen
Editorial Director
Mensa Publications

Sam Cody's Spy School

HI! I'M SAM CODY and before you try the puzzles in this book I'm going to send you to school. Don't worry, it's not the usual sort of school. This is my very own spy school and I'll be teaching you how to crack secret codes. The rest of the book will contain puzzles that help you test just how much you've learned.

Almost all the codes in the book will be taught in this section but, just to keep you on your toes, there are some puzzles where I've given you no clues at all and you'll have to work them out for yourselves.

WARNING
If you would rather try to crack our codes the hard way don't read on, but go to Page 14.

Let's try something easy first. There are some forms of disguised writing that are not really codes at all but they can still be used to convey secret messages. What do you make of this?

CAHE RWDO SAH TSI TTEERLS XIMDE PU

If you look closely you will see that this is just plain English with the letters rearranged. The message reads: "Each word has its letters mixed up."

There are plenty of other really simple forms of disguised writing. Here is another. It looks strange at first but you will soon see that there is only one small trick involved.

KUST DHANGE YHE BIRST OETTER PF DACH BORD

Double Dutch? No, the words are in plain English but the first letter of each has been replaced with a random letter. The message is: "Just change the first letter of each word." Once you have picked up a few tricks like this you can make up all sorts of secret messages. Try taking all the vowels out of your message like this:

MSSGS WTH N VWLS LK VRY STRNG NTL Y GT TH KNCK F RDNG THM

You should quickly realize that this reads: "Messages with no vowels look very strange until you get the knack of reading them." Let's look at just one more simple trick before we get on to real codes.

What do you think this is all about?

SREDAER LAUSAC LOOF LLIW SDRAWKCAB GNITIRW

Stumped? The message is plain English written backwards. There are hundreds of variations on these tricks. Try removing the vowels *and* writing backward, for example. There are hundreds of different variations on these tricks. The only limit is your own ingenuity.

One of the simplest codes was invented by the Roman emperor Julius Caesar and is known as Caesar's Letter. To use this you need to make a code wheel. It consists of two wheels, one inside the other, with an alphabet written around the edge of each. Start off with all the letters on the outer wheel being next to the same letters on the inner wheel.

Now turn your inner wheel clockwise by just one letter. Already you have a secret code! Now instead of writing A you write B, instead of B you write C, and so on. Using this code a word like DOG would come out as EPH. By setting your wheel to different positions you can create 25 different codes. Try this example (the wheel has been turned so that J on the inner wheel is next to A on the outer):

HXD LJW ANJM CQRB FRCQ NJBN

Answer: "You can read this with ease."

Caesar's letter is what is called a 'substitution code' because it simply substitutes one letter for another. However, you don't have to use letters. How about trying numbers instead?

The very easiest sort of numerical substitution code involves giving letters a value based on their position in the alphabet. Using this code A=1, B=2 and so on until you reach Z=26. Now try working out what this means:

14.21.13.2.5.18.19/ 3.1.14/ 5.1.19.9.12.25/ 2.5/ 3.8.1.14.7.5.4/

9.14.20.15/ 12.5.20.20.5.18.19

"Numbers can easily be changed into letters," reads the message. When you have mastered the principle, you can start to work out variations. The obvious one is to number the alphabet backward.

On the other hand you could start in the middle and number the letters from M to A as 1 to 13, and N to Z as 26 to 14. Or you could give the first half of the alphabet odd numbers (A=1, B=3, C=5, etc) and the second half would have the even numbers (N=2, O=4, P=6, etc). All you need is ingenuity.

Another type of code that can be a lot of fun is the grid. We have included three variations on this theme. The first is the simplest but it is also the most useful as it can be used both in writing and for flashing messages with a light or banging them out on the wall of your prison cell.

	1	2	3	4	5
A	**A**	**B**	**C**	**D**	**E**
B	**F**	**G**	**H**	**I J**	**K**
C	**L**	**M**	**N**	**O**	**P**
D	**Q**	**R**	**S**	**T**	**U**
E	**V**	**W**	**X**	**Y**	**Z**

In the diagram above, you will see that the letters have been written into a 5 x 5 grid (I and J share a space). You can now describe the letters by their coordinates. So instead of A you write A1, B becomes A2, and so on. If you wanted to use this code to beat out a message to a prisoner in the neighbouring cell you would use two sets of thumps with a short pause between them. Thus A would be thump-pause-thump and B would be thump-pause-thump/thump.

Try to decode this message just for practice.

E4.A5.D4/A1.C3.C4.D4.B3.A5.D2/E2.A1.E4/D4.C4/ E2.D2.B4.D4.A5/D3.A5.A3.D2.A5.D4.C1.E4

Did you do it? It reads: "Yet another way to way to write secretly". But you are not finished with this code yet! Why not write the letters into the grid in a different order? Backwards, for example. It really doesn't matter what you do just so long as the person receiving your message knows how to decode it.

A mystical sect called the Rosicrucians are responsible for one of the most interesting grid codes ever devised. The trick with this one is to compose your message by leaving out the letters and drawing the relevant section of the grid. Since each section contains two letters you use the dots to indicate which one you mean.

A Ḃ	C Ḋ	E Ḟ
G Ḣ	I J̇	K L̇
M Ṅ	O Ṗ	Q Ṙ

S Ṫ (top)
U V̇ (left) — W Ẋ (right)
Y Ż (bottom)

People being ingenious, they soon came up with a way to complicate the Rosicrucian grid even further. They altered the grid so that each segment except the last now contained three letters. Then they devised a different way of using dots to select the letters. If you showed a section of grid with no dots, then you were to select the first letter from the left. If you showed one dot you took the second letter from the left. Two dots stood for the third letter from the left.

A Ḃ C̈	D Ė F̈	G Ḣ Ï
J K̇ L̈	M Ṅ Ö	P Q̇ R̈
S Ṫ Ü	V Ẇ Ẍ	Y Ż

Take a look at these messages and see if you can decode them. One uses the basic Rosicrucian code and the other the more elaborate version:

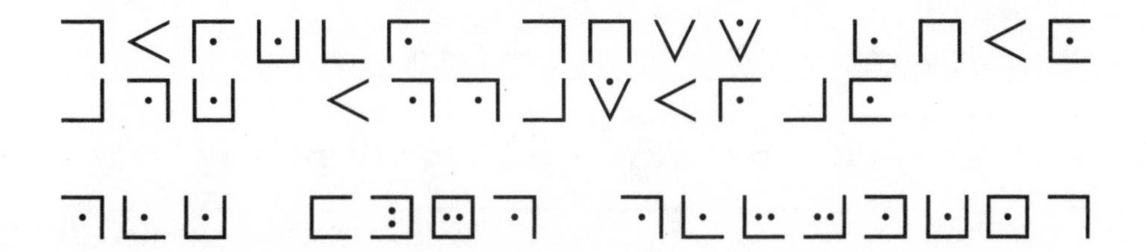

Message 1 reads: "Murder most foul and unnatural." (basic)
Message 2 says: "The plot thickens." (more elaborate)

There are many other forms of coded writing that involve substituting symbols for letters. One of the most interesting was a system that used mystic symbols based on the names of the planets. This was favoured by alchemists who feared that their secret discoveries would be uncovered by a rival. The code would not keep an experienced agent at bay for very long but would outwit most parents and teachers nicely. As it is decorative you could use it for including secret messages within a drawing.

A	B	C	D	E	F	G	H	I	J	K
☉	♃	♄	♆	♅	♁	♀	♂	☿	☾	♉

L	M	N	O	P	Q	R	S	T	U	V
♊	♋	♌	♍	♎	♏	♐	♑	♓	♈	♒

W	X	Y	Z
➢	X	Y	Z

Here is an example for you to work on.

☉♆♆ ♋♅♐♄♈♐Y ☉♌♆ ♓♍☉♆♑
♃♊♍♍♆ ♓♍ ♓♂♅ ♃♐♅➢

The message reads: "Add mercury and toad's blood to the brew."

Morse code, invented by Samuel Morse who telegraphed his first message in 1838, has been widely used to transmit secret information. In the World War II it was a vital aid to members of the Resistance who needed to keep in touch with the Allies. Its system of dots and dashes makes it one of the most adaptable codes in common use.

A	B	C	D	E	F	G	H	I	J	K
.–	–...	–.–.	–..	.	..–.	––.	....	..	.–––	–.–

L	M	N	O	P	Q	R	S	T	U	V
.–..	––	–.	–––	.––.	––.–	.–.	...	–	..–	...–

W	X	Y	Z
.––	–..–	–.––	––..

You can send Morse messages very rapidly by radio, telegraph, flashing lights, sounds, and many other ingenious methods. The code takes very little time to learn (though transmitting and reading at speed are skills that do take time to acquire).

As with other codes it is possible to make changes that will fool an outsider who gets hold of your message. For example, you can exchange dots for dashes and vice versa.

Here is a Morse code message for you to try:

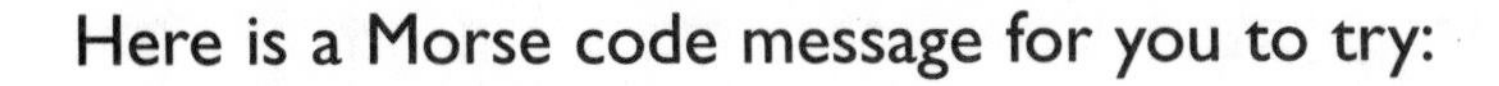

The message reads: "Butch Cassidy spotted in Tucson last Monday."

Another very commonly used code is semaphore, which depends on the sender using flags held at varying angles to represent letters.

The usefulness of semaphore is limited for practical purposes by the fact that the sender needs to be in plain sight of the recipient. This is not a bad way of, for example, sending a message from one ship to another but it is not nearly adaptable enough for espionage work. What does this semaphore message say?

Message reads: "Enemy fleet sighted off the port bow."

Sam Cody's Spy School

Braille, the system of writing devised for blind people, can also be used as an effective code.

A B C D E F G H I J K

L M N O P Q R S T U V

W X Y Z

A system of dots based on a domino layout will allow you to write a message that only initiates will be able to decode. Look out for dots in our puzzles – not all of them are written on dominoes!

Try this message for practice:

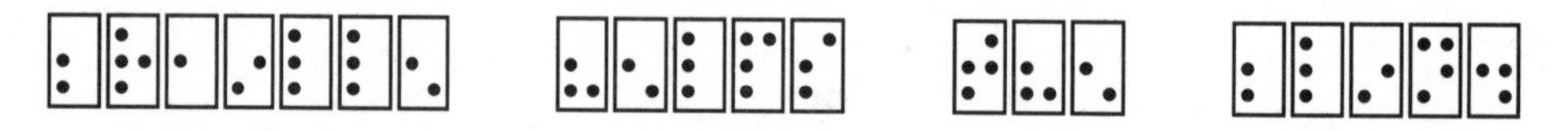

Message reads: "Braille helps the blind."

You can devise symbols of your own to represent letters. Here is a system using differently divided circles.

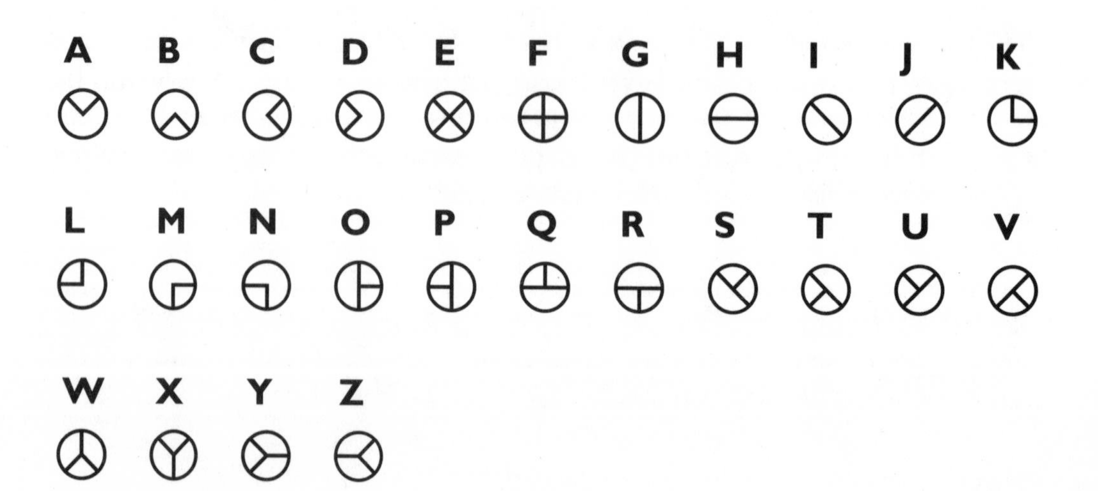

Here is a message using the circle code:

Message reads: "A circular route to understanding."

Finally, here is another code system that was developed for use by the blind. It is called Moon writing after its inventor William Moon.

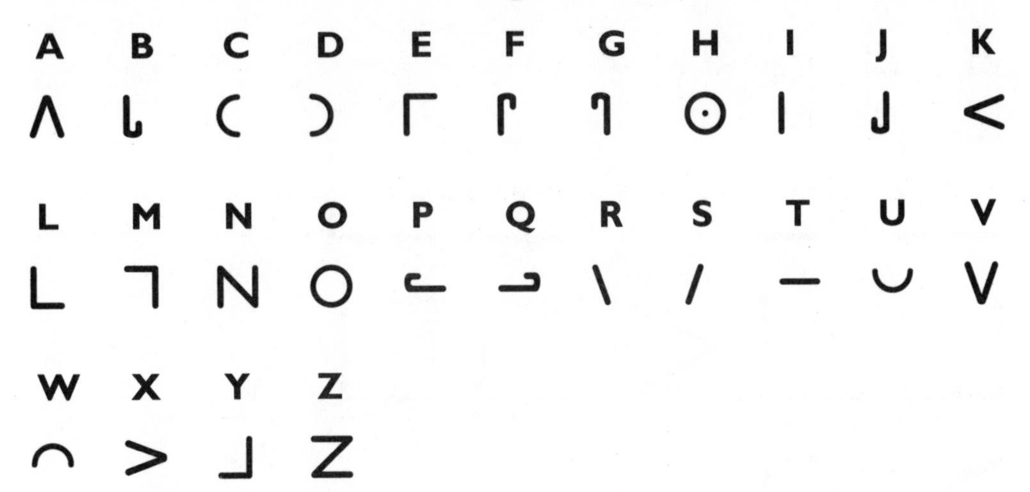

Just like Braille it was intended to be embossed on paper so that a blind person could read it by feeling the bumps with his fingertips.

Here is a Moon message:

Message reads: "You will be over the moon when you read this."

Now you have enough codes to solve all the puzzles in the book. Remember we have sometimes made things just a bit harder by adding variations to the original code. You will need to be on the lookout for tricks and traps.

Templar trouble

Answer Number 28

The mysterious sect of the Knights Templar guards a dread secret. For centuries their members have protected this vital information from prying eyes. However, just one record of their secret exists in written form. You have discovered what you believe is a reference to it in an old book. However, the exact location has been cunningly encoded. Can you work it out?

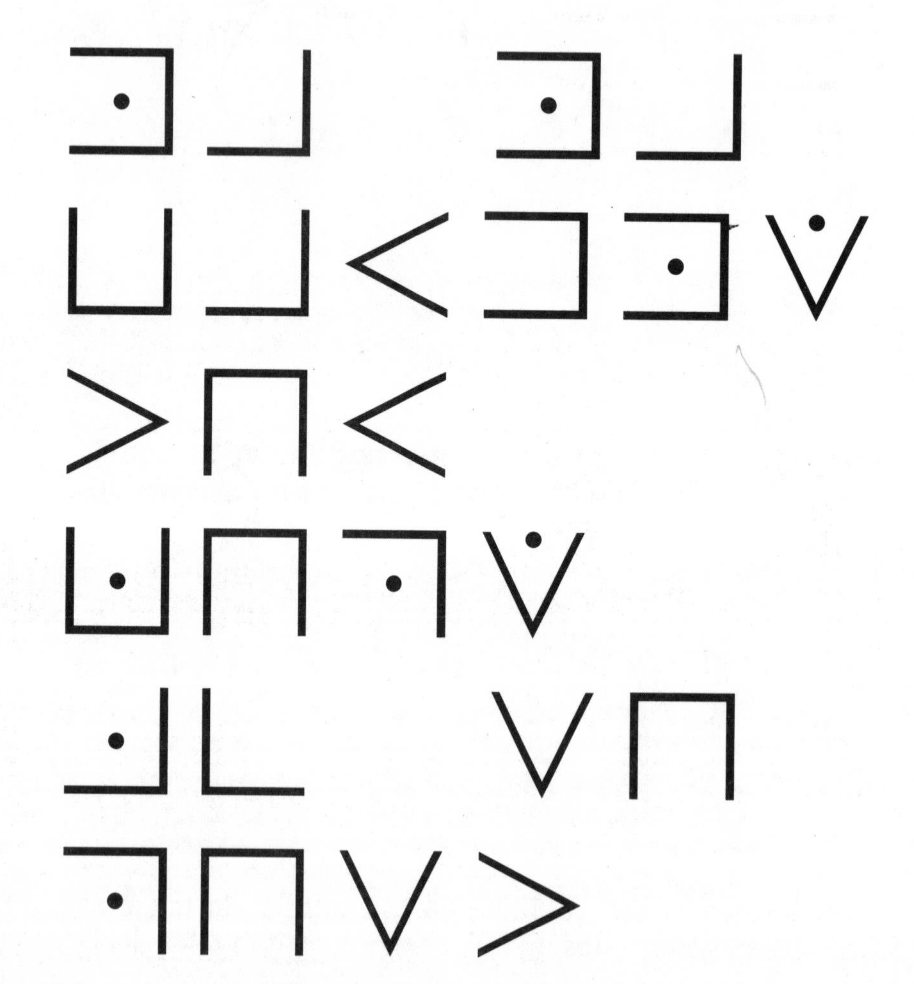

Scout cipher

Answer Number 48

St. Swithin's (Wednesdays) Scout troop have been sent orienteering. The troop leader is not exactly confident he will see any of them again (or sure that he really wants to). However, to give them at least a chance of getting home he has written the following message in chalk on a rock.

Trunk test

Answer Number 85

A trunk containing various anonymous long-lost manuscripts is unearthed in the middle of a farmer's field. Literary experts spend hours toiling over who the author was, but remain completely stumped. A son of one of the experts wanders over to the trunk and absent-mindedly runs his fingers over the mysterious pattern on the lid. His mother is startled when he cries out, "I know the author!" Do you?

Confusing cans

Answer Number 68

Sam went shopping with her bargain-hunting aunt one Saturday morning. They stopped by a basket full of reduced-price cans which had lost their labels, and only had what appeared to be illegible script on their bases. Sam studied the can her aunt had selected and carefully predicted what it would contain. Can you?

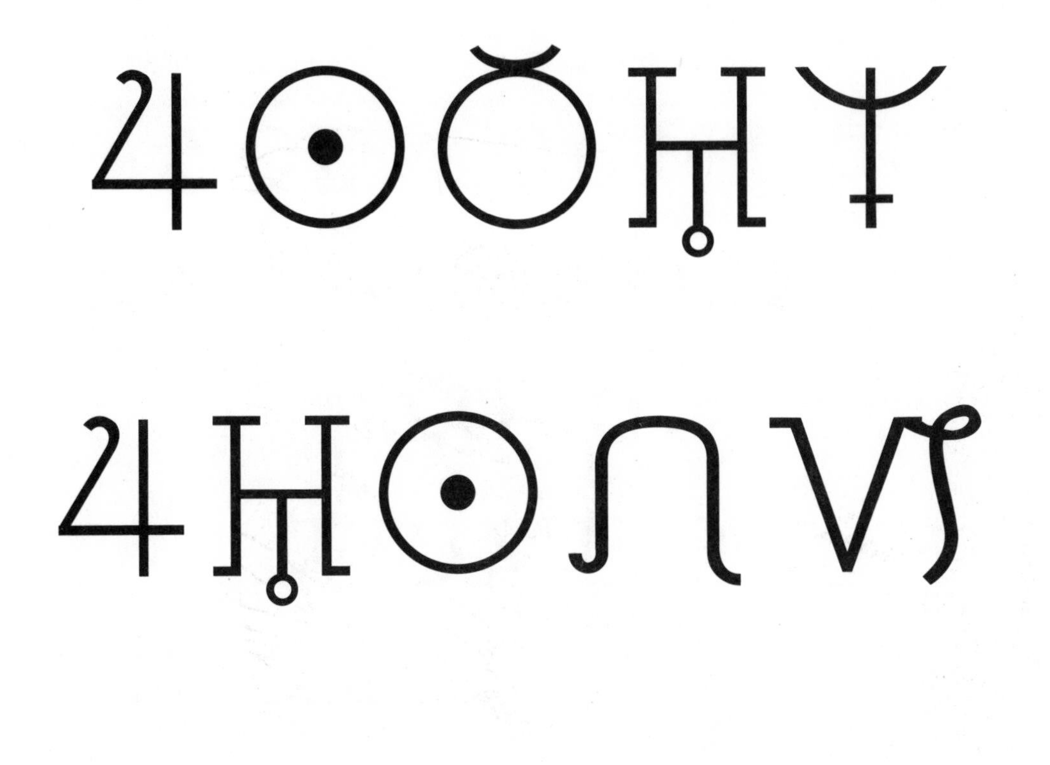

Teacher's travels

Answer Number 17

Class 2B arrive for a history lesson only to discover, to their intense delight, that their teacher, Mr Dullingham, is not at school. However, there is a large message written on the board. They study it with curiosity. Some of the children start to scribble on scraps of paper and then, after a while, they begin to leave the room one by one. What's going on?

U TMHQ NQQZ
OMXXQP MIMK AZ
GDSQZF
NGEUZQEE.
MZKAZQ ITA OMZ
PQOAPQ FTUE YMK
SA TAYQ QMDXK.

Fishy findings

Answer Number 66

Peter Whiting loved to go diving around old wrecks in Highsea Bay. One day, while he was on one of his dives, he came across an old treasure chest buried inside one of the wrecks. The chest was empty but written on the inside of the lid was what seemed to be a foreign language. Peter was intrigued so he brought it up to his boat and began to examine it. Soon he knew the truth and headed straight for shore. What had he discovered? Here is the inscription.

SQDZRTQD HR

ATQHDC HM BZUD ZS

AZRD NE GHFGRDZ

AZX BKHEER

Romans rumbled

Answer Number 1

Professor Potts was excavating a Roman villa when he came across a secret room. He guessed that this might have been a secret gathering place for Christians and when he saw this writing on the wall he was sure his theory was correct. What does it say?

Sam Cody reminds you that the Romans used letters as numbers!

P A 10 5-

O B 1 S 100-

U 1000

Answer Number 29

Janet was going to be in a Shakespeare play at her school. The whole of her family were going to see it but she wouldn't tell them which play it was. However, the family kept on asking her so frequently until finally, in exasperation, she wrote down the last two lines of the play in code, and told them that if they could decipher the code, they would know immediately which play it came from. Can you work it out?

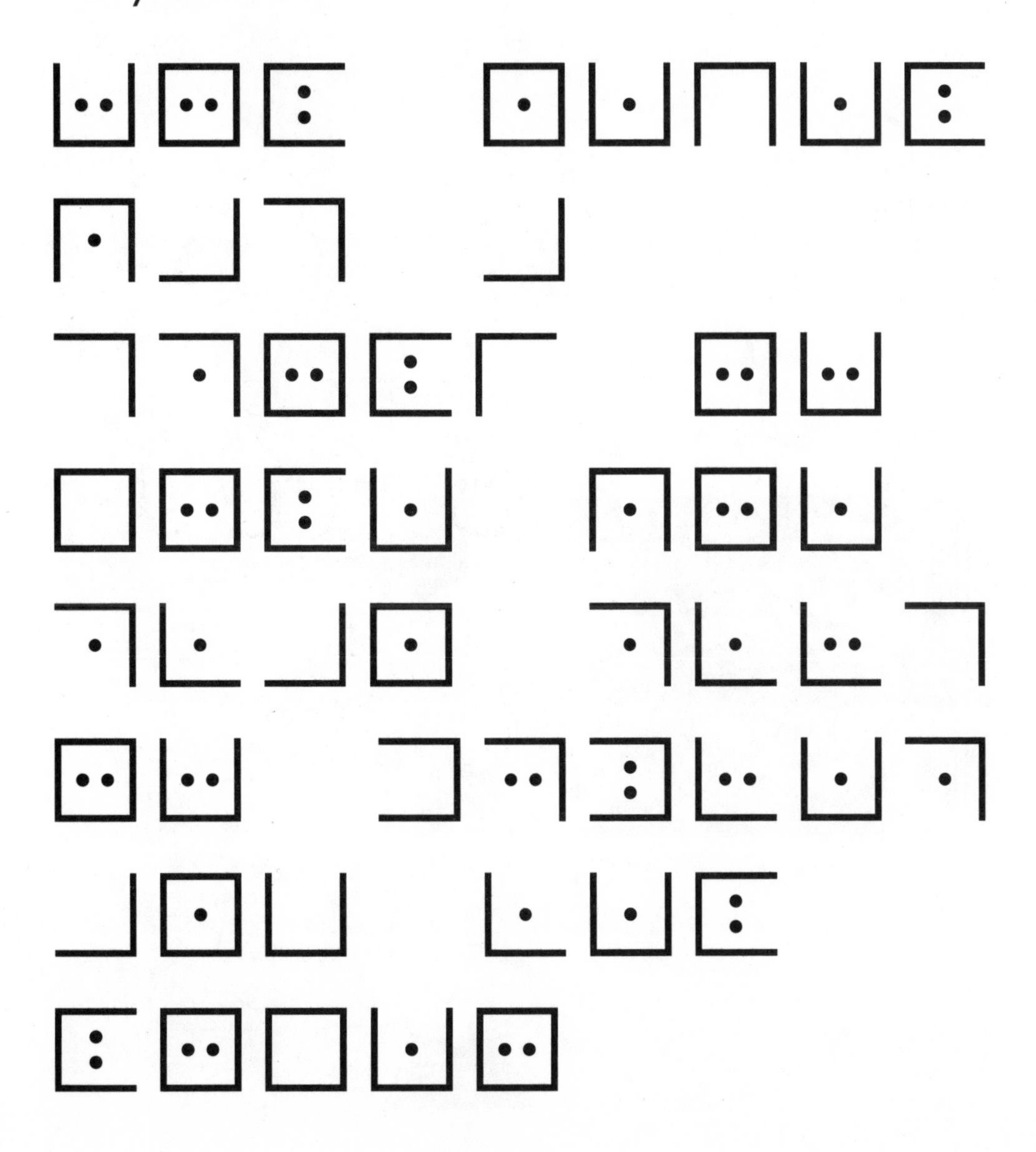

Baffling bard

The test is yet to come

Answer Number 94

Miss McGuckin labels a box containing test papers in code, which appears just to be an abstract pattern, so as to prevent inquisitive eyes from realizing what the box contains, and attempting to find out more. Can you work out what subject the test is for, and when it will be held?

ζ ζγ ζζζ γ ζ

ζγζ

ζζζζ ζζ ζζζ γ

γγγ ζγζ γζγγ

γ ζ ζζζ γ

Answer Number 14

Missing Magnus

Magnus Loot, the newspaper tycoon, couldn't stand the pressure of work one more day. He decided to slip out of the country for a quick break. Naturally he couldn't tell anyone he was going or he would be bombarded with messages the whole time he was away. On the other hand if he were just to disappear there would be a panic to find him. Then he hit upon a plan. He would leave a coded message – not too difficult, just enough to keep them guessing while he made his getaway. This is what his secretary found on his desk:

ONEGO-
THUOT-SFOEN-
CRAFC-ABKRI-
FYAD

Can you work out what Magnus was saying? The code is not at all clever, just a bit mixed up.

PUZZLE 11

Hidden treasure

Answer Number 69

A glossy picture book is published, and creates a great stir as it claims to lead the way to a valuable gold casket covered in diamonds. The race is on to decipher the code which leads to the treasure. Do you know where it can be found?

Muddled matrix

Answer Number 8

Jeff's dad had some slight friction with the tax people over an unpaid bill and had to leave the country rather suddenly. He left his son this note so that he would be able to follow as soon as he was able. At first Jeff thought it was a fiendishly cunning code but, after hours of brain ache, he realized that it wasn't a code at all. It gave his father's route quite plainly! But you have to know where to start.

A	P	O	R	E	U	S
G	H	E	N	S	K	A
N	T	D	A	M	F	R
I	A	R	A	M	R	A
S	T	E	T	S	A	C
K	R	U	F	K	N	H
O	K	G	N	A	B	I

PUZZLE 13

Et tu Brute?

Answer Number 18

Brutus and his fellow conspirators have decided that they have had enough of Julius Caesar. In fact they have clubbed together and bought him a one-way ticket across the River Styx. Brutus has written to Cassius giving him details of their murderous plan. Rather stupidly he has used Caesar's own code (it is the only one he knows). Caesar's agents have obtained a copy of the message. Can you help them crack the code in time?

FN BQJUU BCJK QRV RW CQN OXADV

Answer Number 15

Computer crime

Clive Kilobyte, inventor and computer software manufacturer, was disturbed to find that some of his best commercial secrets were being peddled to his competitors. But how? For weeks he kept watch without discovering anything. Then one day, quite by chance, he spotted a delivery note that was due to be sent out with a new batch of software. The numbers on the docket looked odd. Could they be a code? He tried 1=A but got nowhere. Then suddenly a thought struck him and within minutes he was able to summon the culprit and fire him on the spot. What was the secret?

19.22/19.26.8/26/13.22.4/11.9.12.20.
9.26.14/26.15.14.12.8.7/21.18

13.18.8.19.22.23/18/4.18.15.15/8.22.
13.23/2.12.6/23.22.7.26.18.15.8

26.8.26.11/8.26.14

PUZZLE 15

Desert dilemma

Answer Number 32

You have been wandering through the desert for days and are desperate for water. Suddenly, on the ground you spot four casks that look as if they contain water, but beware, for these casks have been put there by the ancient people of the desert who only reward those who can crack their codes. Those who fail to do so are punished with death. On the outside of each of the four casks is the code. Can you work out which cask is safe to drink from before you perish in the scorching sun?

1.

2.

3.

4.

Card clue

Answer Number 87

Sean received what he believed to be an anonymous Valentine's card, but when he looked at the picture more closely, he discovered a series of symbols which did not seem to fit in with the general design of the card. When one of his friends came round, Sean showed him the card, and was astonished when his friend declared who his secret admirer was. Can you?

Answer Number 59

Dotty digging

For many years archaeologists had admired the exquisite pottery of the Rohoha tribe who had once lived deep in the Amazonian rain forest. Strangely each piece was found to carry the same inscription hidden somewhere within the pattern. What could it mean? Could it be the name of one of their gods, or perhaps some magical formula? No one could decide. Then one day young Dr Marissa Potts was idling away the steamy afternoon hours playing a game of dominoes when the answer suddenly struck her. Can you work it out?

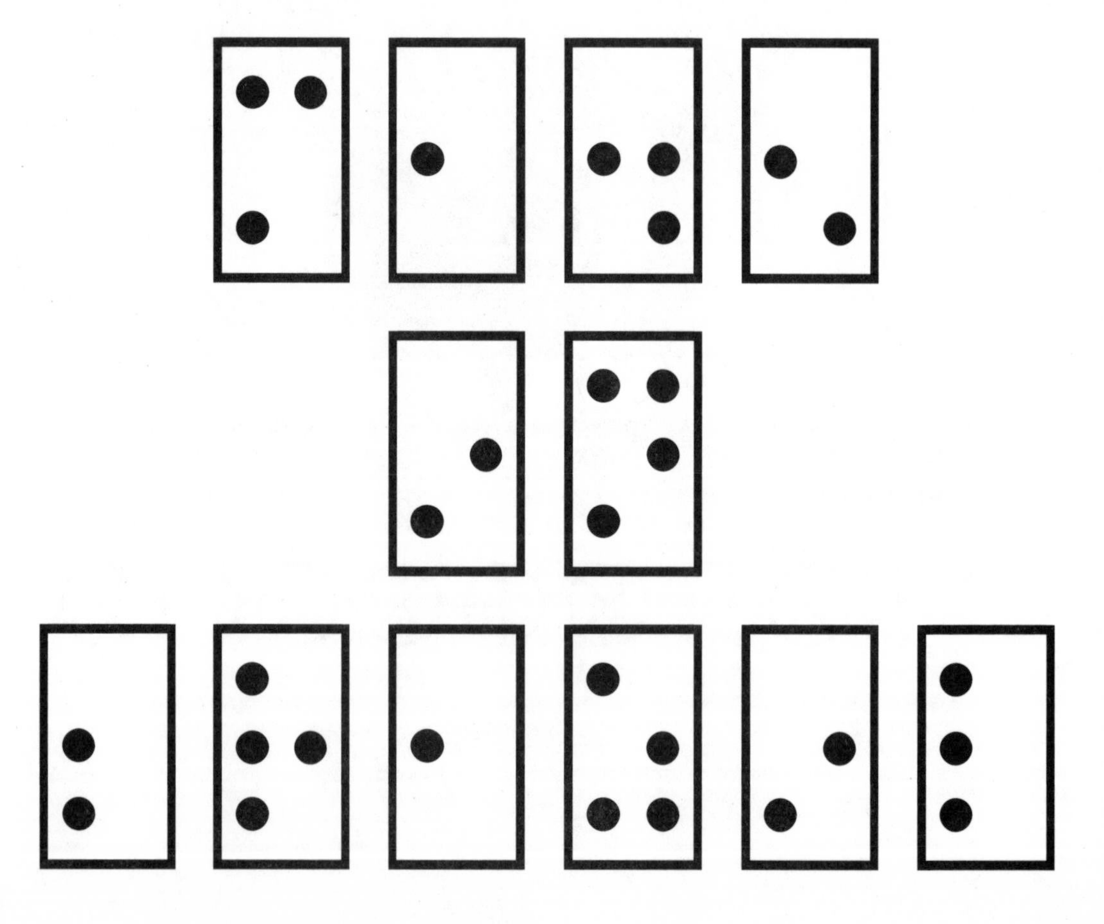

Answer Number 49

You are just sitting watching the latest episode of your favourite police drama, Inspector Bookham, when you notice something very funny about the sound track. There, just below the melody line, is a persistent bleeping that sounds just like Morse code. You quickly jot down as much as you can and then try to decode the message. This is the partial message you have:

Bookham's blues

PUZZLE 19

Much Morsing

Answer Number 50

Ann Tenna is a radio freak. She spends all her spare time up in her bedroom surfing the airwaves. One day she comes across a very strange transmission indeed. Is this someone's idea of a joke, or is it a national disaster? See what you think.

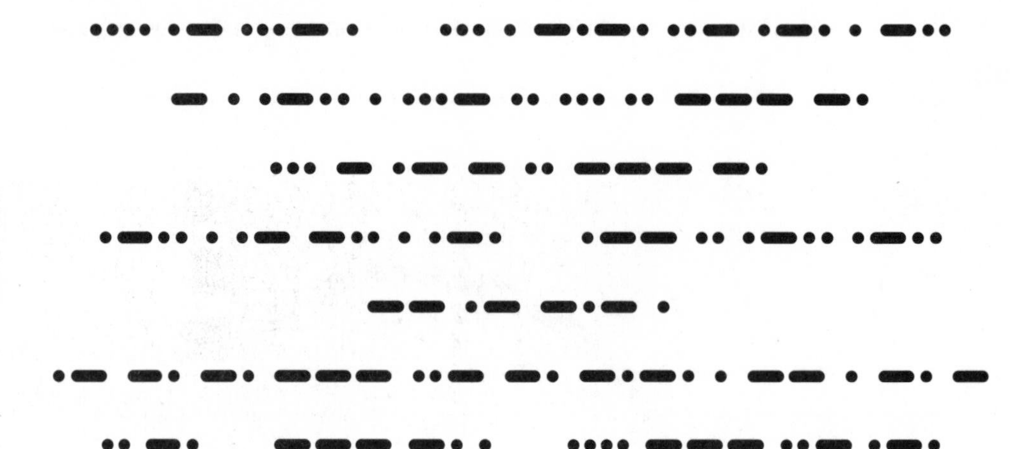

Answer Number 33

Miranda Moneypenny, the famous film star, was being stalked. As all her mail was being read and her phone was tapped, any messages to her had to be written in code. What does this one say?

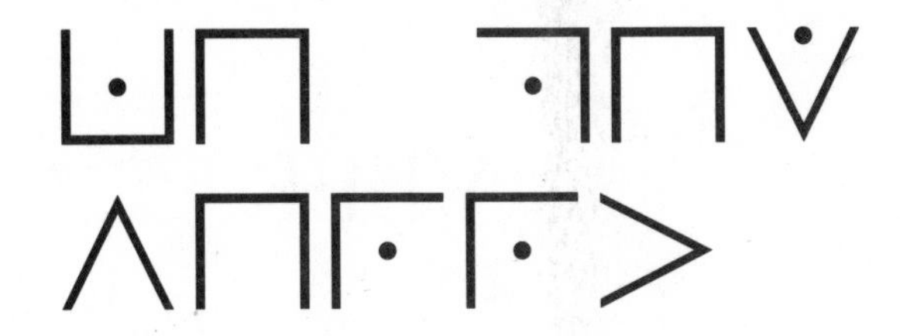

PUZZLE 21

Answer Number 3

Dad in danger

Agent Mucho Macho was on a mission of almost unimaginable danger when he received a message from HQ to say that he had at last become a father. Unable to break the cautious habits of a lifetime he asked his superiors to send his wife this message in code.

OBOE	VEER
MONO	OMEN
SHIN	EYED
BULB	ALLY
DEED	ACTS
KEYS	IBIS

Bolted boxes

Answer Number 75

A local business has a collection of top secret files, all individually labelled in padlocked boxes. To make the theft of any of them troublesome, each label is coded with the subject matter of each document. However one box has been tampered with. According to the code, what does the box contain?

PUZZLE 23

Party pooper

Answer Number 39

Alec Smart decided that he only wanted really clever children like himself at his birthday party. He sent everyone an invitation but put it in code so that only the brightest would know where to go. Unfortunately the code was not as hard to crack as Alec thought. He ended up with 36 guests who had a great time but wouldn't let him join in anything. See if you could have gone to the party. Once you know where to start it's easy.

Sam Cody says that once you get right to the bottom of the puzzle just follow letters that will make words. Beware – sometimes they are spirals, stripes or zigzags. The puzzle may start anywhere.

P	A	W	T	C	O	D	A	E	N
Y	R	O	H	U	M	N	Y	V	E
M	T	L	E	O	E	O	A	T	S
O	Y	L	T	Y	T	M	E	C	A
T	I	O	R	R	O	M	Y	P	L
E	F	F	A	O	F	T	F	E	L
M	Y	O	I	L	I	H	A	V	E
O	O	T	H	G	U	O	N	E	T
C	U	A	R	E	B	R	I	G	H
Y	L	N	O	N	A	C	U	O	Y

Generation game

Answer Number 30

Sam was exploring his grandfather's attic when he came across an old piece of slate with some strange symbols written on it in chalk. He showed it to his grandfather who, after studying it for a while, began to chuckle. He explained to Sam that it was a coded message and part of a game he used to play when he was a child. Can you work out what it says?

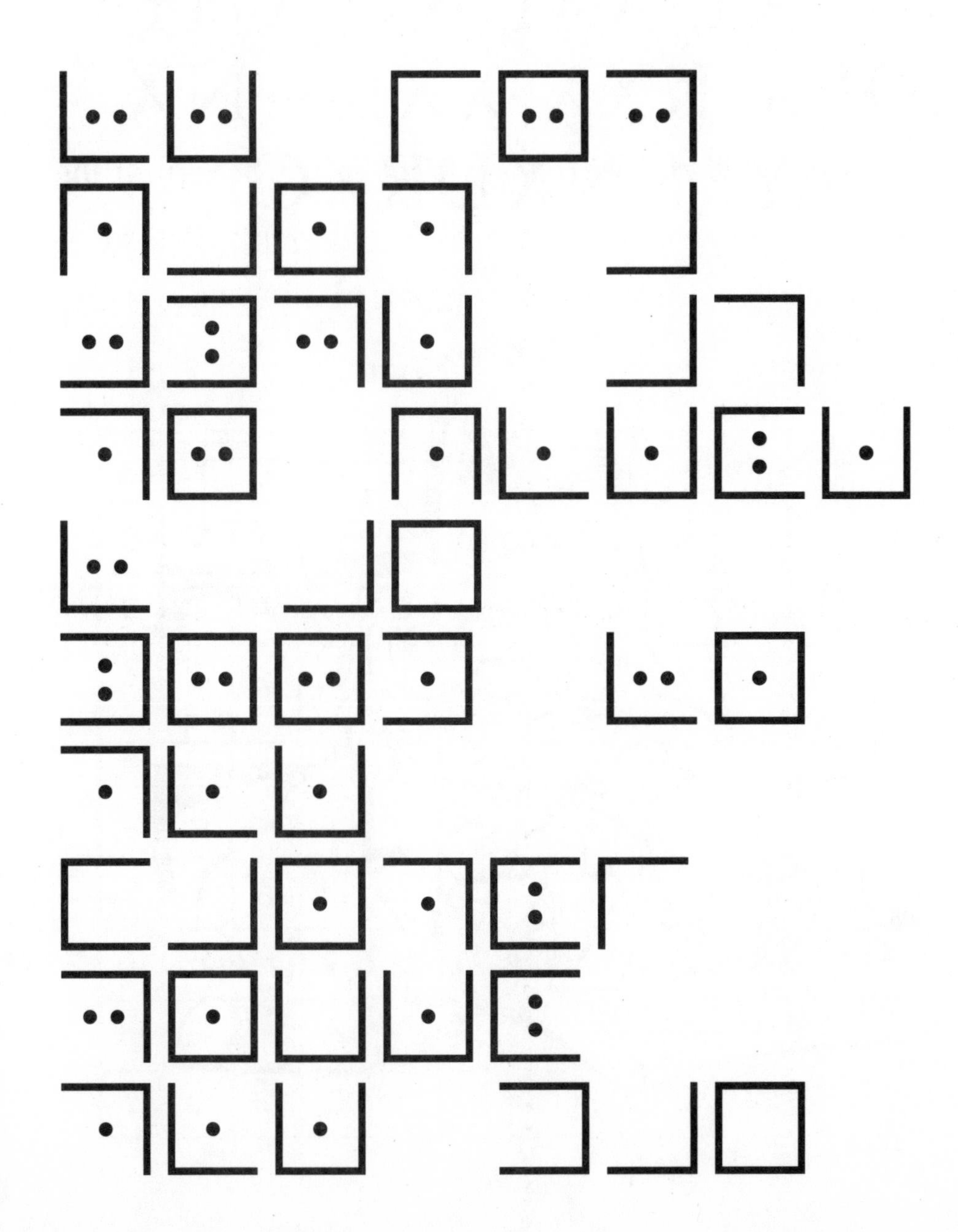

Famous last words

Answer Number 9

Despite being a reformed character, when Ebenezer Scrooge finally died he couldn't resist making it hard for his relatives to get their hands on his wealth. He hid the money and left them this note. Can you work out where the treasure lies hidden?

KXXL RXDNX XHT
DLX KXX XXRT NX
YM NXDRXG

Answer Number 5

Abducted astronaut

Major Mike McQuaid, one of NASA's top astronauts, has been abducted by agents of a foreign power. Days later FBI agents are handed a scrap of paper that a small boy saw thrown from a car speeding from the scene of the kidnap. There is a strange message that appears to be in some sort of number substitution code. They try all the obvious substitutions with no success. Obviously this one is something sneaky. Can you succeed where even the FBI have failed? You might find yourself in the middle of a mystery (hint, hint).

24.18.10.1.14/13.26.6.18.1/13.3
/11.18.22.9.18.13/
12.10.20.18.3.15.13/10.1/11.26.1
.13.26/2.3.1.10.22.26/4.26

A rafty revelation

Answer Number 97

A group of teenagers built themselves a raft during an adventure holiday, and set off excitedly to sail on the huge lake nearby. After several hours on the water, they realised that they had drifted away from their camp, and had no idea how to get back. One lad suddenly noticed movement on the shoreline, and realized that their attention was sought. More movements followed with what appeared to be flags, and the route home suddenly became clear. What message did they receive?

Bridging the gap

Answer Number 34

You are travelling on foot through treacherously rocky terrain when you are confronted with a great, wide canyon – so deep that you can scarcely see the floor of it – which you must cross if you are to go any further. Spanning the canyon are three rope bridges. You must decide which bridge to take, but be careful because choose the wrong one and could find yourself dashed to pieces on the floor of the canyon. Beside each bridge is a coded sign which when decoded, may give you a clue as to which bridge to risk your life on.

1.

2.

3.

Shipping shocker

Answer Number 51

It was Tom Penwithick's last day as a Coastguard. He'd watched the storm-lashed English coast line for over 40 years and now it was time to hang up his binoculars and take a well-earned rest. However, one of the cruellest reaches of sea in the world was not going to let him go without a goodbye to remember. Just as he was about to leave for his farewell party the following message came in over the radio. Tom had one last duty to perform!

... --- ...   ... --- ...

- ....

.-. --- -.-- .- .-..

-.-- .- -.-. .... -

-... .-. .. - .- -. -. .. .-

... .. -. -.- .. -. --.

..-. .- ... -   --. --- -..

... .- ...- .   - .... .

--.- ..- . . -.

Answer Number 60

Bun bonanza

Laura went to her grandma's house every Friday after school. Friday was Grandma's baking day and Laura knew she would always get cakes or buns for tea. However, one day she arrived to find the door unlocked and the kitchen table covered in buns. For a while she was completely puzzled. Then she noticed something strange about the way the currants on the buns were arranged. Laura began to suspect that this was one of Grandma's little pranks. See if you can share the joke.

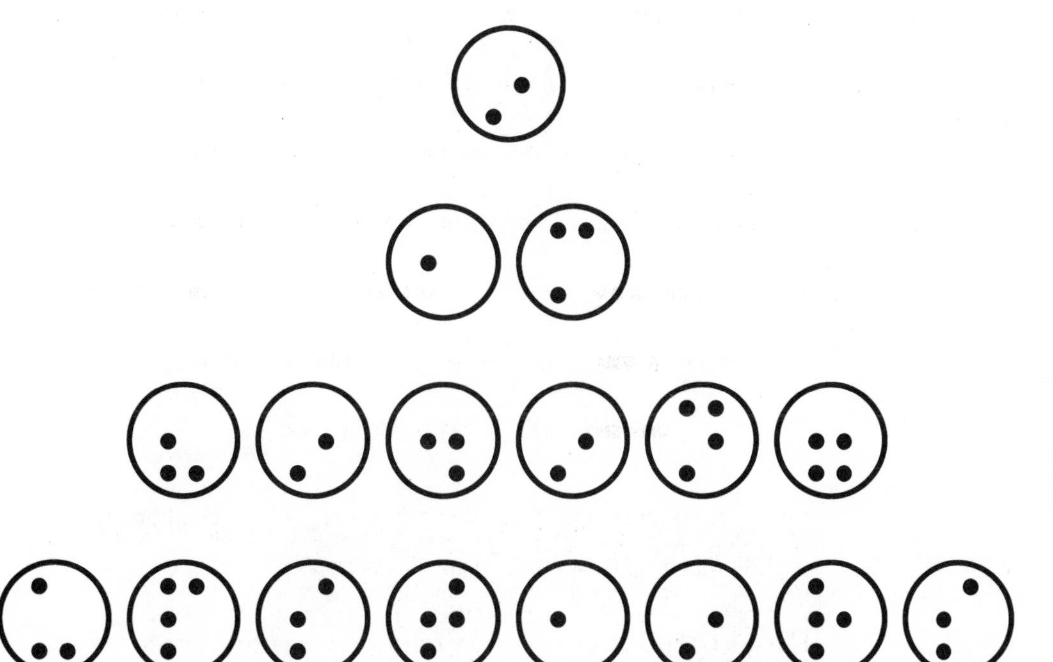

Hackers' horror

Answer Number 81

On a dank and dismal night, computer hackers break into Computer Craze headquarters in an attempt to find documentary details of the code they have been unable, as yet, to discover. They raid the offices and find a curious pattern imprinted on an imposing piece of card. Realizing its importance, they study it for hours to unlock the mystery of the computer code. What is it?

Shakespeare shocker

Answer Number 19

Professor V. Smart has a pet theory that Shakespeare's plays were in fact written by one Albert Grunge, a carpenter who used to live in the same street as Will. After years of campaigning Smart gets permission to open Shakespeare's tomb in search of clues. Among the dust and bones he finds a parchment which appears to be in some sort of code. Eventually he unravels the message but what he finds brings a glow to his cheeks!

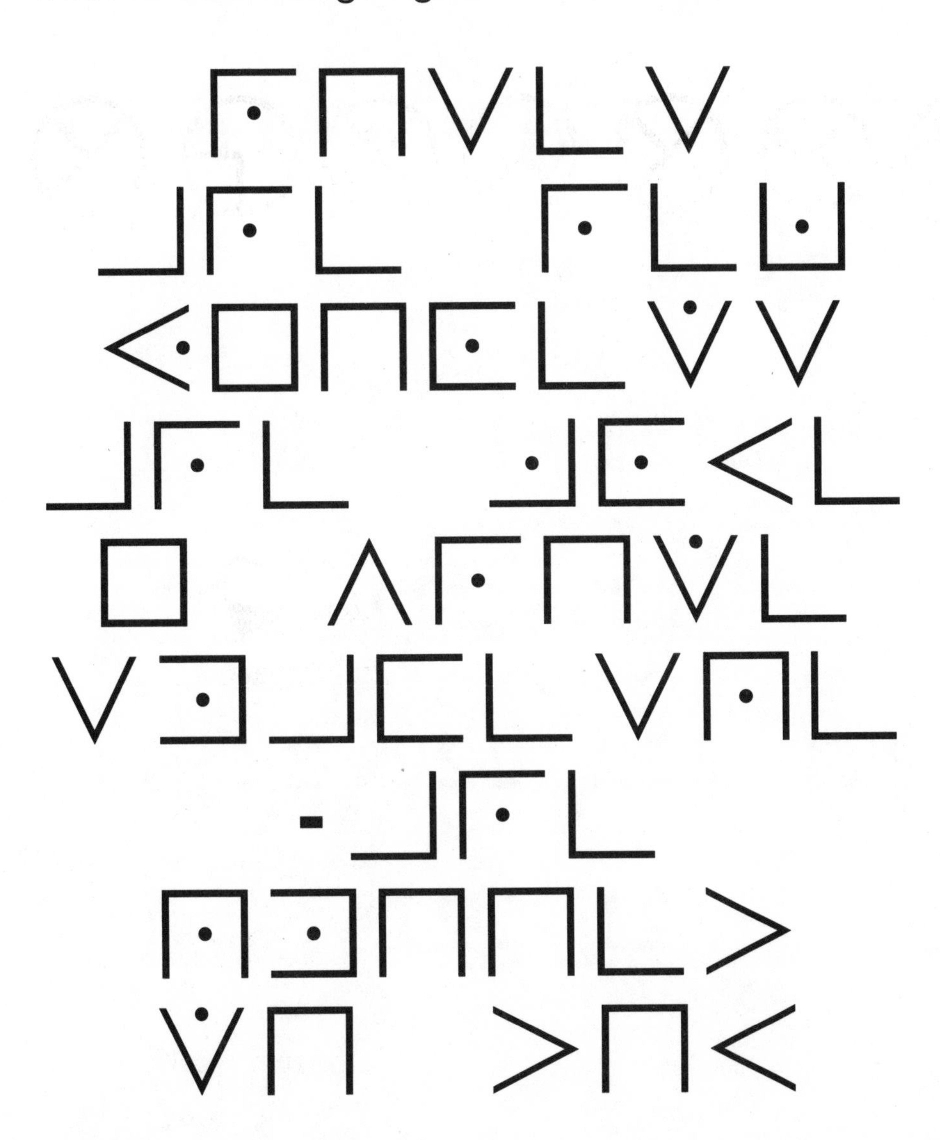

Nautical numbers

Answer Number 96

Captain Routeless received an urgent radio message as he was navigating his ship through stormy waters early one morning. He thought there was interference on the radio as he listened intently to the message, but then realized that the letters were being spelt in the form of a number code easy to detect – the noise of the storm hindered attempts to understand human voices. What message do the numbers spell out?

122 12 121 21 11 21

221

11 2121 1 2111 1

121 221

1211 222 222 22 11

21 221

Shopping strain

Answer Number 77

Rosie discovers a shopping list her mother has written, but the first item had been written in code. She thinks her mother is buying her a surprise for doing well in recent exams, and is anxious to discover what it could be. However, once Rosie has managed to decipher the code, her excitement quickly disappears. Do you know why?

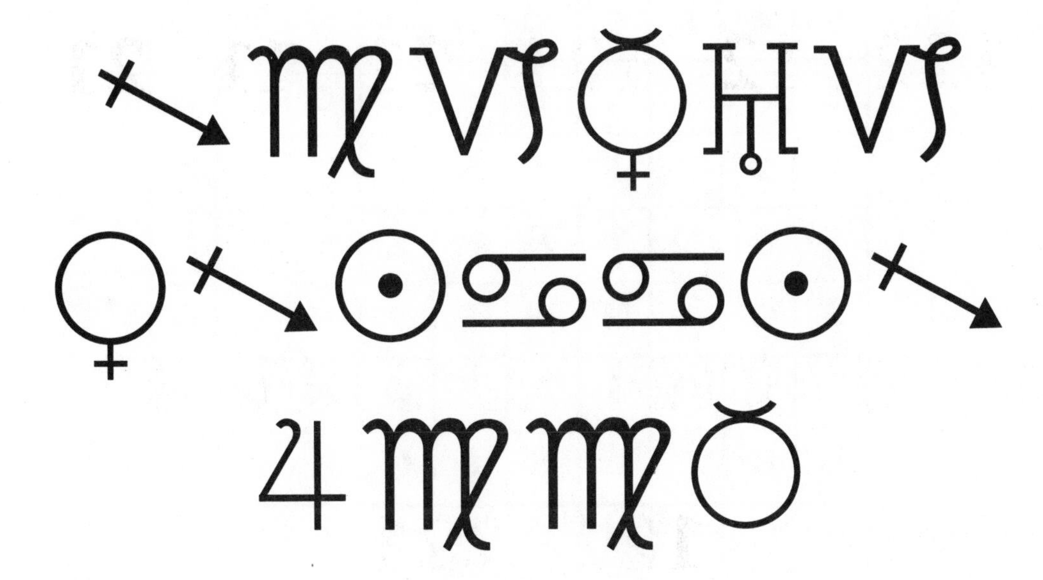

Strange last words

Answer Number 40

Colonel Strange of the US Cavalry is under attack from an enormous Mexican force led by General Sanguinario. Under cover of dark, he smuggles out a messenger carrying a coded plea for help. However, time is short. Unless you can unravel the code, Strange and his men are lost. Get cracking!

L	E	L	L	D	U	O	R	A	W
E	B	A	P	Y	A	N	R	E	E
S	R	A	S	D	O	B	D	R	S
S	A	E	L	E	E	U	D	E	U
L	O	S	I	I	S	R	T	N	D
E	B	O	T	N	A	E	E	N	A
S	C	I	N	N	F	V	N	B	U
T	L	O	S	A	E	O	A	D	M
G	R	E	L	S	S	M	R	L	A
E	N	A	N	O	O	P	E	C	L

Image problem

Answer Number 12

Katie has had a note from an anonymous admirer. Who can it be? She rather hopes the writer is Rick (tall, handsome and so cool he's almost blue) but has a nasty feeling it might be Stuart (fat, spotty, nerd). Unfortunately the note seems to be in some sort of code. Katie has puzzled over it all night but cannot work out what it says. Then suddenly, whilst brushing her teeth, it all becomes clear and Katie, though feeling slightly foolish, has a good laugh. What did the note say?

Dear Katie, Bet you thought this was from lover-boy Rick! Did you spend hours in eager anticipation? Sorry to disappoint you. It was only from your best friend in all the world (who you now hate), Rachel.

PUZZLE 37

Corruptive campaign

Answer Number 35

Snowbridge High School were having student council elections soon and party rivalry was rife. One day, one party's set of notes detailing their election campaign, went missing. No-one could find them until this short letter was found on the floor. After studying it for a while, the notes were recovered and the people responsible were dealt with. What does the letter say?

C2 A1 D4 D4

C3 C4 D4 A5 D3 / A1 D2 A5 / C4 C3 / D4 C4 C5 / B1 C1 C4 C4 D2 / C4 B1 / D3 A3 B4 A5 C3 A3 A5 / A2 C1 C4 A3 B5 / B4 C3 / C1 C4 A3 B5 A5 D2 / C4 C3 / D3 A5 A3 C4 C3 A4 / D2 C4 E2 / A4 C4 E2 C3 / A1 C3 A4 / D4 B3 B4 D2 A4 / B1 D2 C4 C2 / D2 B4 B2 B3 D4

B1 D2 C4 C2

D3 B4 C2 C4 C3

Gang greetings

Answer Number 20

Jodie has been trying for months to join her brother's gang but they keep saying she's too young. At last she receives a coded note and she's pretty sure she knows who it's from. But what does it say? Is it good news or bad? Help her find out.

Answer Number 52

Dotty Dave

The *Daily Bugle* started a Dotty Dave competition. All you had to do was spot a man called Dotty Dave carrying a copy of the *Bugle*, challenge him correctly with the words, "You are Dotty Dave of the *Daily Bugle*" and you would win £100,000. But how would you recognize him? Ah! That was the catch. The newspaper insisted that it had given all the information needed, but for weeks no one could work it out. Then, sitting on a train with her mum, young Georgina had a bright idea. She leapt up and challenged the man sitting opposite. Her mum, who had been cringing with embarrassment, was even more surprised when her daughter won. Look at the picture and see how she did it.

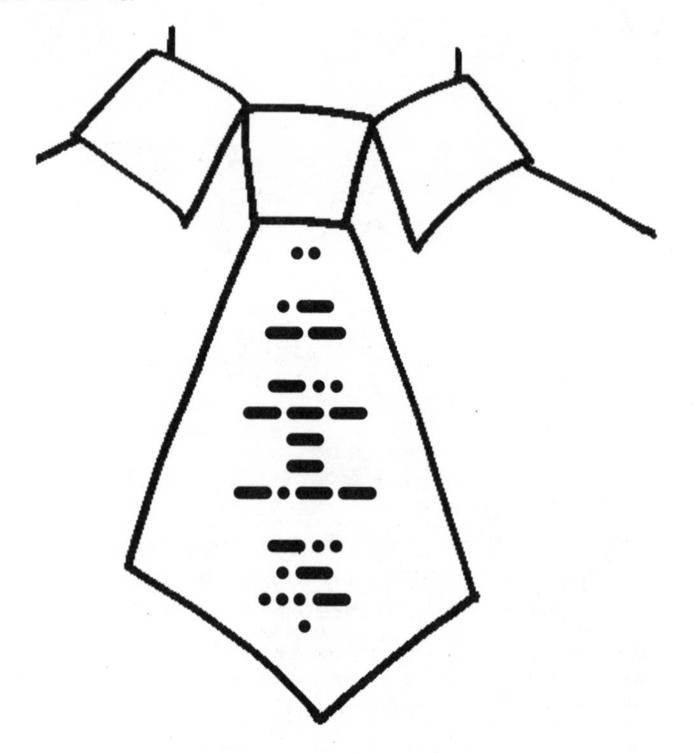

Crate clue

Answer Number 61

The police descended in force on the Dirty Duck, a bar with an evil reputation as the hideout for all sorts of low-life characters. To their surprise their tip-off appeared to be wrong and their informant was also missing. The place was deserted. They searched the premises and found nothing – except for some old beer crates. There was nothing very remarkable about these, or was there? Some of the bottle lids had been punctured with a pattern. Did it mean anything?

PUZZLE 41

Wooden wonder

Answer Number 82

Sally buys a bargain do-it-yourself kit to make a smart desk unit. When she reaches for the instructions, she finds that they're written in an obscure language of which she has no knowledge. However, she finds a series of universal symbols at the bottom of the sheet, and is finally able to work out what to do. What do these instructions say?

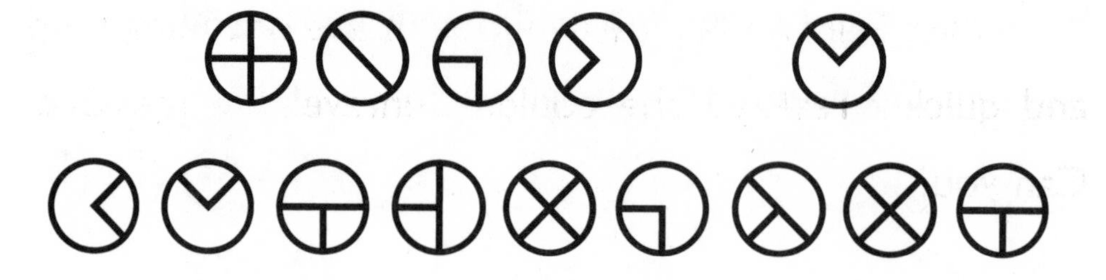

Answer Number 7

Miss Prim caught Becky passing a note to Clare during a Latin lesson.

"And what is this all about?" she enquired acidly.

"It's a note, Miss," replied Becky, helpfully.

"I can see that, but it's in some sort of silly code. What does it say?"

"It's not in code at all, Miss. Can't you read it?"

Miss Prim took a careful look at the offending note and quickly realized she couldn't unravel the message. Can you?

A L E T A H I
T A F N D E R
I T T A G G &
N E E L O R C
L E R O F U O
E M S O O B L
T S C H R A A

PUZZLE 43

Brick bother

Answer Number 88

Bill the builder is working on a new, top-security building used to store vast sums of cash and important documents for a famous company. He has access to the plans of the building, and is approached by Ted who tries to bribe him into disclosing details of the layout. Bill refuses to hold any meetings with Ted so as to avoid suspicion, and instead informs Ted to look for further information, late at night, at an odd-looking wall he has started building. Perplexed, Ted follows instructions and is dismayed when he realizes what Bill wanted to say. What is the news?

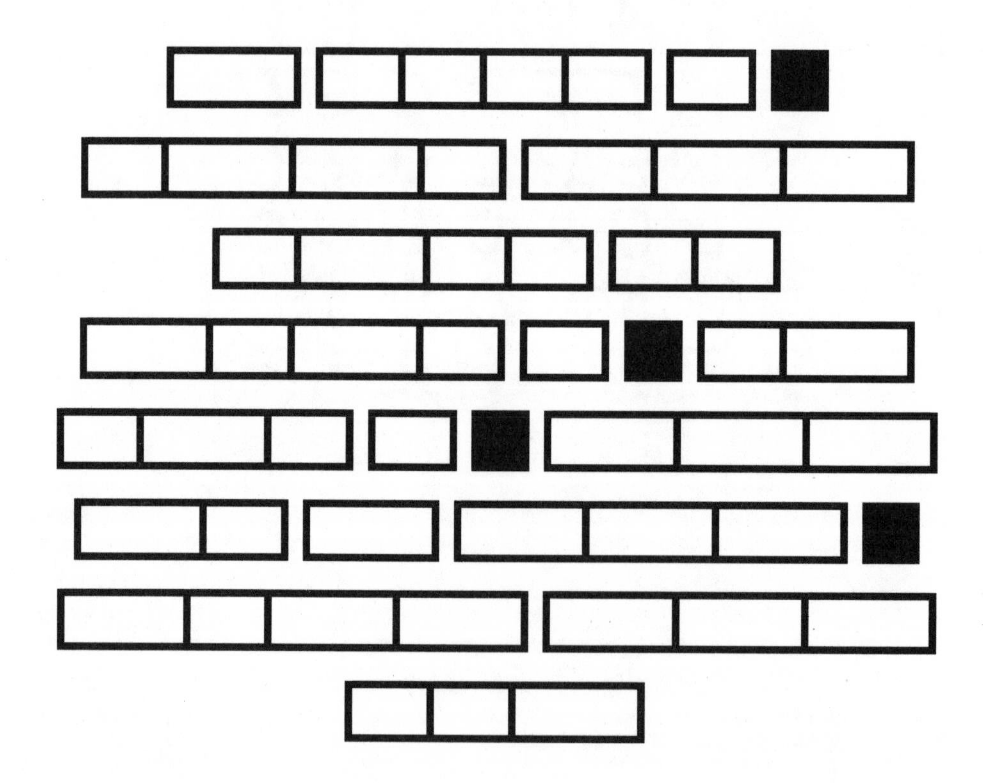

Candle kerfuffle

Answer Number 76

Dame Agelessia is obsessed with hiding the truth about her real age from everyone. However, with her birthday drawing near, you, as a treasured employee, are called upon by her friends to try to discover her age. A massive party is being planned, and the right number of candles for her cake must be used. You come across her birth certificate, but even the date on that has been covered over with a peculiar scrawl. Are you able to reveal her true date of birth?

☉♎♐☿♊

♁☿♐♑♓

♌☿♌♅♓♅♅♌

♁☿♁♓♈ ♁☿♒♅

PUZZLE 45

Answer Number 36

Absent astronaut

During a space mission, one of the astronauts mysteriously disappeared while walking on the moon. With much concern, the other astronauts went down to the surface to look for him after he failed to return to the ship when time was up. On reaching the surface of the moon, there was no sign of him but written in the dust was what seemed to be a coded message. Can you work out what happened to the missing astronaut?

B5 B4 A4 C3 A1 C5 C5 A5 A4 / A2 E4 / D4 B3 A5 / A5 C3 A5 C2 E4

A1 C2 / C4 C3 / D3 C5 A1 A3 A5 D3 B3 B4 C5 / A3 A1 C1 C1 A5 A4 / C2 E4 D1 D5 D2 / D4 E2 C4

B3 A5 C1 C5

Answer Number 53

Jim Hill's parents had brought him all the way from LA to stay at a real English castle. It was a pain! No disco, no computer games, and no burgers. He thought he would die. Then he noticed something strange. The castle was full of odd-looking bugs. At first he thought they were some strange English bug but, when he looked closely, he could see that they were ordinary cockroaches that someone had decorated very delicately by hand. Take a look at one and see what you can make of it.

.--. .-. .. ... --- -. . .-.   .. -.

-.. ..- -. --. . --- -. ...

.... . .-.. .--.

PUZZLE 47

Pecos perplexed

Answer Number 21

Pecos Pete is trying to find a gold mine left to him by his Uncle Josh. However, Josh was a canny old fellow and knew that the location of the mine might be discovered by others. He left directions in code hoping that Pete would be bright enough to follow them.

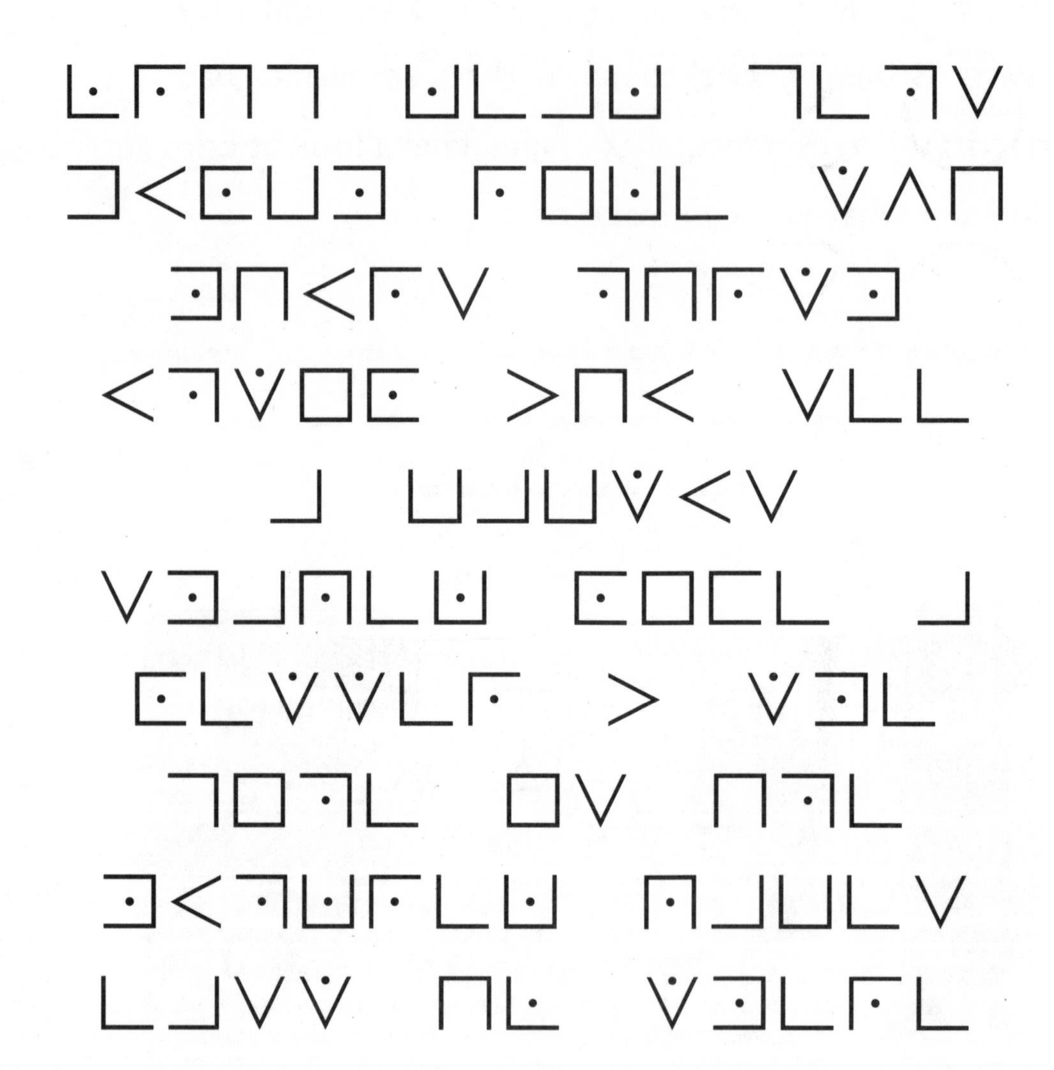

Alien encounter

Answer Number 83

Chris is on a space mission, and lands on Mars. He finds himself surrounded by a group of three-legged, green dwarflings. They attempt to converse with him, but when they realize Chris doesn't speak their language, they start to draw strange shapes in the dusty ground. Just what are they trying to say?

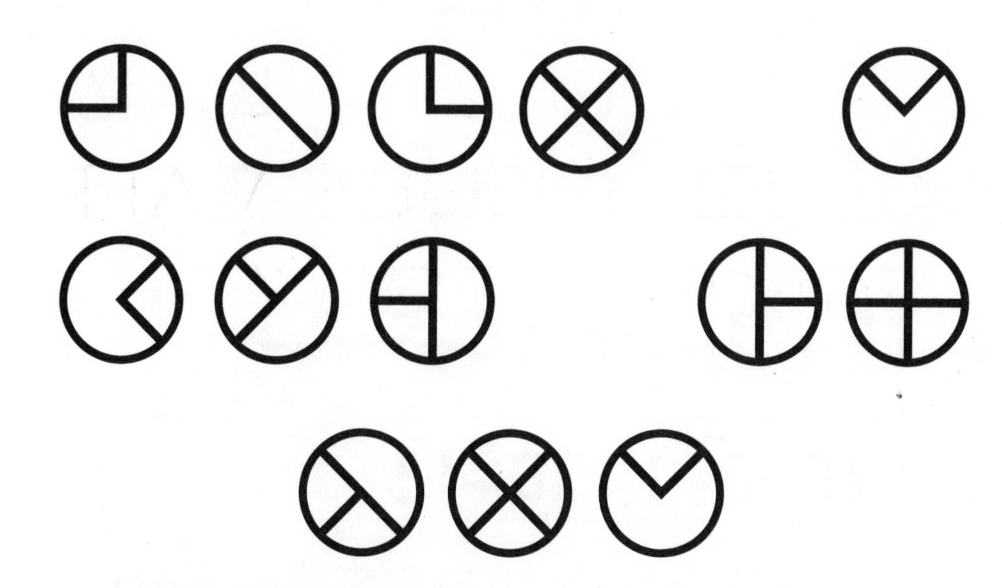

Sharp-eyed sleuth

Answer Number 16

Inspector Sharp was called to the scene of a murder. The victim, eccentric millionaire playboy Piers Short-Sightedly, was lying sprawled on his study floor stabbed through the heart. Among his possessions Sharp came across an address book. At first it looked of no particular interest but, as he looked closer he discovered that some of the numbers were not what they seemed.

Here is what he found:

9–19–21–19–16–5–3–

20–20–8–1–20–13–

25–23–9–6–5–23–1–

14–20–19–20–15–

11–9–12–12–13–5

A novel novel

Answer Number 11

Jeffrey Fletcher, the best-selling novelist, has a slight problem. His computer has gone on the blink and seems to be churning out rubbish. He is supposed to send the manuscript of his new book to the publisher tomorrow but what can he do? Look at a passage from the book. Maybe the computer hasn't gone quite as crazy as Jeffrey assumes.

Szy cght hr brth s sh ntcd th drk hrd mn sh hd sn n th plc phts stndng tsd hr hs. Wht shld sh d? Qckly sh rn t th tlphn nd dlld th mrgncy nmbr.

Answer Number 41

Spurned spy

Beautiful, brainy Susan McSleuth, one of the brightest young things at MI6, has attracted the amorous attentions of fellow agent Duncan Dudd. Susan suspects that Duncan is not quite marriage material but, to be sure, she sends him a coded message. If he can decode it he gets a date, if not she will know that he's as dud as he sounds.

N	A	E	C	V	A	T	D	O	S
S	S	N	E	H	H	A	U	F	A
U	A	N	U	I	E	N	L	N	R
H	O	O	S	R	L	E	D	E	I
C	Y	N	N	E	S	C	V	T	W
E	O	A	S	Y	U	E	H	E	F
T	C	S	M	N	L	A	V	A	Y
U	Y	S	N	C	S	O	L	L	U
O	A	I	S	P	L	L	N	L	O
G	N	A	Y	N	I	O	D	C	I

The conversation's flagging

Answer Number 98

Tim and Claire, two great friends, live opposite each other on a busy road, but have been banned from telephoning each other as the resulting phone bills have been massive. It's a real hassle for them to walk across the road as the traffic is so bad, so they decide to flag messages across to each other. Without the flags, life would be made very difficult for them. Tim sees Claire frantically waving to him one afternoon and rushes to the window to find out what she has to say. What is it that's so important?

Answer Number 102

Dodgy door

Dave found himself trapped in a pitch-black cellar, the storeroom of a hotel whose lights had all failed. He managed to feel his way to the door, but was unable to remember the code needed to get out. However, since the hotel, which was operating on a tight budget, often suffered from power failures, the code could be found embossed on some card near the door which only the staff were trained to understand. What were the words which, when typed into the keypad, would release him?

Domino dilemma

Answer Number 58

To the amazement of astronomers the world over aliens finally made contact with Earth. Their transmission was at first incomprehensible. It looked more like a game of dominoes than a message. After some weeks of work they suddenly made a stunning discovery. It was not only comprehensible but it also contained a surprise no one could have predicted.

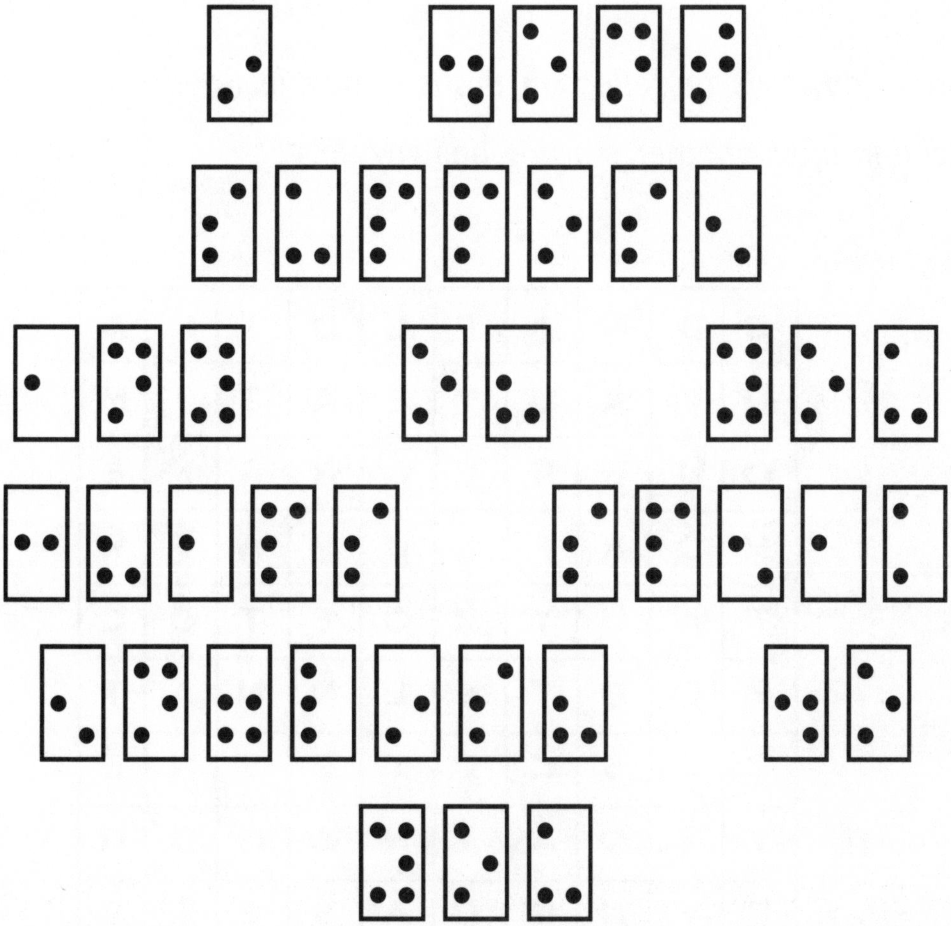

PUZZLE 55

Fruitcake furore

Answer Number 46

For nearly fifty years Ethel Hodgkiss had been trying to get hold of her sister's secret fruitcake recipe. It became an obsession with her and she plotted countless ways to get her heart's desire. Eventually Vi, the sister, died and after the funeral the awful Ethel gleefully rifled through her things to find the precious formula. At last, to her delight, she discovered a cunningly coded note. When she was able to understand its meaning her glee was replaced by more sober reflections.

Sam Cody says, on reflection, this is a toughie. Read one whole column after another, starting halfway up.

G	D	N	I	P	L	D	I	N	A
U	L	A	U	I	E	A	S	I	M
O	U	H	R	C	W	B	A	F	E
H	O	R	F	E	U	V	W	F	R
T	W	U	Y	R	O	E	T	O	C
H	G	D	T	E	L	N	N	A	T
T	E	S	C	D	I	E	T	N	E
Y	T	O	A	I	H	W	H	D	D
O	Y	N	K	D	A	S	E	I	V
U	O	M	E	Y	V	I	C	S	I

Catastrophic car park

Answer Number 64

Sir David Dunethwaite was holding a cocktail party at his huge mansion to celebrate his latest business success. Hundreds of people attended and so, to make parking easier, the staff were told to place guests' cars according to the brand and size. Then six cars arrived that were all exactly the same! How were they going to give the right car back to the right owner? There is a way to do it but, in order to work it out, you must study the registration numbers very closely.

A) Edward	1) B144 SFX
B) Steven	2) T113 VFM
C) Andrew	3) B147 FMB
D) Samuel	4) F423 BSE
E) Thomas	5) T205 WFO
F) Angela	6) U815 NBT

Answer Number 89

Tim buys a second-hand nature book and opens the cover expecting to see the name of the previous owner. Instead he finds a mass of trees carefully drawn out. After taking his book to school one day, the teacher claims to have known the previous owner. Can you work out who it was?

Bungling burglar

Answer Number 70

Security guards dashed out to Doomstead Art Gallery when the alarm suddenly rang out. However, when they went to check on a cherished sculpture, they found that it had been replaced with a coded note. It took the police a while to realize who the infamous culprit was. Can you beat them to it and reveal the contents of the note?

♓♂♅

♃♍♑♑

♑♓♐☿♉♅♑

☉♀☉☿♌

PUZZLE 59

'Mayday' mission

Answer Number 37

You are a member of the space rescue team. After receiving a 'mayday' call from the spaceship Matrix 7 your team arrived to find the ship badly damaged and all the crew dead. In order to find out what happened, you consult the captain's log and the following message comes up on screen:

**D3 B3 B4 C5 / A1 D4 D4 A1 A3 B5 A5 A4 / A2 E4 /
D3 C5 A1 A3 A5 / D4 A5 D2 D2 C4 D2 B4 D3 D4 D3**

**C3 C4 / B3 C4 C5 A5 / B1 C4 D2 / D5 D3 / A2 D5 D4 /
D4 B3 A5 B4 D2 / C3 A5 E3 D4 / D4 A1 D2 B2 A5 D4 / B4 D3 / D3 C5 A1 A3 A5 / D3 D4 A1 D4 B4 C4 C3 / C3 A1 D2 B5 / B1 C4 D5 D2**

D4 B3 A5 E4 / C2 D5 D3 D4 / A2 A5 / D3 D4 C4 C5 C5 A5 A4

Can you work out what the message reads?

Spot on

Answer Number 54

Chris went to see his friend Andy who had measles. He'd never had it himself so he stood at the end of the bed to commiserate. While they talked he started to look more closely at Andy's spotty face and, after a few minutes, he started to laugh so hard he had to run from the room. Andy's mum was totally perplexed. What can you make of the spots on his forehead?

PUZZLE 61

Computer crisis

Answer Number 22

Billy Byte is the school's computer whiz. All his friends have been racing to complete Syko and the Haunted House, but Billy is streets ahead. Until, that is, he comes across a puzzle in code. He's tried everything but to no avail and soon his friends will catch up with him. Can you help him solve the riddle?

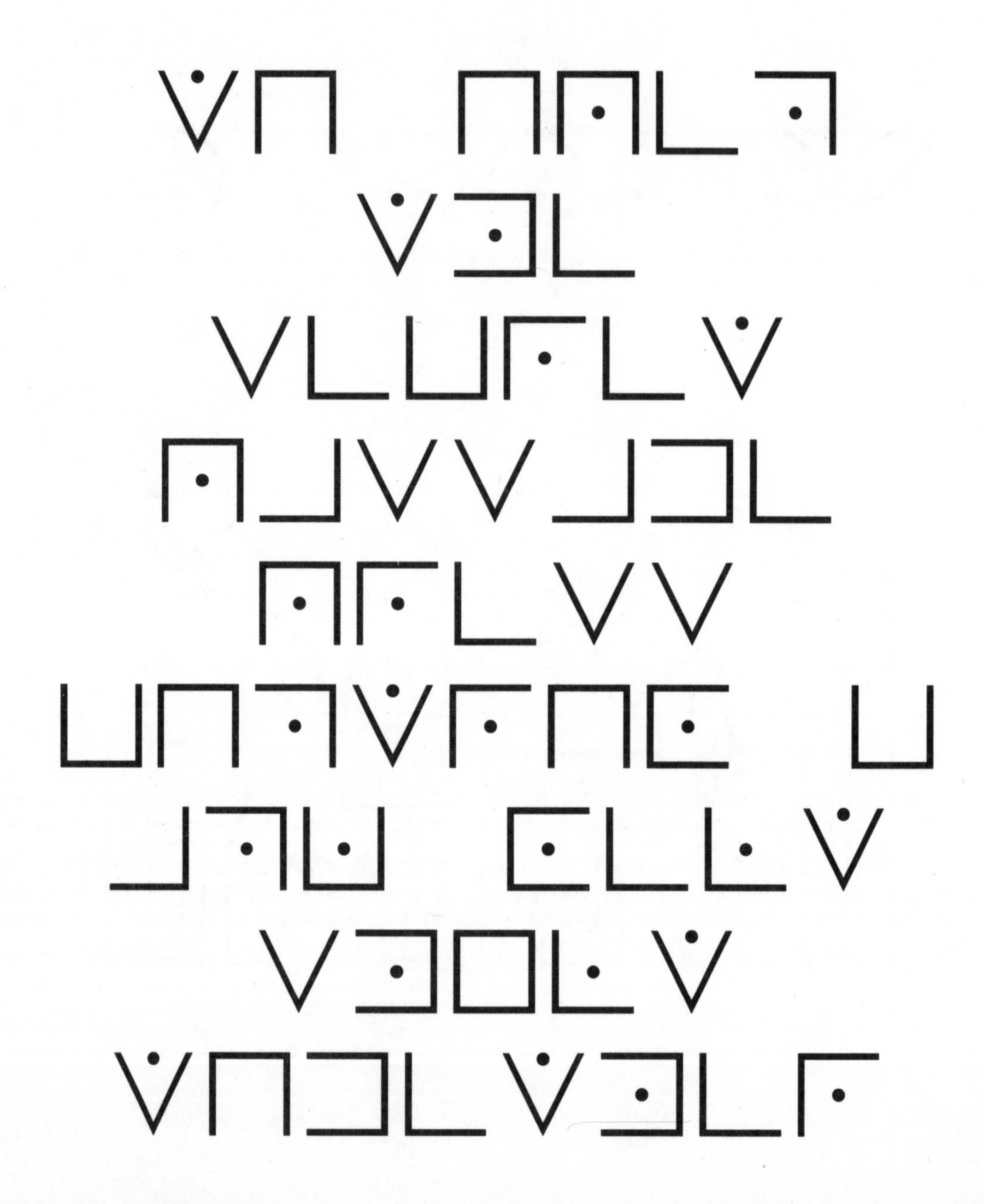

A-mazing message

Answer Number 84

Becky finds herself trapped in the middle of a huge maze, surrounded by hedges which seem to lead to nowhere. She discovers a pile of pebbles carefully arranged on the floor, and stoops down to study the pattern. She realizes it reveals the route to freedom. What must she do?

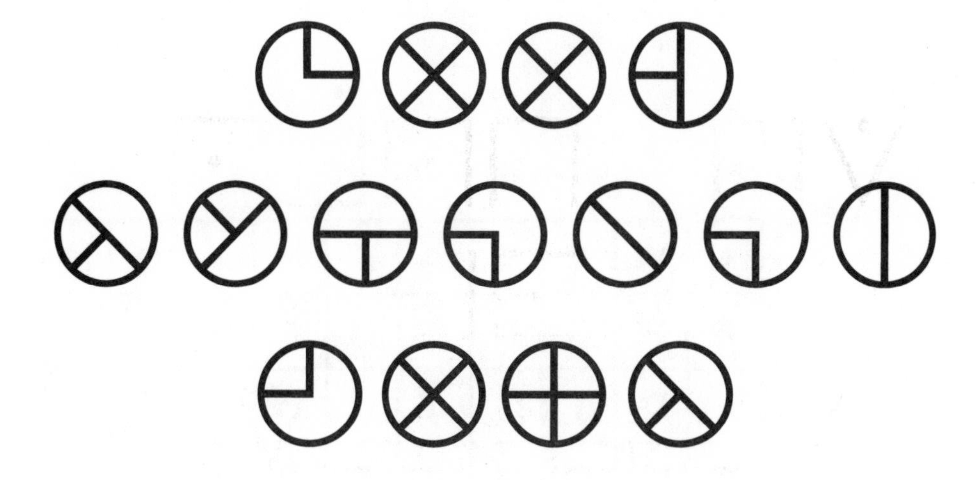

Crew conundrum

Answer Number 42

Captain Stone has been pestered for weeks by young Ben Eager who wants to run away to sea. Stone is not your average pirate. He has brains, which is why he's never been caught. He expects his crew to have brains too. He decides to send Ben a message. If he cracks it he's in, if not he'll be left stranded.

A	V	E	S	A	T	M	I	D	N
E	F	O	R	T	H	E	S	O	I
L	D	J	O	I	N	M	Y	U	G
P	N	O	H	A	R	P	C	T	H
I	U	T	S	O	N	W	R	H	T
H	O	T	D	T	E	I	E	S	O
S	B	N	E	S	S	T	W	E	N
E	E	A	E	N	U	O	Y	A	T
H	D	W	U	O	Y	F	I	S	H
T	I	T	G	N	I	R	P	S	E

The problem's plane

Answer Number 99

Captain Liftorf was carefully moving his private jet plane onto the runway, when an engineer rushed out in front of him, and started to signal an urgent message to him. Realizing the importance of this interruption, he slowed down to study the flags in detail and was horrified when he worked out what he had forgotten. What had he left in the hangar?

PUZZLE 65

Alchemist's almanac

Answer Number 27

At last, after years of searching, Magister Dominicus the alchemist has found the Philosopher's Stone! He is surrounded by jealous rivals who would stop at nothing to snatch his secret and so he decides to write it in the margins of his almanac in a cunningly constructed code. Can you work out what it is? The answer is worth its weight in gold!

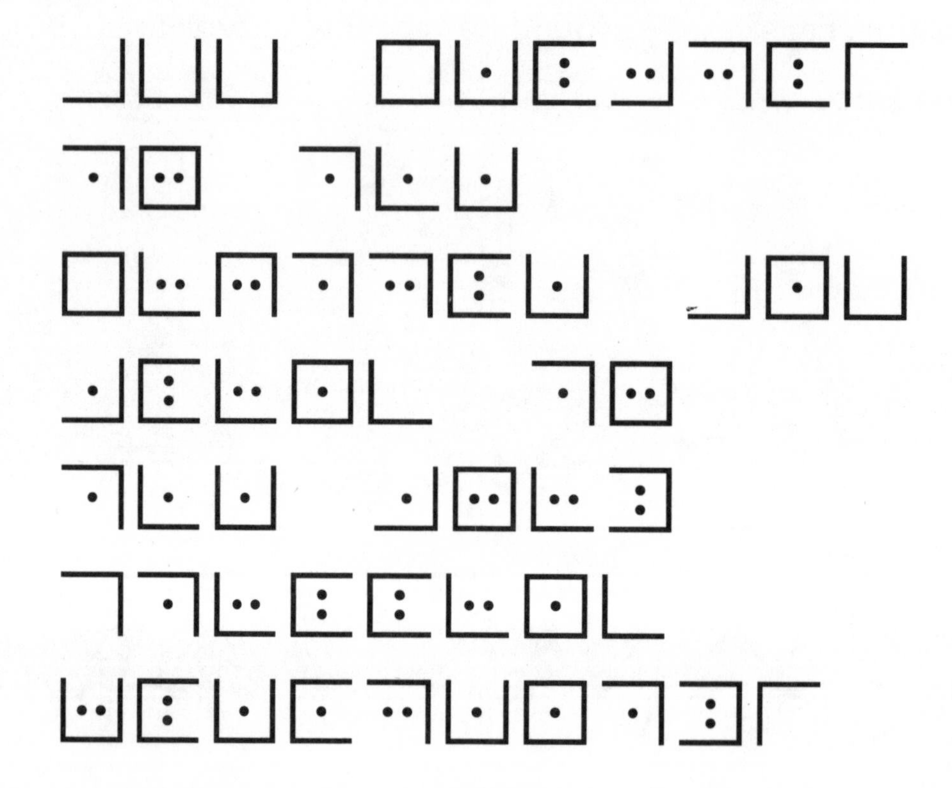

The hole answer

Answer Number 103

Two Scouts were competing in an orienteering competition, following clues to get round the course as quickly as possible. They found themselves facing an old tree, with no obvious clue to lead to the next place. One of the boys found a hole in the tree and slid his hand in the hope of finding the coveted clue inside. But, expecting a piece of card, all he found was a strange pattern marked in the hole, unreadable by being in such an obscure position. From that he found he was able to work out the next place on the route. Can you?

ΓO\Γ/—

∩Λ—Γ\ΓΛLL

Safe Keeping

Answer Number 62

Hans van Helsing, an Amsterdam diamond dealer, has a problem. He has just spent a fortune on a brand new guaranteed burglar-proof safe and now he has forgotten the combination. What to do? It is Christmas and the manufacturers have closed down for the holiday. He simply can't wait until New Year to get at his stock. He remembers that he has to press the buttons on the door and that alphabetical order comes into it somewhere. Can you help him break into his own safe?

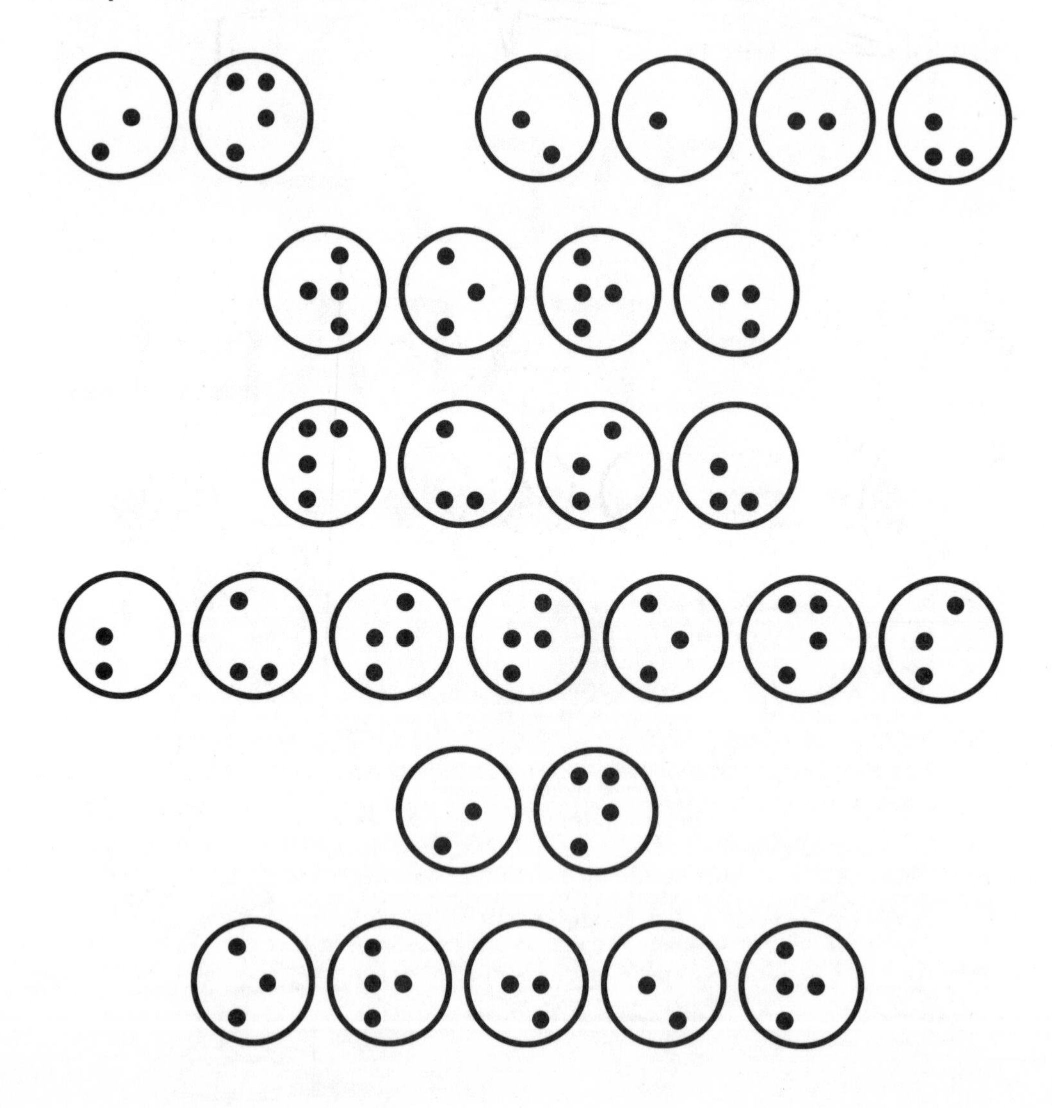

Answer Number 78

The Trotter family are following a trail through a forest, but instead of finding another arrow to lead the way, they find symbols inscribed on a tree. Simon, the eight-year-old, suddenly pipes up with what they have to do. What is the instruction?

Kingly caper

Answer Number 23

King Arthur is just sitting down to a banquet with his knights when a carrier pigeon arrives bearing a message. Naturally it is in code. Merlin cheats and, using his magic powers, reveals the secret in seconds. You, however, will have to do it the hard way.

Sam Cody says: "The word 'castle' appears somewhere."

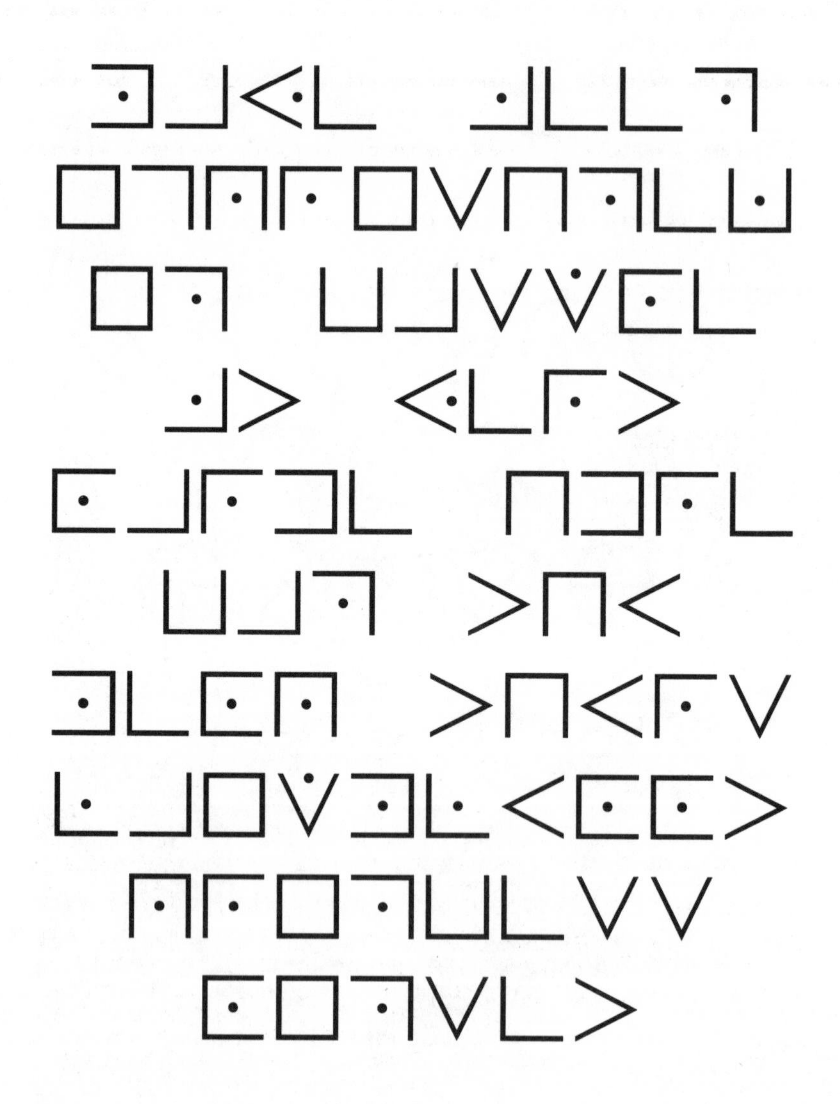

Reel agony

Answer Number 55

Dave is a keen fisherman and spends all his spare time down by the river. One day he gets a shock. When he reels in his line it has been tied in a series of knots and hitches. Who could have done it? What could it mean? Each dot is a knot, and each dash is a hitch.

Answer Number 38

Bemusing blooms

The world famous plant nursery is developing new strains of plants. The problem is that they keep being stolen, so all the names of the plants have been written in code. Unfortunately, the head gardener has a terrible memory and cannot remember how to decipher the code! Can you help him to work out what these special plants are?

Sam Cody says: "Grid codes can work backward too, and it's not just I and J that can share a space."

Nauseating numbers

Answer Number 71

Tom and David were halfway through a tough arithmetic exam when David noticed Tom holding up three fingers. Realizing that he wanted to know how to do question three, but also that the teachers present were on the lookout for any cheating, David scribbled a coded answer on some paper, hoping that if it was found, the teachers would be none the wiser. Tom picked up the paper dropped on the floor and studied it until all became clear. Just what did he have to do?

♁☿♒♅

♓☿♋♅♈♑

♓♂♅

♑♏♈☉♐♅

♍♁ ♑☿X

Puzzling presents

Answer Number 90

Christine knows full well that her children will closely examine their own presents under the Christmas tree if they are labelled with their names, so she puts what the children think is a Christmas pattern on each one. In fact, they spell out each name. So which gift belongs to which child?

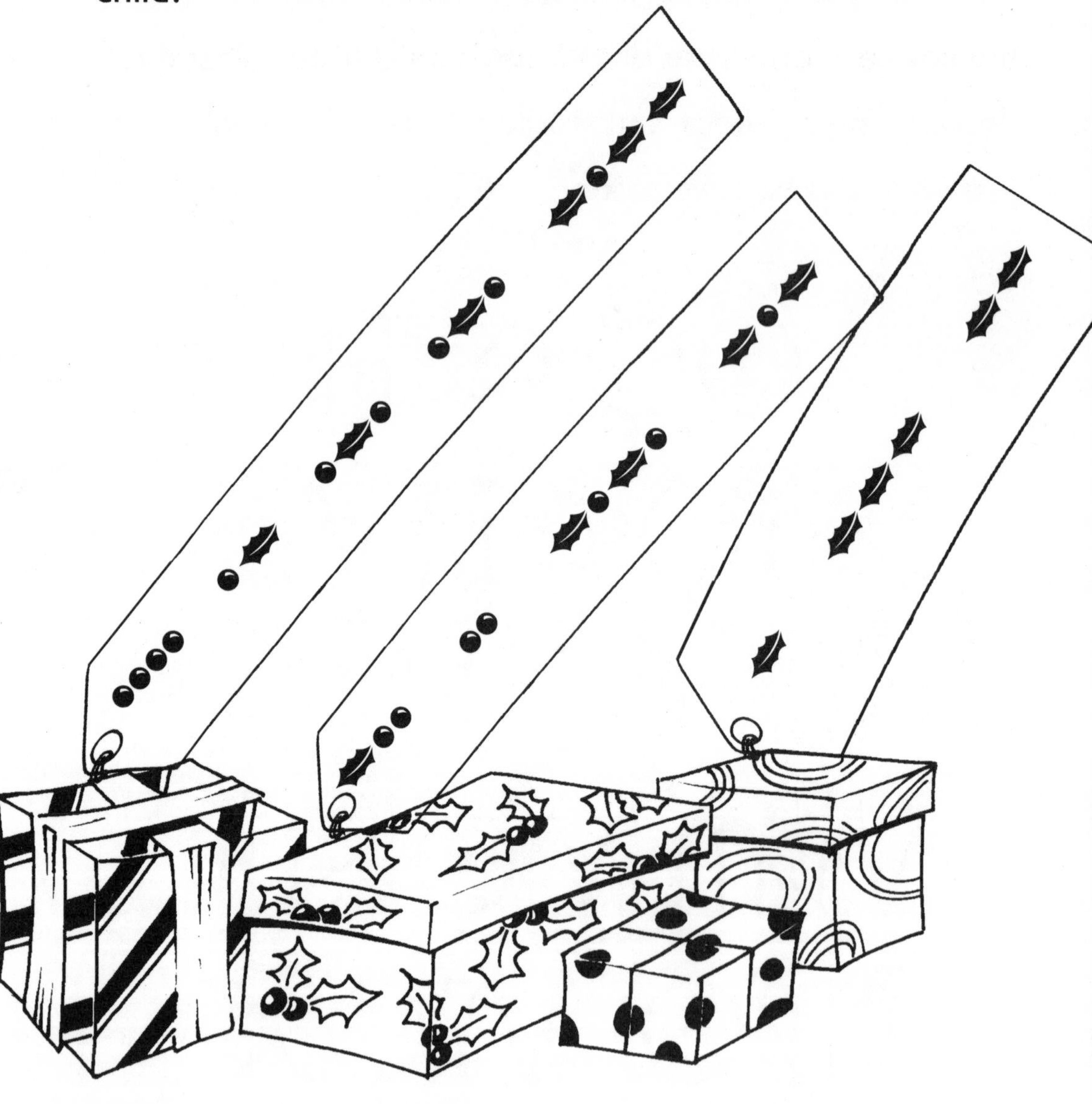

Rainbow riddle

Answer Number 67

The famous explorer, Samuel Gardener, was in the wilds of Africa looking for the lost tombs of the Genmah people. While exploring a cave, he came across a door on which were symbols of Genmah origin. The door was locked. Also on the door was a rainbow pattern with letters written in each of the coloured bands. These held the key to the secret door! Can you work out what it is?

Answer Number 43

Shrewd Sean

To his surprise Sean O'Leary has inherited a castle in Ireland from an uncle he hardly knew. At first it seems a mixed blessing. The castle is beautiful but in need of expensive repairs that he could never afford. Then one day, quite by accident, he comes across an intriguing paper pinned to the wall in one of the outbuildings. At first he can make nothing of it but, just as he is about the give up, he sees his own name hidden among the words. A few minutes later his face is wreathed in smiles. Do you know why?

W	O	L	L	O	F	N	A	E	S
T	I	T	N	U	D	N	U	O	R
H	L	E	H	T	O	T	U	O	D
I	I	H	O	G	E	G	A	Y	N
S	T	E	L	E	H	D	S	S	A
W	E	A	D	R	E	E	S	D	D
I	V	R	B	U	R	I	E	A	N
N	E	T	O	F	M	Y	M	E	U
D	N	T	U	A	L	L	Y	L	O
I	N	G	S	P	I	R	A	L	R

Tribal tension

Answer Number 100

A number of hungry African tribesmen found themselves huddled together on a ridge in the middle of a stretch of desolate wasteland, surrounded by vicious beasts. They saw a group from their tribe in the distance, so they decided to flag a message. What message persuaded the distant tribe to dash over?

PUZZLE 77

Cave confusion

Answer Number 104

Fiona was exploring on holiday when she found herself deep within a cave. Trying to find her way out, she came across two possible tunnels to follow. Unable to decide which would lead to freedom, she started to inspect the rough wall between each route, and, with the help of her torch, found what she believed to be an ancient inscription. Upon closer study, she realized the danger one of the tunnels posed. Which route posed what danger?

Answer Number 63

Form 3B of Densely High School have been taken, kicking and screaming, to an art gallery. They show no interest in culture until Miss Smart shows them The Gamblers and explains that, though it is one of the most famous paintings in the world, nobody has ever known the identity of the artist. Jimmy Toogood examines the picture of some men playing dominoes in an old fashioned tavern with great interest and then suddenly announces:

"I know who done it, Miss," and sticks to his story in spite of threats of punishment. Does he really know? How did he find the name? The clue is in their game of dominoes.

Painter puzzle

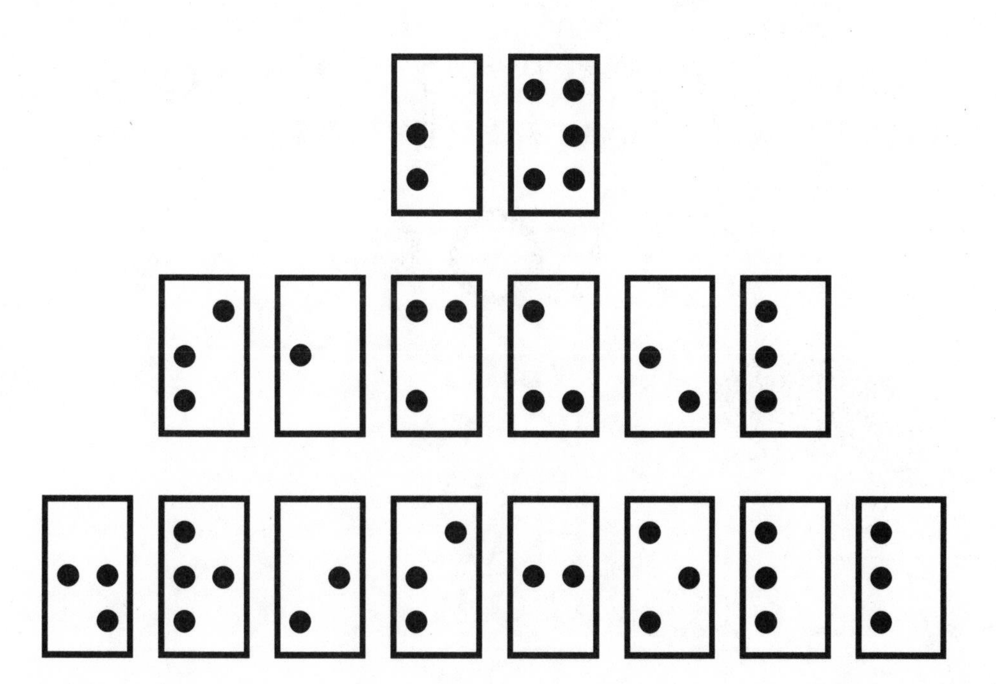

PUZZLE 79

Ape antics

Answer Number 6

It's been said that if you gave typewriters to a group of chimpanzees and they had unlimited paper and unlimited time they would, sooner or later, write the complete works of Shakespeare. But who will make the sandwiches? Never mind. Below you will see what one such group of simian playwrights achieved after a mere 12 million years. The words are all there but in the wrong order. However, we have given you the first letters of all the words in the correct order. Can you work out what they have written?

FRIENDS COUNTRYMEN LEND ROMANS BURY TO ME EARS YOUR COME I PRAISE CAESAR NOT HIM TO THAT EVIL THE LIVES MEN DO THEM AFTER GOOD THE INTERRED OFT IS BONES THEIR WITH CAESAR WITH LET BE IT SO

FRCLM
YEICT
BCNTP
HTETM
DLATT
GIOIW
TBSLI
BWC

Answer Number 91

Chloe decided to go for a walk in her village and, on her travels, she spotted a local football match going on. She decided to wander over and was interested in finding out who her local team were playing against. She asked a spectator who the other team was and was told to look at the crowd to find out. Just who were the opposition?

A troublesome title

Answer Number 72

Sandra was working on her first novel, but wanted to keep the title a secret until all was complete. She had written it down in code to prevent herself from forgetting it, and other unwelcome eyes from seeing it. However, you accidentally find the code and are totally intrigued by what it could mean. Can you solve the mystery and work out the title?

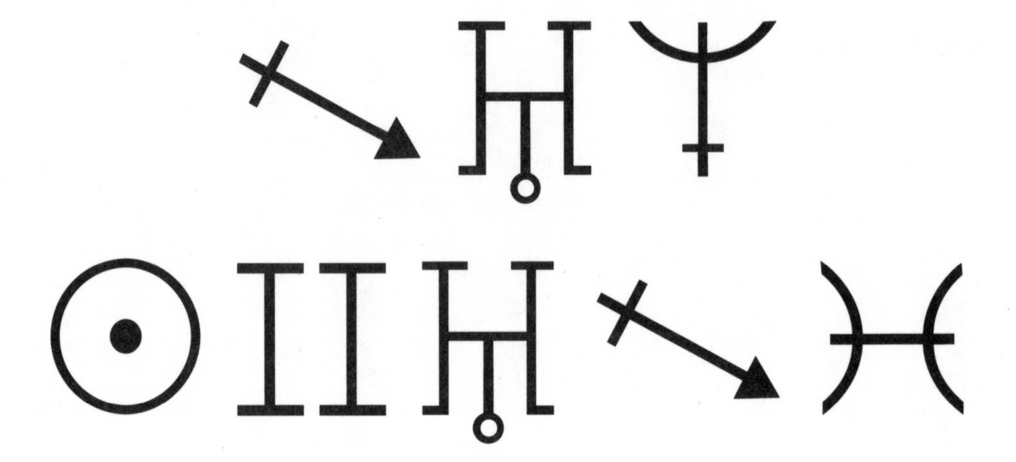

Numbered knocks

Answer Number 2

You have been imprisoned in the dungeons of Schloss Zweitenfrühstuck by the villainous Count Eisschrank. Why? How should I know? However, he does seem very annoyed with you. In fact I can tell you confidentially that a pair of concrete boots and an early morning swim in the lake have been discussed. But don't worry, suddenly you hear someone knocking on the wall of your cell. Could rescue be at hand? You will have to unravel the code to find out. Sounds like some sort of grid code to me. Here are the numbers of knocks.

1.3/3.4/4.5/3.1/1.4/ 5.2/1.5/
1.2/3.4/4.2/4.2/3.4/5.2/ 1.1/
1.3/4.5/3.5/ 3.4/2.1/
4.3/4.5/2.2/1.1/4.2

PUZZLE 83

Dotty dilemma

Answer Number 56

The troop leader is at it again. This time he is going to test the St. Swithin's (Wednesdays) Scout troop to their limit. When the Scouts arrive for their meeting the hut is empty but a message is scrawled on the wall. It looks like Morse code but, wait a minute! There's something wrong. What can it be?

· ·——

·— · ·—·

·— ——· ···· ·· —· ···—   ·—

—·—· —·—· ·· ·· —· ·——·

·· —·

· ···· —

·— —·— ·——· ·—·

Answer Number 24

Eastern escapade

Commissioner Gauden of the police is hard on the trail of the fiendish super-criminal Dr Ah Ti-Shu. Through pluck, fortitude, guts, perseverance and a most outrageous piece of luck he has intercepted a message from Dr Ah to one of his subordinates. He suspects that the message contains details of a meeting of the criminal gang but, as usual, it is in some sort of code. What could it possibly mean? Can you help him to crack the case?

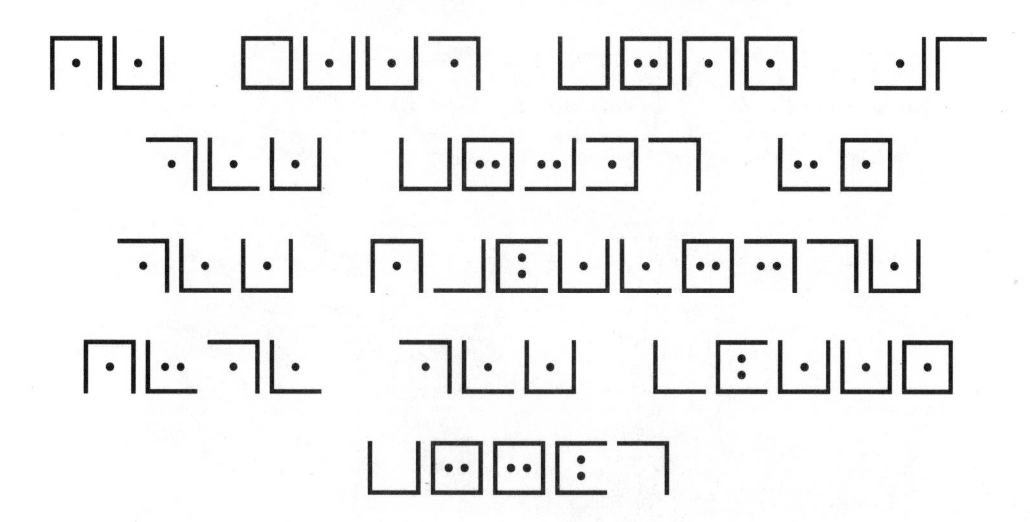

PUZZLE 85

Button blast

Answer Number 79

The Evileyes are planning an invasion of Timidtown. They store the code which reveals which button on the control panel detonates their major bomb in a safe at the Evileye headquarters. However, these premises are broken into by Timidtown spies, who manage to break into the safe, and attempt to crack the code to find the button which they must deactivate. Which one is it?

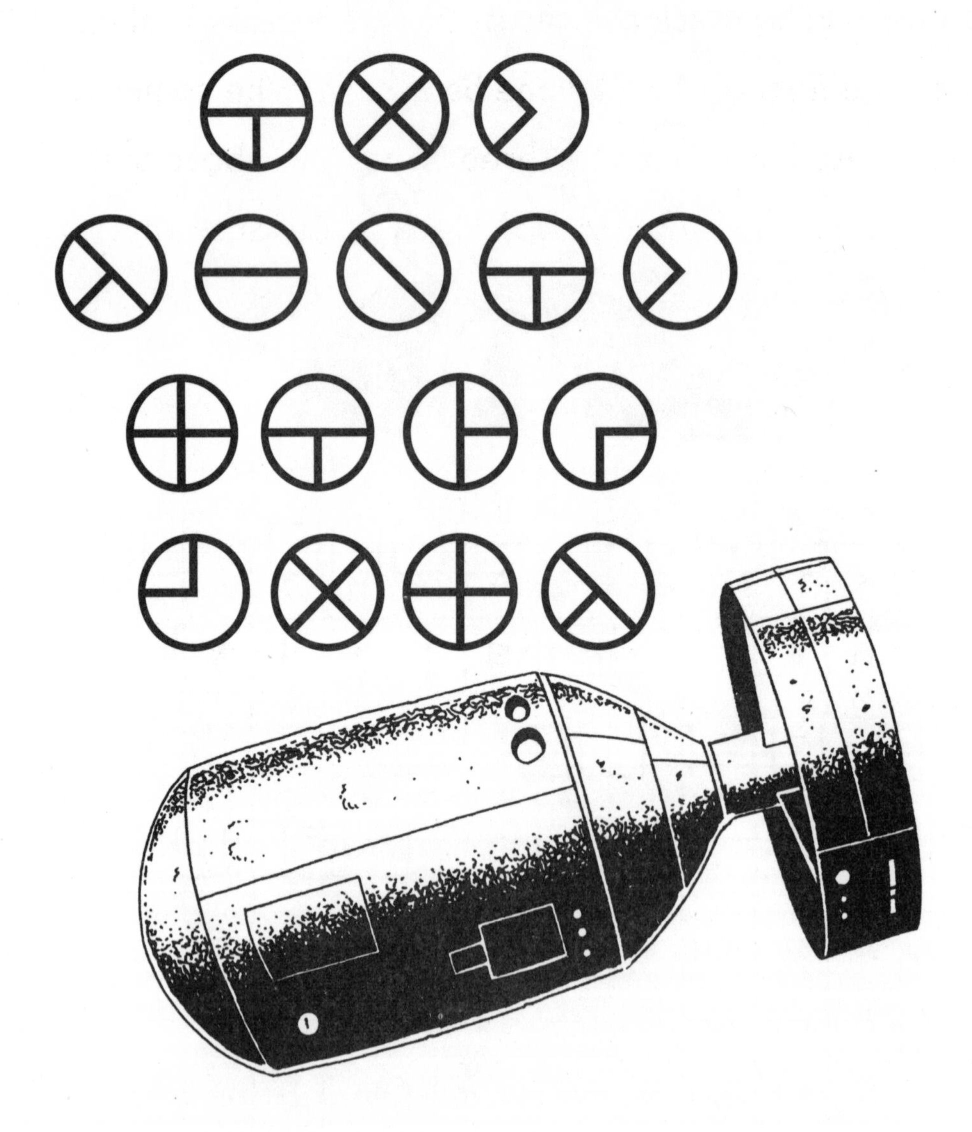

Door dilemma

Answer Number 44

Castle Drak is a place of horror and dread once owned by the evil Count Vlad. But it conceals a treasure of such magnificence that many a young adventurer has dared to enter its gloomy portals in search of it. None has ever returned. Now yet another callow youth has decided to try his luck. Neville Duckworth wants to be a hero. His name is against him but he has courage, fortitude, intelligence and a lucky rabbit's foot. So far he has done really well and penetrated further than anyone before. Then he comes to the final test. He is faced by three doors and, above them, a coded message. What to do? He is pretty sure that to enter the wrong door will mean instant death. Can you help him unlock the coded secret?

E	T	O	N	O	T	F	E	A	R
K	H	D	E	C	A	N	O	N	L
A	E	D	R	R	E	T	E	B	Y
T	S	N	U	C	T	O	F	O	U
H	E	A	S	E	H	F	B	D	N
T	C	R	A	S	E	M	Y	T	H
A	O	O	E	R	T	Y	E	S	O
P	N	O	E	P	L	O	R	O	L
S	D	D	R	A	L	F	E	S	U
U	O	L	I	W	O	O	T	E	T

Answer Number 101

Battle break

During a battle between two rival villages, a soldier standing at the top of a castle starts to wave flags down to the opposition attacking from the ground. The enemy suddenly stop firing their arrows up as they acknowledge the message being relayed. What vital information stops the fighting going on?

Answer Number 47

Grid graduation

Major Sneekly, head of the School for Spies, set his students this test as part of their final exam. It looks just like any other grid code but, to keep them on their mettle, he introduced a variation. Can you spot what it is?

Sam Cody says this is not half as difficult as it looks if you read left to right twice.

I	W	U	O	Y	E	E	N	L	L
R	E	V	E	D	C	N	U	O	Y
I	W	F	O	E	G	D	N	A	T
T	E	L	I	U	K	R	O	W	O
H	T	T	U	O	C	E	S	S	I
E	M	T	E	R	E	G	A	S	S
R	A	F	O	S	E	V	U	O	Y
T	I	D	A	H	B	Y	S	A	E
W	O	N	T	U	U	M	U	O	Y
R	O	W	T	S	D	R	A	H	K

Answer Number 95

Dotty dog

A valuable pedigree Dalmatian is found dashing through town, creating havoc as it runs through the crowds. A young lad who's following the chase suggests to a policeman that they call the dog by its name to grab its attention. However, nobody seems to know it, until the same lad yells out a name and the dog arrives at a sudden unexpected standstill. What was the magic word?

Lost legacy

Answer Number 4

Eccentric great uncle Silas passed away apparently without leaving a will. However, his solicitor, Giles Verry-Boaring, revealed that just before his death Silas sent him a note that appeared to be in code. He left instructions that all his relatives should be shown the note and allowed a chance to decode it. The first one to succeed in finding the will was to be the sole heir. Here is the note. Can you make someone rich? Remember, mighty oaks grow from little acorns grow!

LION (	)OAKS
BEAD (	)CAKE
BLOB (	)OAKUM
COAL (	)SEED
WAIT (	)LILY
ARMY (	)INDEX
MEEK (	)SASH

PUZZLE 91

Lipstick to the rescue

Answer Number 73

Katy finds herself taken hostage by a couple of kidnappers eager to get their hands on her father's fortune. They let her out of the van in the middle of a dense forest while they go off to find their accomplices. Being tied to a wheel, she cannot go far, but manages to clamber onto the roof, and scrawls a message with a bright lipstick she finds lurking in her pocket. The kidnappers return none the wiser, and the journey continues until a helicopter passing overhead radios for help. What message provokes the call for action?

♑♍♑

♑♓♍♎

♓♂☿♑ ♒☉♌

Time trouble

Answer Number 80

A young scientist finds herself trapped in a time machine in a distant century. She discovers that a password must be decoded to activate the time machine which has been installed so nobody else can use the machine. She's getting desperate to leave, but is having trouble finding the password. Can you help her out?

PUZZLE 93

Twain tangle

Answer Number 45

We're not even going to tell you what this one is about. However, if you look carefully you will find the names of two well-known young Americans who are in a spot of bother and need your help. Once you have found them the rest should be simple.

T	O	W	Y	C	K	H	A	R	S
M	A	E	U	L	N	V	E	H	E
S	R	H	E	N	E	B	I	R	T
A	D	B	I	F	B	D	A	E	L
N	E	F	O	O	E	D	L	O	D
R	Y	U	R	O	T	L	E	C	B
R	N	E	U	N	L	H	A	N	Y
D	H	T	O	O	T	V	W	T	R
T	B	D	O	N	E	O	H	O	E
U	T	K	I	S	D	E	F	S	T

Answer Number 106

Party planing

Sinbad was organizing a surprise party for his sister, and was writing out invitations. Knowing that his sister would want to know what he was doing, he wrote them in code, declaring that he was working on some linguistic research. He sent the invitations out to family and friends – but when and where was the party to be held?

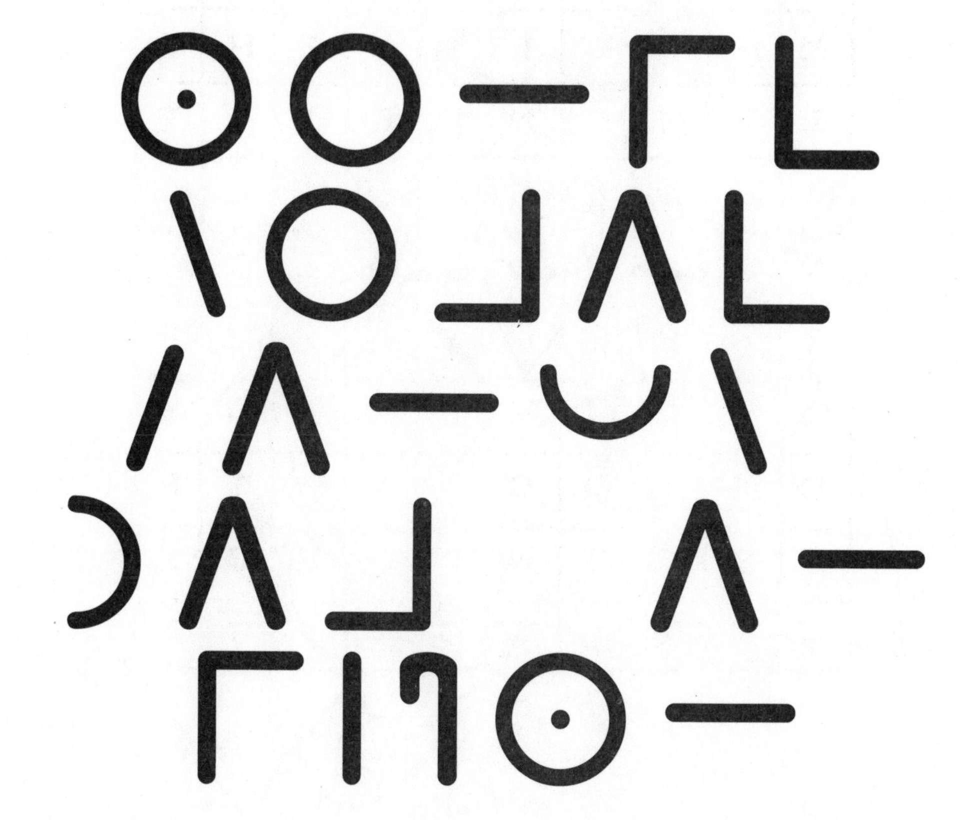

PUZZLE 95

Designer difficulty

Answer Number 96

A famous eccentric movie star arrived at her latest film premier dressed in a space-age outfit of which all the reporters were eager to know the designer. The actress, when pressed with the question, mysteriously replied, "Just look at the dots." The confused reporters were momentarily silenced. Can you name the designer for them?

Moriarty in memoriam

Answer Number 25

Having finally killed off the infamous Professor Moriarty, Sherlock Holmes is taking a well-earned rest. While playing his violin in his study his peace is disturbed by a brick being hurled through his window. At first he takes this as a critical comment on the quality of his playing. But no! On closer inspection the brick is found to have a note attached to it written in some villainous code. Naturally the genius detective unravels the mystery in minutes. It may, however, take you slightly longer.

PUZZLE 97

Answer Number 57

Mixed Morse

Now here's a puzzle for you! The tireless leader of St. Swithin's (Wednesdays) Scout troop has arranged an initiative test. They are to travel cross country responding to instructions he flashes to them from afar with his torch. All goes well until he decides to really test their initiative with a dirty trick. Here is the message he sends. Can you work out what's gone wrong?

.-.. ... --. .- - - .-- . ...

.--- - -.

.-.- -.-- - ---. - -.-

--- .-.- ... --. . . ...

-.. ... -.- .-. ... --. .

-.. ---- -. . -- ---. -

.-- ... .- -

Answer Number 65

Literary loot

Chief Inspector Cornfield has had an anonymous tip-off that a major robbery is about to take place but he doesn't know when or where. A few hours later he receives a piece of paper in his mail. After looking at it for a while he suddenly rushes for the town library! Why? Here is what was written on the paper:

The arrangements have been booked. Everything you need will be found inside:
38 28 E 22 6 I 8 38 E 24 36 A 16 6 50
4 38 E I 40 I 6 O 46 40 12 O E 24 A
40 A

PUZZLE 99

Time travel

Answer Number 31

You are an assistant to an absent-minded professor who has just built a time machine. To prevent anyone from using it without his permission, he has written the instructions to start the machine in code. The time has now come to test it but unfortunately the professor has been taken ill and this is the only time for the next six months when a gap in time is available. The professor has therefore nominated you to try out the machine but forgot to tell you how to crack the code. Can you work out how to start the machine before the gap in time disappears?

1.

2.

3.

Answer Number 92

Diary dilemma

Cheryl's mother picks up her daughter's diary which she knocked on the floor as she went to move it. It falls open on the fourth of February, and she cannot help but see what has been written. However, Cheryl, fearing that her mother may find her diary, has written the entry in coded symbols. Her mum thought that Cheryl went to the cinema with some friends on that evening, but where did she really go?

PUZZLE 101

Rocky revelation

Answer Number 74

A couple move into an old house and spend a day trying to sort out the garden. Helen uncovers a rock by the pond with what she believes to be an ancient inscription. Full of excitement, she takes it to the local museum where the expert on duty reveals that the rock is of no value whatsoever. When she asks why, the expert tells her the true meaning of the code. What is it?

Answer Number 13

Lost lyrics

Fading pop star Danny Devine had written a new song that he just knew would storm to the No. 1 spot and save his crumbling career. At first he had it scribbled on the back of an envelope but then he was suddenly afraid that someone would steal his idea. So he decided to throw away the envelope and write the lyrics in code in the inside of his guitar case. He had only got as far as the title when he was called away to answer the phone. When he came back his guitar case was gone! This is what he had written. Can you decode it?

Sam Cody reminds you that there are five vowels and you don't have to stop where you're told to!

2F3.L2.HT.N3.Y1.D1

PUZZLE 103

Castle conundrum

Answer Number 26

Robin Hood has just received a strange message by carrier pigeon. Naturally he and his merry men are just itching to dash off on another swashbuckling adventure but where to? This looks like some sort of grid code, but how does it work?

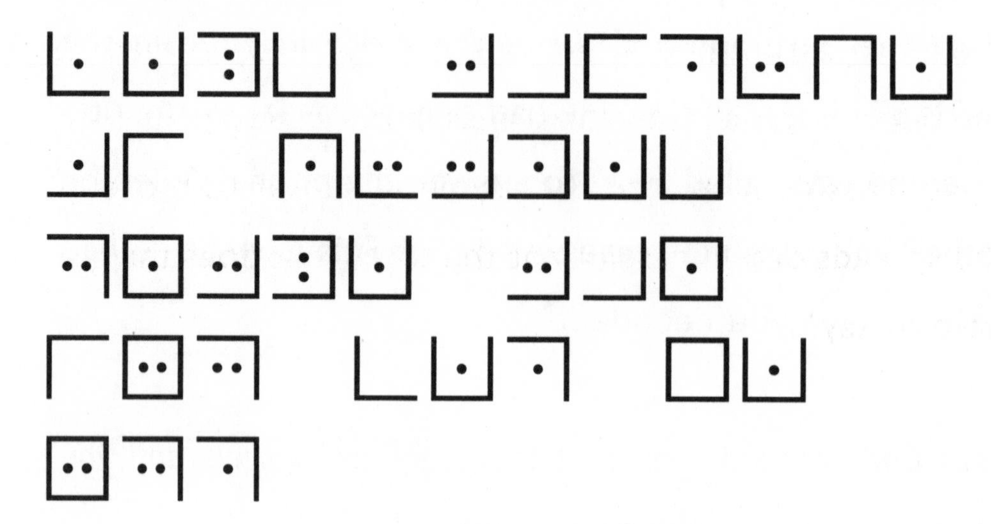

Spread survey

Answer Number 86

Shona is undertaking a survey to gather data on whether children can detect the difference between a range of butters and margarines. She labels the products in code with the real name of each spread, and finds that no child is able to identify many of the spreads correctly. She is therefore astonished when one girl correctly names all the butters and all the margarines, but then looks further at her answer sheet and finds symbols similar to those of the spreads drawn carefully at the top. What does the girl have to say?

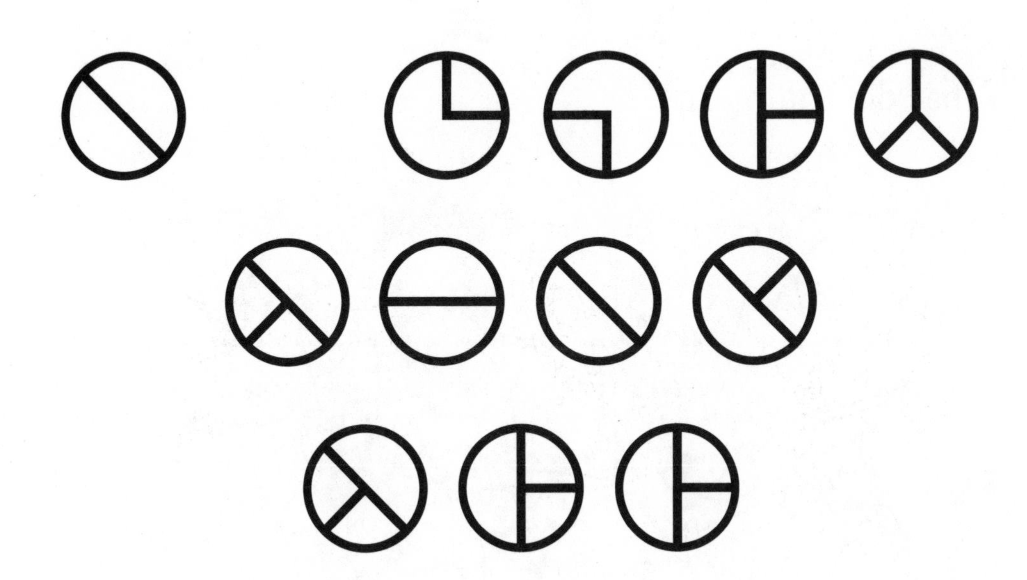

Answer Number 10

Even very small changes to a message can help to conceal the meaning. Laura Lane is only six and hasn't been writing for very long but even so she worked out a way of turning a message into code. This is the caption she put on one of her drawings.

DHIS GS HY KOG
DITTING DN FIS
BOGHOUSE GITH
S VONE.

What did she mean?

Answer Number 105

A relief mission was dropping essential food supplies over an isolated village suffering from a severe drought in the middle of nowhere. Being unable to land, and the crew having no knowledge of the native language, they scribbled a note on some paper in what they hoped was a language they would understand, knowing that blind people lived on the camp. The message was vital if the food was to be consumed safely. What must the natives do to some of the supplies to avoid illness?

Answers

1 **Romans rumbled**
Pax Vobiscum (Latin for 'Peace be with you'). The Roman letters that can also be used as numbers have been turned into Arabic numerals.

2 **Numbered knocks**
'Could we borrow a cup of sugar'. What size do you take in concrete boots?

3 **Dad in danger**
OVER MOON SEND BABY DADS KISS. The first and last letters of words in the left-hand column form the first and third letters of the new words. The first and third letters of words in the right-hand column form the second and fourth letters of the new words.

4 **Lost legacy**
LOOK BACK (of) BOOK CASE WILL AMID MESS. Take the first and third letter of each word and put them into the brackets.

5 **Abducted astronaut**
"Being taken to secret hideout in Santa Monica, LA." The alphabet is numbered from the middle. The odd numbers start at N (1) and go to Z (25). The even numbers start at M (2) and go to A (26).

6 **Ape antics**
Friends, Romans, Countrymen, lend me your ears, I come to bury Caesar not to praise him. The evil that me do lives after them, the good is oft interred with their bones, so let it be with Caesar.

7 **Teacher torture**
"I hate Latin. Let's meet after school and go for a burger & cola." Start with the I at the top right.

8 **Muddled matrix**
"Amsterdam, Frankfurt, Athens, Karachi, Bangkok, Singapore, US." Start at the A in the exact middle and go in a clockwise direction.

9 **Famous last words**
"Look under the old oak tree in my garden." The words are written backwards and every vowel is replaced with an X.

10 **Initially puzzling**
The first letter of each word is replaced with a random letter. The message reads: "This is my dog sitting in his doghouse with a bone."

11 **A novel novel**
"Suzy caught her breath as she noticed the dark haired man she had seen in the police photos standing outside her house. What should she do? Quickly she ran to the telephone and dialled the emergency number." All the vowels have been removed.

12 **Image problem**
Dear Katie, Bet you thought this was from lover-boy Rick! Did you spend hours in eager anticipation? Sorry to disappoint you. It was only from your best friend in all the world (who you now hate), Rachel.
This is mirror writing. Katie guessed that whilst she was looking in the bathroom mirror to brush her teeth. Hold the page up to a mirror and you will see the answer.

13 **Lost lyrics**
"A Day in the Life" (sorry Danny, it's been done!). The words are spelt backwards and with numbers in place of the vowels. The full stops are there to fool you.

14 **Missing Magnus**
"Gone to South of France back Friday." The dashes are there to mislead.

15 **Computer crime**
"He has a new program almost finished I will send you details ASAP – Sam." This substitution code works backwards (i.e., 26 = A, 1 = Z).

16 **Sharp-eyed sleuth**
"I suspect that my wife wants to kill me." This is a simple number code (1 = A, Z = 26), and the only problem is working out where to break up the strings of numbers.

17 **Teacher's travels**
"I have been called away on urgent business. Anyone who can decode this may go home early." This is a simple letter code: M = A, L = Z, etc.

18 **Et tu Brute?**
"We shall stab him in the Forum." This is a simple letter code: J = A, I = Z, etc.

19 **Shakespeare shocker**
"Roses are red, violets are blue, I wrote Shakespeare, phooey to you!"

20 **Gang greetings**
"You can join our gang as soon as you can read this note."

Answers

21 **Pecos perplexed**
"From Dead Men's Gulch ride two hours north until you see a cactus shaped like a letter Y. The mine is one hundred paces east of there."

22 **Computer crisis**
"To open the secret passage Press Control C and Left Shift together."

Kingly caper
23 "Have been imprisoned in castle by very large ogre. Can you help? Yours faithfully, Princess Linsey."

Eastern escapade
24 "We meet down by the docks in the warehouse with the green doors."

25 **Moriarty in memoriam**
"Good try, Holmes, but I still live and will return."

26 **Castle conundrum**
"Held captive by wicked uncle. Can you get me out?" The message is from Maid Marian.

27 **Alchemist's almanac**
"Add mercury to the mixture and bring to the boil stirring frequently."

28 **Templar trouble**
"Ha ha. Caught you! Don't be so nosy!"

29 **Baffling bard**
"For never was a story of more woe
Than this of Juliet and her Romeo."

30 **Generation game**
"If you want a clue as to where I am look in the pantry under the jam."

31 **Time travel**
1. Put solid fuel in tank one and liquid fuel in tank two.
2. Key in date time and location.
3. Press red blue white and green buttons in that order.

32 **Desert dilemma**
1) Death water
2) Killer drink
3) Water of life
4) Poisonous potion
(Therefore cask 3 is the safe one to drink from.)

33 **Filmstar frights**
"Do not worry. Police have put their plan into action and the culprit is about to be caught."

34 **Bridging the gap**
1) Deadly drop
2) Safe and Secure
3) Plummet point
(Bridge number 2 is therefore the bridge to take.)

35 **Corruptive campaign**
Matt. Notes are on top floor of science block in locker on second row down and third from right. From Simon.

36 **Absent astronaut**
Kidnapped by the enemy. Am on spaceship called Myqur Two. Help!

37 **'Mayday' mission**
Ship attacked by space terrorists. No hope for us but their next target is space station Nark Four. They must be stopped.

38 **Bemusing blooms**
1) Black iris
2) Yellow geranium
3) Golden larkspur
4) Blue chrysanthemum
5) Lilac lily

39 **Party pooper**
"You can only come to my party if you are bright enough to follow the trail I have left for you. Come to my place Monday at seven." Just follow the trail from the bottom right corner.

40 **Strange last words**
"We are surrounded and badly outnumbered. Please send all available reinforcements as soon as possible – Colonel Strange." This is a zig-zag message.

41 **Spurned spy**
"I could only fall in love with a spy as clever and cunning as myself. So unless you can read this note you have no chance – Susan." This is a zig-zag message.

42 **Crew conundrum**
"The ship leaves at midnight on the spring tide. If you want to join my crew you need sharp wits – Stone." This is a spiral from the bottom left corner.

Answers

43 **Shrewd Sean**
"Sean – Follow this winding spiral round and round until it eventually leads you to the heart of my message – gold buried here." This is a spiral from the top right corner.

44 **Door dilemma**
"The secret of my treasure can only be found by those resolute to follow a perilous path. Take the second door and do not fear." This starts on line four, column six and follows winding path out.

45 **Twain tangle**
"Tom Sawyer and Huckleberry Finn have found the robbers' hideout but don't dare tell. Look in the old caves down by the forest." This is a zig-zag.

46 **Fruitcake furore**
"Thought you would get your hands on my fruitcake recipe, did you? Well, I have v. bad news. It was in the coffin and is cremated – Vi." Imagine this is a mirror, so read from halfway up, then from halfway down, starting at the left column.

47 **Grid graduation**
"You will need every ounce of wit and guile to work out this secret message. So far you've had it easy but now you must work hard." Read from row one column five to column one, then from column ten to column six.

48 **Scout cipher**
I will meet you by the pond near the old barn.

49 **Bookham's blues**
"...thought you'd never wake up. The murderer is the old lady in the red hat."

50 **Much Morsing**
"Have secured Television studio. Leader will make announcement in one hour."

51 **Shipping shocker**
SOS, SOS. This is Royal Yacht Britannia. Sinking fast. God save the Queen.

52 **Dotty Dave**
"I am Dotty Dave." The message is on the man's tie in Morse code.

53 **Cockroach conundrum**
"Prisoner in dungeons. Help." The pattern is on the bug's back.

Answers

54 **Spot on**
"Not really ill. Wanted to miss English test." The dots on Andy's face have been painted on.

55 **Reel agony**
We're fed up with this. Why don't you take up soccer? Kind regards from the fish.

56 **Dotty dilemma**
"We are having a picnic in the park." The order of letters in each word is changed.

57 **Mixed Morse**
You need to be a clever Scout to work out what I've done. (The dots are dashes, and the dashes are dots.)

58 **Domino dilemma**
I don't suppose any of you chaps speak English, do you?

59 **Dotty digging**
Made in Brazil.

60 **Bun bonanza**
I am hiding upstairs.

61 **Crate clue**
They suspected trouble and ran. Will report again ASAP.

62 **Safe keeping**
"In each word push buttons in order."

63 **Painter puzzle**
The dominoes on the table read: "By Samuel Driscoll".

64 **Catastrophic car park**
A4, B5, C1, D2, E6, F3. The letters on registration plates are advanced by one from corresponding letters in each person's name. The numbers are A = 1, Z=26 from corresponding letters in the name.

65 **Literary loot**
The book to look in is *A Tale of Two Cities* by Charles Dickens. The numbers give a message written backwards, with the vowels uncoded but the consonants are represented by a number that is double their alphabetic value.

Answers

66 **Fishy Findings**
"Treasure is buried in cave at base of Highsea Bay cliffs." Letters are replaced by the one before in the alphabet.

67 **Rainbow riddle**
Each band contains the name of a colour. If you delete these letters the ones that are left give you the message. It reads: "To enter push three times on star."

68 **Confusing cans**
Baked beans.

69 **Hidden treasure**
The oak tree, Luckyhull.

70 **Bungling burglar**
The Boss strikes again!

71 **Nauseating numbers**
Five times the square of six.

72 **A troublesome title**
Red Alert.

73 **Lipstick to the rescue**
SOS stop this van!

74 **Rocky revelation**
Adam was here, May, Nineteen eighty-nine.

75 **Bolted boxes**
Mr Richkid's accounts.

76 **Candle Kerfuffle**
First of April, Nineteen fifty-five.

77 **Shopping strain**
Rosie's grammar book.

78 **Perplexing paths**
Follow the river.

79 **Button blast**
Red, third from left.

80 **Time trouble**
"Action stations."

81 **Hacker's horror**
Systems go.

82 **Wooden wonder**
Find a carpenter.

83 **Alien encounter**
Like a cup of tea?

84 **A-mazing message**
Keep turning left.

85 **Trunk test**
Dickens.

86 **Spread survey**
I know this too!

87 **Card clue**
B. Sotted.

88 **Brick bother**
The police are onto you. A long brick is a Morse dash, a short one a Morse dot.

89 **Nature's mysteries**
C. Camore. A large tree is a Morse dash, a small one is a Morse dot.

90 **Puzzling presents**
Tom, Dick and Harry. One name appears on each present. A holly leaf is a Morse dash, a holly berry is a Morse dot.

91 **Football fun**
Winnertown. A tall fan is a Morse dash, a short one is Morse dot.

92 **Diary dilemma**
Matt's party! A triangle pointing up is a Morse dash, one pointing down is a Morse dot.

93 **Nautical numbers**
Warning – iceberg looming. 1 is a Morse dash, 2 is a Morse dot.

94 **The test is yet to come**
Easter history test. ζ is a Morse dash, γ is a Morse dot.

95 **Dotty dog**
Blackie. The name is in Braille dots along the dog.

Answers

96 **Designer difficulty**
Spacini. Reading down the dress, the letters are spelled out in Braille dots.

97 **A rafty revelation**
It's behind you!

98 **The conversation's flagging**
We are moving.

99 **The problem's plane**
Left wing missing!

100 **Tribal tension**
Dinner's ready!

101 **Battle break**
Coffee time.

102 **Dodgy door**
Open sesame.

103 **The hole answer**
Forest waterfall.

104 **Cave confusion**
Left leads to sheer drop.

105 **Mission complete**
Must grind beans well.

106 **Party planning**
Hotel Royal, Saturday at eight.

Contents

Introduction

Although you have decided to study Psychology at AS or A Level, you may not have come across the subject before. Most people have the idea that psychology is about understanding why people do things. Although this is an aim of psychology, a more formal definition sees psychology as the *scientific* study of brain and behaviour.

Today, psychology is seen as a science, and studying Psychology will give you a real understanding of how to think scientifically. You will be introduced to the scientific method in the **Research methods** section, but essentially it means using the methods of science such as observation, measurement, and experimentation to study behaviour. Throughout this book you will be introduced to many examples of psychological studies and their findings, and learn how contemporary psychology works.

Because human behaviour is complicated, psychology has used a number of different **approaches** in trying to explain behaviour. These include learning, cognitive, and biological approaches in A Level Year 1 and AS, with psychodynamic and humanistic approaches added for the A Level Year 2. Knowledge of these approaches provides an essential background to the explanations and theories you will be studying during your course.

Structure of the book

This book is designed specifically for students new to Psychology who are following the AQA specification. All the authors are experienced teachers and examiners, and the content matches the AQA specification. Besides being introduced to the scientific method and approaches, you will also be introduced to topics representing the core areas of psychology. In A Level Year 1 and AS, these are **Social influence**, **Memory**, **Attachment**, **Psychopathology**, and **Biopsychology**. Throughout each topic there is reference to relevant approaches and research studies.

Research methods is a key area of psychology. As a science, it is critical that you understand the methods that are used to investigate behaviour and experience, and that you develop the skills to plan and carry out practical investigations. This topic covers the basics of the scientific approach. However, as research methods underpin all areas of psychology, throughout the topics covered in this book there is discussion of research methods issues, and you will also be given guidance on the sorts of studies you might try.

Key features of the book

A LEVEL ONLY

Some content is only relevant for students studying the full A Level, and will be clearly labelled.

EXAMPLE EXAM QUESTION

Example exam questions are given throughout the book on the full range of topics.

Exam hint

Exam hints accompany example exam questions, giving you expert guidance on what to look out for.

KEY STUDY

Certain research studies are described in detail. All studies mentioned in the AQA specification are provided as 'key studies'.

THINKING SCIENTIFICALLY

'Thinking scientifically' features contain important information about how to evaluate key studies.

Research methods link

Link boxes appear throughout the book and link back to the **Research methods** section.

Key term

These are the terms given on the specification that you will need to be able to define and understand.

ACTIVITIES

Short activities for home or the classroom aim to develop your understanding of the subject.

PRACTICAL ACTIVITY

A suggestion for a practical investigation is included at the end of each chapter.

Exam focus

At the end of every chapter there is an example exam question, model student answers, and examiner feedback.

Assessment objectives

During your course you will need to develop skills relating to the following assessment objectives.

AO1 – Demonstrate knowledge and understanding of scientific ideas, processes, techniques and procedures

AO2 – Apply knowledge and understanding of scientific ideas, processes, techniques and procedures:

- In a theoretical context
- In a practical context
- When handling qualitative data
- When handling quantitative data

AO3 – Analyse, interpret and evaluate scientific information, ideas and evidence, including in relation to issues, to:

- Make judgements and reach conclusions
- Develop and refine practical design and procedures

You will need to develop the ability to analyse and evaluate psychological theories, concepts, studies, and findings. This may involve what we call methodological evaluation of studies to determine whether they are valid and whether the findings are reliable. In addition, the significance of findings for our understanding of behaviour is a major issue in evaluating studies. Finally, in some questions you will need to be able to apply your knowledge and understanding to unfamiliar situations. For instance, can you apply your knowledge of eyewitness testimony to explain how to help a witness give an accurate account of an incident?

Throughout the specification there is an emphasis on research methods and findings, and your understanding of these will be assessed in the examination. However, you will acquire this understanding gradually as you progress through the year. It involves such skills as relating research findings to theories and models, understanding how to carry out psychological investigations, and the ability to select appropriate methods. Additional skills include evaluation of research methods in terms of, for instance, validity and ethics, and the application of psychological findings to the real world. As you can see, many of these skills relate to the Research methods topic. Others overlap with the analytic and evaluative assessment objectives mentioned earlier. This is why it is important not to worry too much over which assessment objective you are dealing with at any particular time.

The examination is designed so that if you answer the question set you will automatically be satisfying the various assessment objectives, so do not waste time worrying whether a question is AO1, AO2, or AO3. You must read the question carefully and look for the command words – e.g. explain, discuss, briefly outline, outline, evaluate – and do what it asks. For instance, if there is a scenario and you are asked to answer the question with reference to the scenario, then you must do this to have a chance of full marks. For more guidance on the exam and how to develop your exam skills, see page 300.

Assessment at AS

There will be two papers at AS, and in both, all questions will be compulsory. Therefore, you will need to have covered all of the AS specification. Both papers will use a variety of question styles, from multiple-choice to short essays. Remember that in many areas of psychology there is no one right answer. It is essential that you develop the ability to weigh up evidence in order to identify the most appropriate explanation.

The sequence of topics in the book follows the AS specification precisely and the examinations are organized in the same order. Paper 1 (Introductory topics in psychology) covers social influence, memory and attachment. Paper 2 (Psychology in context) will have sections on approaches in psychology (including biopsychology), psychopathology and research methods. Note, however, that research methods questions can be asked in any of the sections across both papers.

You have come into Psychology at a time when it has become one of the fastest growing subjects in schools, colleges, and in higher education. We hope that, besides introducing Psychology and preparing some of you for the AS examinations, this book also shows you that Psychology is a varied and exciting subject. And the second year is even more exciting...!

Simon Green, Rob Lewis, and Julia Willerton

Research methods

Introduction

The goal of psychology is to describe behaviour, predict behaviour, and ultimately control or change behaviour. This is not an easy task. Whilst people are naturally drawn to observe the behaviour of others and develop their own theories to explain what they see, humans are, alas, characterized by their biased and faulty thinking. We cannot therefore rely on such observations to be free from things like prejudice and emotional distortion.

Psychological evidence must be gathered as dispassionately as possible, and this is achieved through the use of the scientific method. This emphasizes the use of empirical evidence, i.e. evidence gathered by means of objective observation and measurement. It is an orderly, systematic approach to finding things out, and the knowledge gained through scientific procedures is considered the most dependable. It is the scientific method that has enabled the accumulation of a vast knowledge-base about behaviour. In order to be able to understand its value and appreciate how psychologists come to the conclusions they do, it is essential to know about the research processes that created this knowledge.

In this section we will be looking at some of the most important scientific methods used in psychological research. We will also look at the kinds of data gathered by this research, how this data is analysed, and how conclusions about behaviour are drawn from this data.

What is covered in Research methods?

Research methods and experiment designs

Experimental methods

A great deal of psychological knowledge has been gained by the use of experimental methods. In experiments, psychologists seek to control and manipulate events in order to establish precise cause-and-effect relationships. There are a number of types of experiments: laboratory, field, natural, and quasi-experiments.

Laboratory experiments

A **laboratory experiment**, sometimes referred to as a 'true' experiment, has three key features: direct manipulation of an independent variable, control, and randomization.

Direct manipulation of an independent variable

The **independent variable (IV)** is something that is altered by the researcher to bring about a change in behaviour. This change is measured as the **dependent variable (DV)**. It is important that these variables are **operationalized**. This means that it must be clear what the variables are and how they are measured. For example, if a researcher was interested in looking at the influence of alcohol on memory then he or she would need to be clear about the type and quantity of alcohol, and how exactly its effects on memory are going to be tested. A lack of such clarity can have serious consequences for the findings and conclusions of research.

The logic behind manipulating the IV to see the effect on the DV is returned to frequently elsewhere in this chapter.

Control

Control is achieved when, other than the independent variable, all other variables (known as **extraneous variables**) are held constant, so that the dependent variable can only be due to the manipulation of the independent variable. Control is also accomplished by having a control group and one or more experimental groups. Participants in the experimental group receive the independent variable treatment and participants in the control group do not. The control group then provide a baseline measure. If all other variables are controlled then any difference in outcomes between the control and experimental groups must be due to the independent variable. Control is discussed further on page 13.

Randomization

Participants are randomly allocated to conditions, for example by flipping a coin or using odds and evens with a random numbers table. This is to ensure that any extraneous influence associated with the participant is as likely to affect one group as the other and will therefore have little or no influence on the dependent variable. Other things are randomized too, for example the order in which stimuli are presented to participants, and the order in which participants take part in the experiment. Randomization is discussed further on pages 11–12.

Key terms

Laboratory experiment: an experiment that is carried out in a controlled environment where the independent variable is manipulated and extraneous variables are controlled, and cause-and-effect relationships are established.

Independent variable (IV): the variable that is manipulated in an experiment.

Dependent variable (DV): something that is measured following manipulation of the IV.

Operationalization of variables: how variables are defined and measured.

Extraneous variable: an unwanted variable that adds error to an experiment.

ACTIVITY 1: LABORATORY EXPERIMENTS

Look through the Key Studies in the chapters on Social influence, Memory, and Attachment. Select one laboratory experiment and identify the following features:

(a) The independent variable (IV)
(b) The dependent variable (DV)
(c) Variables that were controlled.

Field experiments

Field experiments are controlled studies that take place in natural settings. Like a laboratory experiment, the independent variable is manipulated in an effort to find a causal relationship. As this method seeks to measure natural behaviour, participants are often unaware that they are involved in research. The dependent variable is the behaviour of the participant.

Key terms

Field experiment: an experiment that takes place outside a laboratory environment, where the independent variable is manipulated and cause-and-effect relationships can be inferred.

Natural experiment: an experiment where naturally occurring changes in independent variables are observed.

Quasi-experiment: an experiment where participants cannot be randomly assigned to experimental and control groups.

ACTIVITY 2: FIELD EXPERIMENTS

Look through the Key Studies in the chapters on Social influence, Memory, and Attachment. Identify one field experiment and answer the following questions:

(a) What was the independent variable (IV)?
(b) What was the dependent variable (DV)?
(c) What extraneous variables were controlled?
(d) What did the researchers fail to control that might have had an effect on the results?

Natural experiments

In a **natural experiment** the independent variable is unplanned and has occurred because of a naturally occurring event. Sometimes, practical and ethical reasons dictate that this is often the only experimental method that can be used. Because the event is not planned by researchers, there is no control over variables and no direct manipulation of the independent variable. As a consequence, it is more difficult to pinpoint a cause-and effect relationship due to particular variables.

Quasi-experiments

In many kinds of research participants cannot be randomly assigned to experimental and control groups. In such cases, rather than random assignment to conditions, participants are often matched in some way, for example males may be in one condition and females in another, but they are matched for age, educational background, or other important variables. Strictly speaking, there is no control condition in a **quasi-experiment**, rather there is a comparison condition; for example, if we are comparing males to females in some regard, one is not providing a control (baseline) condition but a point of comparison between the two conditions.

The terms quasi- and natural experiment are often used interchangeably, or the natural experiment is considered a type of quasi-experiment. One key way to identify the difference between a quasi- and a natural experiment is regarding the extent to which there is planned manipulation of the independent variable. It is not possible to do this in natural experiments, but it is possible in quasi-experiments.

Strengths and limitations of experiment types

	Strengths	Limitations
Laboratory experiment	• High levels of control of extraneous variables. • High degree of replicability. • Cause-and-effect relationships can be uncovered.	• Reduced ecological validity. • Increased risk of investigator effects and demand characteristics. • Participants are often required to behave in ways that are artificial.
Field experiment	• Cause-and-effect relationships can be uncovered. • Higher levels of ecological validity than a true experiment. • Reduction in demand characteristics.	• Reduced control over extraneous variables. • Often more time consuming.
Natural and quasi-experiment	• Useful where it would be impractical or impossible to manipulate variables. • High levels of ecological validity.	• Not always possible to clearly identify cause-and-effect relationships.

Table 1 Strengths and limitations of different types of experiment

Experimental design

A basic experiment involves two conditions: one in which the variables are held constant (the control condition) and another in which the independent variable is manipulated (the experimental condition). If all variables other than the independent variable are held constant, then any difference in outcomes between the two conditions must be due to the independent variable. In each condition there are participants, and a decision has to be made when designing an experiment whether participants will take part in one or both conditions.

There are three types of experimental design: independent groups, repeated measures and matched pairs.

Independent groups design

In the **independent groups design**, different participants are used in each of the conditions, i.e. each group of participants is independent of the other. In a true experiment, the condition in which each participant is placed is decided randomly. By random allocation it is hoped that participant variables balance out across conditions, although of course there is always the chance that they will not. The effect of participant variables on results can be reduced by increasing the size of the sample – 'outlier' scores (extreme scores) have less effect when there are more scores.

Key term

Independent groups design: an experimental design in which each participant takes part in only one of the conditions of the experiment.

An example would be when a sample of 20 participants is selected to take part in a study on working memory. They are divided into two groups by the toss of a coin. Ten participants will be in the control condition, where they will silently read through a list of words before being tested for recall. The other ten participants will be in the experimental condition and read through a list of words while repeating the word 'the' out loud. They are then tested for recall. The performance of participants in one group is independent of the performance of participants in the other (see Fig. 1).

Control condition	Experimental condition
Participant 1	Participant 11
Participant 2	Participant 12
Participant 3	Participant 13
Participant 4	Participant 14
Participant 5	Participant 15
Participant 6	Participant 16
Participant 7	Participant 17
Participant 8	Participant 18
Participant 9	Participant 19
Participant 10	Participant 20

Fig. 1 An example of independent groups design

Repeated measures design

In the **repeated measures design**, the same participants are used in each of the conditions of the experiment. So for example, participants in one condition might be required to read through a list of words whilst repeating the word 'the' out loud before being tested on their recall of the list. The same participants would also read through a list of words in silence before being tested for recall (see Fig. 2).

Key term

Repeated measures design: an experimental design where each participant takes part in all conditions of the experiment.

This design avoids the problem of participant variables encountered in independent groups designs. Any difference in scores between the two conditions cannot be because people in one condition just happen to be better at the task than ones in the other condition. There are drawbacks with this design however. For one, two sets of stimulus materials will need to be developed, and these will need to be carefully assessed as being equivalent to one another in all respects. Also, it may be that the scores in the two conditions are different because the same participants were used. For example, they may have improved through practice, or become fatigued. These are order effects, and researchers must take steps to minimize these when using a repeated measures design. There are two principle methods of dealing with order effects: counterbalancing and randomization.

Control condition	Experimental condition
Participant 1	Participant 1
Participant 2	Participant 2
Participant 3	Participant 3
Participant 4	Participant 4
Participant 5	Participant 5
and so on	and so on

Fig. 2 An example of repeated measures design

Key terms

Counterbalancing: a strategy for reducing order effects by ensuring that participant variables occur with equal frequency in all conditions of the experiment.

Randomization: the process of using chance to decide the order in which participants experience the experimental or control condition when using a repeated measures design. It is also used to decide the order of use of stimuli.

Matched pairs design: an experimental design where participants in each condition of the experiment are matched according to important variables.

Confounding variable: an uncontrolled variable that has an effect on the dependent variable.

Counterbalancing

The **counterbalancing** strategy for reducing order effects has half the participants doing one condition first, and the other half of the participants the same condition second. In this way, any order effects are balanced between the two conditions and thus should have no greater effect on the overall scores of one condition than another. For example, if we label the experimental condition 'A' and control condition 'B' then, as can be seen in Figure 3, we can counterbalance so that some participants do A first and some do B first.

Participant 1 – A	Participant 1 – B
Participant 2 – B	Participant 2 – A
Participant 3 – A	Participant 3 – B
Participant 4 – B	Participant 4 – A
Participant 5 – A	Participant 5 – B
Participant 6 – B	Participant 6 – A

Fig. 3 An example of counterbalancing: order effects are balanced between the two conditions

Randomization

This strategy involves **randomizing** the order of trials. Rather than participants alternately experiencing one condition first then the other, researchers randomly assign whether or not participants do one or other condition first. As in other cases where researchers use the mathematical properties of chance, such as in random sampling, this is an example of researchers using chance to control variables.

Matched pairs design

In the **matched pairs design**, participants are matched as closely as possible with another participant. They are then randomly allocated to one condition or the other. For example, if researchers were investigating the effects of watching prosocial films (films that promote social acceptance) on the behaviour of children, they might want to match children on their prior levels of prosocial behaviour. Once two children are matched on this important variable, one child could be randomly assigned to the experimental condition (exposure to prosocial films) and the other to the control condition (no exposure to prosocial films).

In some ways matched pairs could be seen as a design somewhere between independent groups and repeated measures – it allows researchers to use the same stimulus materials for all participants, thus eliminating one potential **confounding variable**. As the pairs are matched on the important variables, it also reduces participant variables and the impact of individual differences. However, these benefits are dependent on the ability of researchers to both identify the key characteristics that need matching and then to effectively match pairs on this variable. This is a complex and indeed often impossible task, leading some researchers to argue that the only true matched pairs design is one using identical twins.

Design	Strengths	Limitations
Independent groups design	• There are no order effects. • As both conditions can be tested simultaneously, there is a potential saving of time and effort. • As participants are involved in one condition only, potential investigator effects and demand characteristics are reduced.	• Participant variables may affect the results. By chance, participants in one group may differ in some crucial way to participants in the other. • Participants are only doing one condition, therefore twice as many participants are needed for this design compared to repeated measures.
Repeated measures design	• Uses fewer participants – get two or more scores per participant, saving time, effort and money. • Participant variables are not a concern.	• There is a risk of order effects and, because of the need to limit these, the design can be a complex one. • The cost of a loss of participants is greater, since data for both conditions is lost compared to one in independent groups design.
Matched pairs design	• Good control of participant variables. • Eliminates order effects.	• Matching participants is very difficult.

Table 2 Strengths and limitations of experimental designs

Variables and control

A defining feature of the laboratory experiment is the manipulation and control of variables. By only having one thing differing between conditions (the independent variable), researchers can conclude that any difference in the measured behaviour of participants (the dependent variable) must be due to this one thing that differs. That researchers can say that the manipulation of the variable caused the difference is the great strength of the experimental method. However, this can only be said to the extent that all other important variables have been controlled, so that researchers can confidently say that only the manipulation of the IV caused the change.

Control is essential to the experimental method. However, the reality is that it is virtually impossible to eliminate interference from unwanted variables. These variables that have unwanted effects are called **extraneous variables**, and an essential part of the design of an experiment is to ensure that extraneous variables have as little influence on the outcome as possible.

Key terms

Extraneous variable: an unwanted variable that adds error to an experiment.

Standardization: a means of ensuring that all participants in an investigation have exactly the same experience.

Extraneous variables can come from *random error*. A random error is something that cannot be predicted, such as a participant's state of mind during the experiment, or something physical like having a cold (or even being cold!). Because random errors are just that – random – then the only way to deal with them is by randomly allocating participants to experimental and control conditions, so that the effect of errors might be balanced out and therefore have minimal impact. One source of random errors comes from a lack of **standardization**. Standardization means that all participants in a study have exactly the same experience, so that individual experience does not cause some participants to engage with the study differently. Procedures therefore need to be standardized to ensure that all participants have the same experience. For example, the instructions given to participants need to be exactly the same so that if there is an error in interpretation it then affects all participants in all conditions.

Extraneous variables can also come from *constant error*. These errors are more serious than random errors because they have more of an effect on one condition of the experiment than the other. A typical source of constant error is when participant characteristics affect one condition more than the other, often a result of failing to counterbalance or randomize. Randomization in this sense is not just used to randomly allocate participants to conditions in a repeated measures design, but also to randomly allocate order or use of stimuli. For example, an extraneous variable might arise from the order of words presented to participants in a memory recall task – perhaps the words at the end of the list are less familiar than those at the start.

A constant error that remains uncontrolled in an experiment becomes a confounding variable. This is something that has an effect on the dependent variable, thus making it is impossible to say that the DV is the result of the IV – it could well be one or more constant errors causing the difference.

ACTIVITY 3: CONTROLS

A psychologist is conducting an experiment to investigate whether time of day influences reaction time. The psychologist invites participants to complete a computer-based game during which coordination errors are recorded. Participants complete this game either at 12 midnight or at 6am.

(a) Identify one likely source of random error.
(b) Identify one likely source of constant error.
(c) Outline three controls that you would use in this experiment to deal with extraneous variables.

Observational techniques

Observational techniques are useful when the researcher wants to study natural behaviour. This might involve, for example, discovering the circumstances under which certain behaviours occur and their frequency. On the face of it, this resembles what we as humans do anyway – 'people-watch'. We are constantly watching the behaviour of others and inferring causes and origins for what we see. Observation as a scientific method, however, involves making objective systematic observations. What is to be recorded from observations is planned in advance, before the observations begin, based on clear and testable hypotheses. This ensures that observations are recorded as objectively as possible.

Types of observation

There are different types of observation, varying in the degree to which they reflect natural behaviour, the extent to which the participants know they are being observed, and the level of involvement of the researcher in the observational context.

Controlled versus naturalistic observation

Laboratory experiments often involve observations of behaviour. For example, a psychologist might investigate the likelihood of a person administering electric shocks to another participant with and without another person present. This would be an example of a **controlled observation**. Alternatively, researchers may want to observe behaviour in entirely natural settings. For example, they may wish to investigate the queuing behaviour of shoppers. There is no control of the setting and people make their own choices about how they behave. This is called **naturalistic observation**.

	Strengths	Limitations
Controlled observation	High level of control. Easier to establish cause-and-effect relationships.	The environment is artificial, therefore you may not get natural behaviour.
Naturalistic observation	High degree of natural behaviour meaning findings can be generalized to everyday life.	No control of variables so difficult to establish cause-and-effect relationships.

Table 3 Strengths and limitations of controlled and naturalistic observations

ACTIVITY 4: CONTROLLED OBSERVATION

Ainsworth's Strange Situation (page 164) is an example of a controlled observation.

(a) State one limitation of this example of a controlled observation.

(b) How might researchers make this controlled observation a naturalistic one? What drawbacks might they face in doing this?

Covert versus overt observation

Psychologists will often choose to observe behaviour without revealing themselves, so that participants are not aware that they are being observed. Observations may take place from hidden viewpoints, from secret cameras, or from behind two-way mirrors. A psychologist might even become a member of a group in order to observe behaviour of individuals, hiding their true intentions and identity. These are known as **covert observations**.

When participants know that their behaviour is being watched and recorded they are taking part in an **overt observation**. With overt observation the psychologists are usually open with the participants about the purpose and scope of the research.

	Strength	Limitation
Covert observation	More valid results from participants because natural behaviour is being observed.	Lack of informed consent means there are ethical issues
Overt observation	Ethically sound as participants know they are being observed and will have given consent.	Participants may not behave naturally if they are aware of being observed.

Table 4 Strengths and limitations of overt and covert observations

Participant versus non-participant observation

Participant observation involves the researchers becoming part of the group or situation that is being observed. For example, if the queuing

Key terms

Controlled observation: observation that takes place in a highly controlled environment such as a laboratory setting.

Naturalistic observation: observing people in their natural environment without control over variables.

Covert observation: observation that takes place without the knowledge or awareness of participants.

Overt observation: observation that takes place with the full knowledge and awareness of participants.

Participant observation: data is gathered by the psychologists whilst being part of the observed group or situation.

Key terms

Non-participant observation: data is gathered 'from a distance' without the psychologist being involved in the observed group or situation.

Behavioural categories: a detailed list of all behaviours to be recorded during an observation.

behaviour of shoppers is being investigated, then a psychologist might do their observations in the role of a shopper in a queue.

On the other hand, behaviour may be observed at a distance so that the researchers are not involved in what they are observing. In the example of queuing behaviour, the psychologist may pretend to be another shopper at a distance while observing behaviour, or record the behaviour from hidden cameras. This is **non-participant observation**.

	Strengths	Limitations
Participant observation	Greater insights into behaviour are gained by being part of the group/situation, increasing validity of findings.	Objectivity of observations are affected by being part of the group/situation.
Non-participant observation	Lack of direct involvement ensures greater objectivity.	Data lacks richness of that provided by participant observation, e.g. feelings and motivations of participants.

Table 5 Strengths and limitations of participant and non-participant observations

Observational design

To reduce observer bias and ensure that observations really are guided by the hypotheses, it is essential that the 'what' and 'how' of observations are planned in advance. Researchers have to be clear about exactly what behaviour is being observed and exactly how that behaviour is going to be measured and recorded. Without careful consideration of this it is possible that the result will not do what it claims to be doing (i.e. it will lack validity) and that there will be observer bias. Designing observations carefully is essential for reducing observer bias. People in everyday life often interpret the same events differently and it is important that, as far as possible, this tendency is eliminated from psychological research. This is done by making observations systematic and objective through the use of a coding system.

Behavioural categories

It is important to be clear about what the target behaviour actually is. For example, if researchers were interested in observing aggressive behaviour of primary-aged children during school breaks, then at the start researchers would need to decide on what exactly constitutes aggressive behaviour. Aggression can be defined in a number of ways, and many activities in a playground that might look aggressive to a casual observer might not constitute aggression from a psychological perspective. Clarifying what is meant by aggression will involve creating an exhaustive list of all possible behaviours in the playground that would fit the definition of aggression.

This list gives the researchers their **behavioural categories**. The next step would be to develop a coding system so that observations can be made efficiently and objectively. These behavioural categories and codes would be used on an observational checklist, which is used to record the observations. If the researchers want an indication of the degree to which something has occurred, such as a measure of the response to an aggressive behaviour from another child, then they might also include a scale.

Once an observational checklist has been created, a decision has to be made about how the observations will be conducted. For instance, how long the observational period will be and how frequently the observations will be recorded on the checklist.

Event sampling

One option for recording behaviours is to use **event sampling**. This is basically to record on the checklist the number of times a particular thing occurs. For example, researchers might record the number of shoves, kicks and punches observed during the school playtime (see Fig. 4). The chronological order of events is not taken into consideration; this is nothing more than a frequency count.

Key terms

Event sampling: a record on an observational checklist of the number of times an event occurs.

Time sampling: a record of an event made on an observational checklist after a standardized interval.

Slap	III
Kick	I
Push	IIII
Pinch	I
Poke	II

Fig. 4 Example of behavioural categories using event sampling in a study of types of playground aggression

Time sampling

It might be that the order of events is important in the observation. In this case the researchers would record when an event occurs. For example, observations could be taken at predetermined intervals of 30 seconds which are then recorded chronologically (see Fig. 5).

Behaviours	1 (30 secs)	2 (30 secs)	3 (30 secs)	4 (30 secs)	5 (30 secs)	6 (30 secs)	7 (30 secs)
Slap	I		I	I			
Kick				I			
Push	I		I	I		I	
Pinch		I					
Poke					I		I

Fig. 5 Example of behavioural categories using time sampling in a study of types of playground aggression

Although careful design of an observational checklist should maximize the objectivity of observations, in practice it is difficult to be absolutely certain that observations of behaviour will be recorded in the same way by all observers (that is, to ensure that observations are absolutely reliable). There are a number things that researchers can do to ensure a high degree of agreement between observers, and these are discussed in the section on reliability on page 41.

Self-report techniques

As the title suggests, **self-report techniques** require participants to somehow report on themselves. This is typically done by getting participants to answer questions or respond in some way to statements. Two principle methods of doing this are questionnaires and interviews.

Strengths	Limitations
• Allows more detailed access to participant thoughts and feelings. • Enables psychologists to investigate what participants might think, feel, or do in the future.	• They rely on participants being honest, articulate and insightful, which might not always be the case. • Participants may feel they need to give socially desirable answers.

Table 6 Strengths and limitations of self-report techniques

Questionnaires

A **questionnaire** is a list of predetermined questions to which participants must respond. By asking questions the researcher typically seeks to find out what people think and feel about something – in other words, they want to establish the attitudes of people.

Key terms

Self-report techniques: a research method which requires participants to report on themselves.

Questionnaire: a self-report method where participants are presented with a set of predetermined written questions.

There are a number of ways in which a questionnaire can be administered, each having their own advantages and disadvantages depending on such things as the content of the questionnaire, and how important it is that participants do not conspire or are distracted.

- In presence of researcher: questionnaires could be given out to individuals to complete, or to groups of individuals. It may even be conducted over the telephone.
- In absence of researcher: questionnaires could be sent through the post or, as is increasingly the case, via the internet as an email or web page.

Strengths	Limitations
• Can be cost-effective and time-efficient since they can be quickly administered to large numbers of participants. • When completed privately and anonymously they can provide honest data, improving reliability. • The reduced involvement of the researcher lessens the risk of investigator influence on the behaviour of participants.	• Response rates can be poor when administered in absence of the researcher. It can then be difficult to generalize findings. • It may be that only certain people return them, e.g. those who are motivated or who have the time, so that results only represent a certain type of person. • It is difficult to phrase questions in ways that are not open to interpretation by the participants.

Table 7 Strengths and limitations of questionnaires

Questionnaire construction

An effective questionnaire needs a good response rate and needs to be well designed. A poorly designed questionnaire does not become better because lots of people have completed it. There are a number of important considerations when constructing a questionnaire. One is to consider the sequence of questions. For example, it is usually better to start with easy questions that put respondents at ease rather than make them defensive. Some questions might be included that have little relevance to the research aim. These can be useful in obscuring the main purpose of the research so that demand characteristics are reduced (you can read more about demand characteristics on page 34). Another thing to consider is the format of the questions. Questions need to be written in a way that not only makes them clear and not open to interpretation, but also in a way that makes them easy to analyse. There are two basic types of question: open and closed questions.

Closed questions

Closed questions only allow participants to respond in certain kinds of ways. Typically, the questionnaire will provide a fixed number of responses from which the participant selects the one that applies to them. These could be yes/no responses, multiple category choices, or even rating scales where participants are asked to indicate on a scale the extent to which they agree or disagree with something.

'I love Psychology.'

Yes ☐

No ☐

Don't know ☐

'I find Psychology stimulating.'

|___|___|___|___|___|___|

1 2 3 4 5 6

Not very Very

A Level Psychology	Excellent	Good	Fair	Poor
Text book				
Class materials				
Classroom				
Topics				

Fig. 6 Some examples of closed questions

Strengths	Limitations
• Good when asking questions with finite, clear-cut answers. • Provide control by requiring answers and in a particular way. • Require minimum effort to answer. • Saves time, especially in analysis.	• You need to know the range of answers to the questions. • Can frustrate respondents, e.g. when their preferred answer is not available. • Can create a lack of engagement. • Longer questionnaires cause fatigue.

Table 8 Strengths and limitations of questionnaires

Open questions

Open questions allow respondents to answer freely without restriction. They allow respondents to answer in more depth, giving opportunities to explain answers and express opinions, providing good qualitative data. Open questions may even contain unexpected content that gives the researchers new lines of enquiry.

What do you feel is the best thing about your Psychology course?

....
....
....
....
....

If you could change one thing about A Level Psychology, what would it be and why would you want the change?

....
....
....
....
....

Fig. 7 Examples of open questions

Strengths	Limitations
Offers flexibility to the respondent in the way he/she responds. Good when you do not know the range of possible answers to put into closed questions. Good way of accessing motivations and feelings.	Provide qualitative data which can be difficult to analyse. More time consuming for participants to answer. Questions may not be answered in helpful ways, e.g. difficult to interpret.

Table 9 Strengths and limitations of open questions

Interviews

Interviews involve researchers and participants engaging in a face-to-face conversation, so that rather than participants responding to written questions they respond to the verbal questions of the investigator. The way that questions are asked can either be very fixed or can have a considerable degree of flexibility.

Key terms

Interviews: a self-report method where participants answer questions face-to-face.

Qualitative data: descriptive data that typically relate to things that cannot be easily measured, such as how people think and feel about something.

Strengths	Limitations
• A well-conducted interview can address sensitive complex issues that other methods are unable to. • Interviews are a good source of **qualitative data**.	• Participant responses can be influenced easily by researchers. • Interviews work best with participants who are confident, honest and articulate. • Interviews are highly dependent on the skills of the interviewer, especially with unstructured interviews.

Table 10 Strengths and limitations of interviews

Structured interviews

Structured interviews involve the use of a set of predetermined questions. The structured interview can appear in many respects like a questionnaire, but the questions are asked rather than written down for the participant to answer themselves. The responses of participants are recorded, either electronically, manually, or a combination of both.

Unstructured interviews

In **unstructured interviews**, the researcher works more to a framework than a set of predetermined questions. There may be questions that are formulated in advance, but the structure of the interview is more likely to be guided by themes than explicit questions. This allows the interviewer to respond to the answers given by the interviewees; for example, to seek clarification or expansion and to pursue new lines of enquiry. It is therefore a much more flexible way of conducting interviews.

Key terms

Structured interviews: an interview that follows a predetermined set of questions.

Unstructured interviews: a flexible interview based around themes rather than fixed questions, allowing interviewers to respond to the answers of interviewees.

	Strengths	Limitations
Structured interviews	Because all participants have the same questions it is possible to compare responses and thus identify trends and patterns.	More time consuming than a questionnaire, often with little obvious additional benefit.
Unstructured interviews	Allows the interviewee to go into more depth and detail than a structured interview.	The information gathered is difficult to analyze objectively. There is an increased risk of investigator bias. Requires considerable skill on the part of the interviewer to be done well.

Table 11 Strengths and limitations of structured and unstructured interviews

Design of interviews

In many respects, the considerations that apply to questionnaire design also apply to the design of interviews.

Interviews can contain open and closed questions, although the latter is less usual. Since the aim is to get as much useful information from participants as possible, it is important to give very careful consideration to the questions being asked. A number of factors will influence this, not least whether the interview is going to be structured or semi-structured. It is important to ensure that the questions being asked are the right questions to get the right kind of information from interviewees with the desired detail. Also, the questions must be worded in such a way so that they cannot be misinterpreted and do not trigger a social desirability response in the interviewee. For example, if a researcher was interviewing a parent about their child-rearing practices, a question such as 'How often do you beat your child?' might not get a very accurate response. It may be that some of the interviewees 'beat their child' but trying to access this information with a question like that is almost certainly going to be unsuccessful.

It is usually good practice to start interviews with basic factual questions and questions of less importance to the research. Interviewees are likely to be most nervous and guarded in their responses at the start of an interview, giving poorer answers to questions. The questions most likely to give the detailed information you want are therefore best left to later in the interview.

Research has shown that the type of interviewer is a factor in interviews, depending on the nature of the interview. For example, the age and gender of the interviewer might influence responses in interviews dealing with sexual matters. Another example is the potential cultural biases that might arise when the interviewer is from a different ethnic group to the interviewee.

Consideration must not only be given to the characteristics of the interviewer but also to interviewing skills. It is not easy to conduct a good interview as it requires well-developed communication skills and lots of practice in interviewing. Often considerable training is needed to ensure that the interviewer has the skill to make the interviewee feel at ease, and that they appear trustworthy so that the interviewee gives full and natural answers.

Correlations

Key terms

Correlation: an analysis of the relationship between co-variables.

Co-variables: the variables measured in correlational analysis.

When two or more variables are in some way associated we say they are **correlated**. Correlational studies therefore are ones that look for relationships between variables. The variables being measured are known as **co-variables**. Rather than being a research method as such, correlation is more of a technique used to analyse data. It could be that observational or self-report methods were used to gather data, but correlation techniques are used in the analysis of that data.

Correlational studies only allow researchers to infer relationships between variables, and are particularly useful in situations when it would not be possible to do experimental studies. For example, researchers have found a strong correlation between smoking tobacco and lung disease. It would not be possible to do an experiment to prove that smoking causes lung disease as the practical and ethical difficulties are insurmountable. However, the correlation is so strong, even when important factors like lifestyle are taken into account, that it is generally accepted that the relationship is best explained as a causal one.

A correlational analysis will tell us what kind of relationship exists between the variables. Relationships are positive, negative, curvilinear, or zero correlations.

- A **positive correlation** is when as one variable increases, the other variable increases.
- A **negative correlation** is when one variable increases as the other variable decreases.
- A curvilinear correlation is where there is both a positive and a negative relationship between two variables, for example a relationship may start off being positive but end up being negative (see page 59 for a further discussion of this).
- A zero correlation is when there is no clear relationship between variables.

Key terms

Positive correlation: a relationship between co-variables where one variable increases as another variable increases.

Negative correlation: a relationship between co-variables where one variable increases as another variable decreases.

Correlation	Example
Positive	People of less attractiveness tend to choose less attractive dates.
Negative	The more that people are vaccinated for a specific illness, the less that illness occurs.
Curvilinear	As temperature increases so do levels of aggression, but as temperature continues to increase levels of aggression decrease.
Zero	There is no relationship between intelligence and the amount of ice cream eaten.

Fig. 8 Some examples of correlations

Strengths	Limitations
• Correlations allow researchers to investigate situations that could not be done experimentally. • Correlations do not just indicate a relationship but the strength of that relationship.	• Correlations are seriously affected by sample size – the smaller the sample the less accurate the coefficient (see page 24 for more about coefficients). • Correlations cannot reliably establish cause-and-effect. • Correlations only work for linear relationships; they do not work for curvilinear ones.

Table 12 Strengths and limitations of correlations

Key term

Correlation coefficient: a statistical measure of the relationship between two variables, i.e. the degree to which changes to the value of one predict changes to the value of another.

Analysis and interpretation of correlations

Correlational analysis tells us more than just whether the variables are related in some way; it also tells us something about the strength and direction of the relationship. The direction, and to some degree strength, of the relationship can be represented visually on a graph called a scattergram (see page 58 for a description of a scattergram). However, the key way that the strength and direction is indicated is by something called the **correlation coefficient**. This is a numerical representation of the relationships between co-variables, calculated by a statistical test, for instance Spearman's rho. It ranges between +1 and –1, the sign indicating whether the correlation is positive or negative. +1 represents a perfect positive correlation: as one variable increases the other variable will always increase. –1 represents a perfect negative correlation: as one variable increases the other variable will always decrease. In reality, psychological investigations simply do not result in perfect correlations like this. The coefficient sits on a sliding scale somewhere between 0 and +1 or –1. The closer the coefficient is to + or –1, the stronger the correlation is. The correlation grows weaker as it nears 0. At 0, there is absolutely no correlation. The sign in front of the coefficient only indicates the type of correlation, not its strength. For example, +0.6 is exactly the same strength correlation as –0.6, the only difference being that one is a positive correlation and the other is negative.

As a 'rule of thumb', when the calculated coefficient falls below 0.5 (either – or +) then it indicates that the coefficient may not be significant (i.e. large enough for us to be confident that there really is a relationship between two variables). This is not always the case however; for example, coefficients below 0.5 can be significant when larger amounts of data are being analysed. As large coefficients are statistically more likely to occur by chance when the sample size is small, researchers need to be cautious about jumping to conclusions in these circumstances when they find a big and impressive coefficient. (The section on inferential analysis on page 64 will explain the process of how it is decided whether or not findings are significant.)

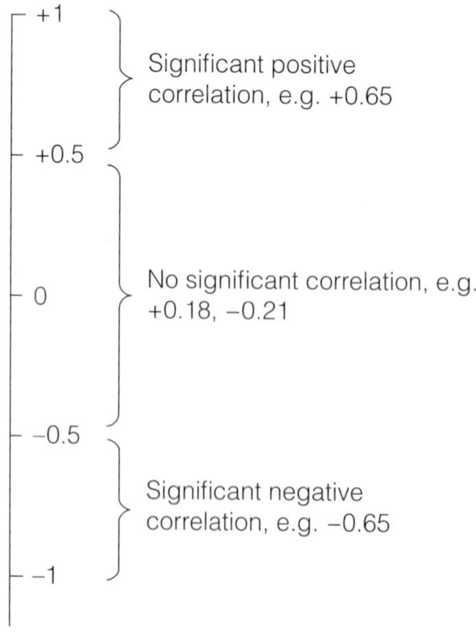

Fig. 9 Correlation scale

The difference between correlations and experiments

The key difference between a correlational study and an experiment is that, unlike experiments, correlations do not reliably point to cause-and-effect relationships. A correlation study gives us an indication of the nature of the relationship between the co-variables, for example if the correlation is positive or negative, but it does not tell us why the co-variables are related. In other words, a correlation does not imply causation.

If, after correlational analysis, a relationship between co-variables is found, the researcher has a decision to make about how the relationship is interpreted. Correlations can occur for a number of reasons, and which reason is selected should be based on a combination of theoretical knowledge and a clear understanding of the data and sample used. For instance, extreme scores (or 'outliers') can distort coefficients considerably, especially with small samples. Also, when a sample is small it is less likely to truly reflect the population it supposedly represents, so conclusions should only be drawn with great caution. As a rule, for statistical reasons, greatest caution should be taken when the sample size is less than 100.

The choices are:

1. **A cause-and-effect explanation.** The researcher could decide that one variable actually caused the other variable to either increase or decrease as the other increased or decreased. However, even though we might elect that a causal relationship is the most likely explanation, the correlation does not prove that this is the case.
2. **A third variable explanation.** Something in the background, other than the measured variables, is creating the apparent relationship between co-variables. For example, there is a relationship between school results and income in later life. School results do not cause increased income, but rather they appear related because of another variable – people who get good grades tend to be harder working.
3. **A chance relationship.** The relationship between co-variables has no meaning beyond chance. Sometimes things appear to be related when in fact they are not – it is just a statistical anomaly, which occasionally happens even with large samples. For example, there is a correlation between teacher salaries and the price of alcohol – as one increases, so does the other. You might look for background economic factors that make these two things look related, but it is almost certainly a chance correlation.

Content analysis

Key term

Content analysis: the analysis of the content of media, such as text or audio/visual sources.

With **content analysis**, behaviour is not directly studied. Rather, it is a process of investigating the content of the medium in which behaviour is recorded. This may be mass media (e.g. TV, film, magazines, etc.), historical documents (e.g. crime records), or any other recorded source. For example, a psychologist might be interested in the different ways in which tabloid newspapers stereotype genders when they describe men and women in their stories. Content analysis is employed when the kind of information sought is either too costly, or not possible or practical to obtain in other ways. It is particularly useful when it is used in conjunction with other methods (known as a 'mixed methods' approach), as the evidence obtained can be used to corroborate data gathered through other methods.

Strengths	Limitations
• It can be relatively straightforward to get access to media that provide rich sources of information. • As the method does not require direct contact with people, investigators cannot influence behaviour.	• There may be a lack of objectivity, since researchers have to make decisions about what behaviour to look for and how to categorize it. • It is a description of behaviour rather than an explanation of it.

Table 13 Strengths and limitations of content analysis

Content analysis and coding

Content analysis is basically a statistical process that involves categorizing and quantifying events and aspects of behaviour as they occur in some selected medium. In many respects, the challenges presented by content analysis resemble those in observational studies, the categorizing and coding of events and behaviour. Decisions have to be made very early on about what is being investigated and how this can best be measured. As with other methods, research starts with an operationalized hypothesis, informed by existing theory and research.

As content analysis involves converting content into some kind of objective measure, one of the first considerations is deciding on a coding system relevant to the medium (or 'population') of interest, for example newspaper, film, or web content. Sometimes it is possible to use a pre-existing coding system, validated by previous research. Usually, however, it involves researchers developing their own coding systems. This can be relatively straightforward when dealing with such things as how often a particular word is used, or how many people are involved. Coding is a little trickier when dealing with subjective elements of media, such as interpreting the meaning of what people say or judging emotional responses. Researchers would always need to establish a reliable coding system by repeatedly trialling it, and adjusting it as necessary against samples of material very similar to that which will be used in the eventual study.

As with the observational method, it is important that the reliability of coding is established. This would usually involve at least one independent person using the coding system alongside the researchers, and checking all the coding for close agreement (see page 41 for a description of inter-observer reliability). Following the coding process may be a further thematic analysis of the data, so that the findings are categorized into themes and concepts.

Steps involved in content analysis

Step 1: State the aims and hypotheses. For example, researchers are interested in how mental health is represented in tabloid newspapers and how such reporting might perpetuate negative attitudes towards individuals with mental illness. They hypothesize that tabloid newspapers portray mental health in negative and stereotyped ways.

Step 2: Decide on the sample, that is, the limits of what is going to be analysed. For example, daily tabloids *The Sun* and the *Mirror* published Monday to Friday, over a period of six weeks from the first Monday in May.

Step 3: Decide on units of analysis and develop a coding system. For example, researchers might include the frequency with which mental health issues are reported, the kinds of words used in the reporting, and the emotional content of the reporting.

Step 4: Establish reliability in the coding system. This might be trialled against editions of *The Sun* and the *Mirror* from a period different to that under investigation. Make any adjustments and check for reliability, making further adjustments to the coding system as necessary.

Step 5: Analyse the findings and interpret them in terms of the hypothesis. For example, use qualitative methods (e.g. thematic analysis) and/or quantitative methods (e.g. inferential and descriptive analysis), as appropriate.

Thematic analysis

Thematic analysis is a technique used to identify patterns of meanings and themes within qualitative data. It is used with methods such as case study, content analysis and self-report. Thematic analysis often begins with a process of developing codes with which to label data. The 'data' in this instance are the ideas that you are interested in identifying (i.e. the 'themes'). Having a code which applies to a particular theme makes recording instances of that theme much easier. For example, you may be analysing the content of an interview you have conducted with someone about their childhood school experiences, and this might run to many pages when in text form (called a 'transcript'). Given the context of the research, an example of what you might be looking for could be references to positive feelings about teachers. You might code this 'theme' as 'teacher positive' or 'TP' and note this on the transcript whenever it appears. Negative references to teachers might be coded and recorded as 'NT', and so on (see the discussion of content

Key terms

Thematic analysis: a method for analysing qualitative data that focuses on identifying themes and patterns in the data.

analysis on page 26). Researchers will often be already aware of existing theory and research of themes that may emerge from data, and therefore may directly search for themes. Sometimes, however, themes emerge from the analysis which have not been identified in advance.

The data is searched for themes, and similar themes are sorted together. Themes may change as more data is analysed, and new themes emerge. This means that themes are constantly adjusted and data is returned to for further searches of new themes that have emerged. After thorough analysis the themes will be categorized and meaning and patterns within the themes may be identified. When the report is written up, the data within each category provides the evidence for the themes, perhaps presented as, or supported by, direct quotes.

Thematic analysis carries an inherent risk of subjectivity and hence researcher bias. The identification of themes and patterns requires a degree of interpretation, and it is possible that researchers' beliefs may cause differences in how qualitative data is analyzed. While steps should be taken to ensure that subjectivity and its effects are minimized, such as openly identifying possible sources of bias, it is unlikely to be completely eliminated. Such drawbacks, however, are balanced against the richness of data provided by this form of analysis.

Case studies

Key terms

Case study: an in-depth study of one person or a group of people.

Quantitative data: data that can be measured (quantified) in some way, e.g. level, number, speed.

A **case study** is a detailed investigation of a single individual. It can also be an investigation of an identifiable group of people. Case studies often take place over a period of time, and information is gathered using such methods as observation, interview, psychological tests, and analysis of records (for example, school or medical records). Individuals being studied are often those who are in some way unique or different, such as those displaying the effects of brain damage or consequences of some personal trauma.

Strengths	Limitations
• A great deal of qualitative and **quantitative data** can be gathered, giving a very detailed insight into the person or group. • Allows researchers to study things that they may not be able to any other way.	• A detailed investigation of one person cannot be replicated so it lacks scientific rigour. • The researcher can become too deeply involved with the person or group being studied, affecting objectivity. • The focus on a very small sample means that it is difficult, or sometimes impossible, to generalize the findings.

Table 14 Strengths and limitations of case studies

Scientific processes

Aims and hypotheses

One of the first steps in conducting research is the development of **aims** and hypotheses. An aim is a general statement outlining the purpose of the investigation. It is not invented as such, but derived from a theory. For example, based on what is known about factors that influence human memory, a psychologist might state an aim of research as being 'to investigate the influence of noise on memory'. This is a very general aim. There is nothing wrong with it, but in all likelihood the psychologist will be more informed by existing theory and research, and will have decided what is meant by 'noise' and what 'memory' actually refers to. In this case the aim might be more focused, for example 'to investigate the effects of loud continuous noise on ability to recall random word sequences'.

Having stated the aim the psychologist must now formulate a hypothesis. This is a specific prediction about the outcome of the investigation – a statement that will be tested in the investigation. For example, the psychologist might predict that loud continuous noise will have a negative effect on memory.

However, this is still not a fully written hypothesis. One more thing that must be done is to operationalize the hypothesis. This means that the nature of the variables and how they will be measured must be clear in the hypothesis, and only then will the statement become a testable hypothesis. Having operationalized the variables, the hypothesis might now look something like 'Participants who are exposed to a continuous 100 decibel noise during a task requiring them to learn a random word sequence will have poorer subsequent recall of the word sequence compared to participants who do the task in silence'.

Research hypotheses have different names, depending on the research method. In this case, the hypothesis is predicting that there will be a difference in the performance of participant scores. As this is a hypothesis for an experiment (there is an IV and a DV), it is known as an **experimental hypothesis**. Obviously, hypotheses used with other research methods would not be called 'experimental' hypotheses. When used with correlations, observations, and self-report studies, they are generally referred to as **alternative hypotheses**.

An investigation is carried out to test the hypothesis. It is possible that the results do not support the hypothesis. Does this then mean that the researchers have found nothing? Of course not – in the example of the effects of noise on memory, they will have found that there is no significant difference between the recall of random word sequences in noisy and silent conditions. (The use of the word 'significant' is important here – it is unlikely that there is no difference

Key term

Aim: a general statement describing what the study intends to investigate.

Experimental hypothesis: a testable statement used in an experiment to predict what will happen in an investigation, i.e. that there will be differences between scores in two or more conditions.

Alternative hypothesis: a testable statement used in a non-experimental method to predict what will happen in an investigation.

whatsoever but more likely that the difference was not big enough to be statistically important. This is the idea of statistical significance, which is discussed on pages 64–68.) What the researchers have to do now is reject their experimental hypothesis in favour of something else. This is called the null hypothesis. Inevitably, one hypothesis will be supported and the other will be rejected.

So, whenever researchers formulate hypotheses for their research they will also have constructed appropriate null hypotheses. This is not simply stating the opposite of the experimental or alternative hypothesis – that can just look like another research hypothesis! The null should predict that there is no difference, or relationship, or association, and so on. The null hypothesis is not an afterthought – it is crucial to the scientific method. This is discussed further in the 'Features of science' section on page 44.

Directional and non-directional hypotheses

There are two types of alternative/experimental hypothesis. One type is known as a **directional hypothesis** because it predicts the direction of the results. When hypotheses contain terms like 'greater than' or 'less than' they are being specific about the outcome, and usually indicate that the hypothesis is directional. For example, the following hypothesis is directional because it says that performance in one group of participants will be slower than the other group:

> Reaction time speeds will be slower in participants who have consumed four units of alcohol than in participants who have not consumed alcohol.

A directional hypothesis would be used when previous research indicates that results will go in a particular direction, or when the study is a replication of another which used a directional hypothesis.

Another type of hypothesis is the **non-directional hypothesis**. This is less specific than the directional hypothesis in that it does not predict the direction of the results. When hypotheses contain terms like 'affect' or 'alter' they are not being specific about what the exact outcome will be, and they are usually non-directional hypotheses. For example, the following hypothesis is the previous hypothesis on reaction time but now written as a non-directional hypothesis:

> Drinking four units of alcohol will affect participant reaction time speeds.

Notice that the hypothesis does not predict the particular direction of the effect, only that alcohol will have some kind of effect, maybe speeding it up or maybe slowing it down.

So, when researchers formulate their hypothesis, not only does it have to be written as either an alternative or experimental hypothesis, but it also has to be either directional or non-directional.

Key term

Directional hypothesis: a hypothesis that predicts a very specific direction of outcome of a study, e.g. one thing will be greater than or faster than the other.

Non-directional hypothesis: a hypothesis that does not state a specific direction of outcome of a study, e.g. one thing will affect the other thing.

ACTIVITY 5: HYPOTHESES

Read through each hypothesis and indicate:

(a) Whether it is an experimental/alternative hypothesis or null hypothesis

(b) Whether it is directional or non-directional.

1. People who drive sports cars drive faster than people who drive family saloons.
2. Children exposed to television violence behave more aggressively than children not exposed to television violence.
3. There is a relationship between personality variables measured during childhood and personality variables measured during adolescence.
4. People are more likely to make risky decisions when in a group than when alone.
5. Mood influences the amount of time 10-month infants spend looking at complex patterns.
6. As the number of school absences increase exam scores decrease.

Sampling

People who are studied by researchers in order to test theories are known as participants. The selection of participants to take part in research is known as **sampling**. The first step in selecting a sample of participants is to identify the target **population**. The target population is the particular group of people of interest to the research. For example, if you wanted to uncover attitudes to academic work in Year 12 A Level students, then your target population would be Year 12 A Level students. Studying everyone in this population would be impractical – there are many thousands of A Level students in hundreds of schools and colleges. The alternative is to select a number of participants from this population who are representative of everyone else in the population. If the participants in the sample are typical of the people in the population, then the findings can be generalized from the sample to the population. So, if our sample of Year 12 A Level students is representative of the Year 12 A Level student population, whatever we find from our sample could be applied to everyone else in the population who was not part of the study. If the sample is not representative of the target population, then the sample would be biased and we would not be able to apply our findings to anyone other than those who took part in the study. It could be that certain types of people are over- or under-represented. For example, it may be that the sample consists entirely of male students attending a college in a specific area. We could not be sure that the attitude to academic work is either the same or different in schools, in males and females, or even regionally. Our sample is biased, and we have made what is called a sampling error.

Key terms

Sample: the participants selected from a target population to take part in research.

Population: the wider group of people identified as those that findings should apply to.

To minimize the likelihood of sampling errors we also need to consider the sample size. Generally speaking, the larger the sample the more representative it is of the target population. A large sample however is not always representative. In the above example, our sample could be 500, which appears impressive, but if they are all boys attending private single-sex schools it would be a biased sample. Smaller, more representative samples are better than larger samples that are not representative. Basically, researchers need their sample to be both as large as possible and representative of the population to avoid a biased sample.

Sampling techniques

There are a number of ways of selecting samples in psychological research. Each technique has its strengths and limitations in terms of bias and generalization.

Random sample

In a **random sample**, all members of the target population have an equal chance of being selected to participate in the research. The selection is made according to chance. The logic behind this is that chance selection of participants should mean that no participant characteristic is more likely than another to appear in the sample. This should then reduce (though not eliminate) the likelihood of a biased sample.

Key terms

Random sample: a sample in which all members of the target population have an equal chance of being selected to participate in research.

Stratified sample: this sampling method aims to ensure that the key characteristics of the population are represented in the same proportion in the sample.

Systematic sample: a mathematical selection of participants, where the population size is divided by the sample size to dictate which participants are selected for the sample.

There are a couple of ways to create a random sample:

1. **Use computer selection**. For example, all potential participant names or identifying numbers are entered into a program that then selects the required sample size randomly from that data list.
2. **Lottery method.** This is the 'names from a hat' method, where each participant is given a number that is then entered into a lottery. The quantity of numbers selected at random is equivalent to the size of the sample.

Each method has practical implications in terms of how and when they would be used. These can largely be dealt with by common sense. For example, if a population is already recorded as a data set then computer selection would seem logical, and if the population is large then you would have to question how sensible it would be to use the lottery method.

Stratified sample

The **stratified sample** method ensures that the key characteristics of the population are represented in the same proportion in the sample. For example, we might decide that in our study of attitudes to academic work the most vital similarity between the sample and the population is in the proportion of sexes. Now, if the population has 60 per cent female and 40 per cent male, it is essential that our sample also contains 60 per cent female and 40 per cent male participants. We would select the proportions of male and female students by random sampling.

Systematic sample

The **systematic sample** method of selecting participants involves selecting every nth participant from the list of available participants. For example, if the population consists of 200 people and researchers want a sample size of 20, they would divide 200 by 20 giving 10, and every 10th person from the list would be selected to take part. Although participants are selected mathematically, this does not make it a random sample. In the example, every 10th person is selected, but those on the list before the 10th person do not stand a chance of being selected, and the same applies to those lying 11th to 19th, etc.

Opportunity sample

The **opportunity sampling** technique simply is that the researchers used whoever was conveniently available. It could be a friend, or someone passing along the corridor at the time.

Volunteer sample

The **volunteer sample** is also called the self-selected sample, which gives a strong hint as to the nature of this sampling technique. Typically, people volunteer themselves as participants in response to adverts in the media, or posters on notice boards. For example, if a psychologist was interested in studying attitudes to weight loss in active dieters, then they might use a notice board in the local health centre where a dieting class is held every week.

Key terms

Opportunity sample: a sample that consists of participants who were selected because of their availability.

Volunteer sample: a sample where participants self-select.

ACTIVITY 6: SAMPLING

A government report has noted that teachers in England rely less on textbooks than teachers in other countries. Researchers decided to investigate the attitude of Key Stage 5 students in England towards the use of textbooks.

(a) What is the target population in this study?
(b) Identify which sampling technique is most likely to give a representative sample and explain why.
(c) Describe how you would go about gaining a sample of participants using this sampling technique.

Sampling technique	Strengths	Limitations
Random	As the researcher has no control over who is selected, investigator bias is avoided.	Although based on sound laws of mathematical probability that predict that by chance samples should be representative, there is still a possibility that they will not be, thus limiting generalizability.
Systematic	The only input the researcher has is deciding the sample size, therefore it avoids investigator bias.	As with a random sample, there is still a possibility that the sample will not be representative, thus limiting generalizability.
Stratified	By guaranteeing that all key characteristics of the population are present in the sample, it not only avoids investigator bias afterwards, but it is also representative and can be generalized.	If all the key features of the population are not identified then the sample may not be representative, thus limiting generalizability.
Opportunity	Since the selection of participants is very straightforward it is less time-consuming than other techniques.	The researcher may consciously or subconsciously show bias in sample selection, thus limiting generalizability.
Volunteer	Since the selection of participants is very straightforward it is less time-consuming than other techniques.	Sample bias is likely as only certain types of people are motivated to volunteer for research, thus limiting generalizability.

Table 15 Strengths and limitations of sampling techniques in terms of bias and generalization

Pilot studies

Conducting research usually involves a great deal of time, effort and money. It is important therefore that it is right, and that it is not flawed. A key element to this is ensuring that before the researchers conduct their study for real they do a small-scale trial run. By doing this they can check all aspects of their research. For example, as a result of trying out a questionnaire they might discover that certain questions were unclear to participants, or by trialling an experiment they might discover important investigator effects that they should be avoiding. As far as possible, participants who take part in pilot studies should be typical of those expected to take part in the real study. They can offer important insights into their experience of taking part in the study; for example, if boredom had an effect or if they had guessed the purpose of the study and consequently adjusted their behaviour. As a result of the pilot studies, researchers can adjust their design, procedures, and analysis of findings, increasing the reliability and validity of the final research.

Demand characteristics and investigator effects

Key terms

Demand characteristics: subtle clues that make participants aware of what the researcher expects to find or how the participant is supposed to behave.

Investigator effects: the ways that researchers can influence the results of their research, e.g. by unconscious bias.

When taking part in research, participants sometimes try to guess the purpose of the research and change their behaviour accordingly. This change in behaviour is often unconscious, but it can be a deliberate conscious change. The things in the research that give rise to these changes in behaviour (i.e. give hints as to the purpose of the research) are called **demand characteristics**.

There may be a range of motives behind participants altering their behaviour; for example, the participant may be wanting to please the researcher, they may just be nervous, or participants may even be attempting to sabotage proceedings. Whatever the motive, the effect is the same – demand characteristics change what participants do and think, and are confounding variables that can alter the outcome of studies.

It is important that researchers minimize the likelihood of demand characteristics affecting their research. Careful design of a study can often pre-empt demand characteristics and minimize their effects. One way of dealing with them more directly, however, is to use deliberate deception, by telling participants that the study is looking at something other than what it really is. For example, Asch (see page 74) did not tell his participants that they were really taking part in an experiment on conformity. There are of course ethical issues with deliberate deception, so it is not something researchers should do without careful consideration.

The more usual solution to demand characteristics in an experiment is to adopt a single blind technique of control. In a true experiment, participants are randomly assigned to a control or experimental condition. Being single blind means that the participant does not know which condition they are in, therefore making it harder to guess what the study is about.

It is also the case that researchers can influence the results of their research. These are called **investigator effects**. It could be that participants react to something about the investigator, for example their sex or ethnicity, accent or mannerisms. It could even be something subtle in the behaviour of the investigator that, at an unconscious level, biases participants towards the prediction of the study. This latter possibility has been demonstrated many times in psychology. In a classic study by Rosenthal and Lawson (1964), students were given rats that they were told were either 'maze bright' or 'maze dull' and instructed to test their maze-running ability. Those given 'maze bright' rats found that their rats navigated mazes faster than those given 'maze dull' rats, even though the rats were in fact allocated randomly. The students were influenced by what they had been told about the rats beforehand. Rosenthal and Lawson referred to this as 'experimenter expectancy' – the researchers were unconsciously influenced by what they expected to find.

ACTIVITY 7: INVESTIGATOR EFFECTS

A psychologist went into a local school to conduct a study with students. She wanted to know whether gender stereotyping in films had any effect on the attitudes of students towards the opposite sex.

(a) Identify potential investigator effects in this study.

(b) Explain ways in which the study could be designed to minimize these investigator effects.

The most common way to reduce investigator effects is to use a double blind technique of control. This is where neither the participants nor the researchers know the aims and/or conditions of the study. While this still requires an investigator in charge overall, the participants do not come into contact with investigators who can give information or clues about aims, conditions, etc. It has the benefit of not only reducing investigator effects, but, as mentioned previously, demand characteristics too. The double blind technique is a difficult control to set up in a study, but when it is used it is an indicator of good quality research.

Ethical issues

All scientific and professional bodies have codes of conduct governing the behaviour of individuals who operate under their influence. Doctors, for example, are expected to behave in ways that meet the guidance for standards and ethics laid out by the General Medical Council. Psychologists working in the UK have a Code of Conduct and Ethical Guidelines, produced by the British Psychological Society (BPS). This covers the conduct of psychologists working in all contexts, including research. It is extremely important that psychologists carefully consider the ethics of their research. Simply put, ethics are moral codes that guide behaviour. As research has the potential to directly or indirectly harm people, researchers have responsibilities to participants to conduct their research in ways that prevent psychological, physical, or cultural harm. Psychologists also need to consider wider issues. For example, some topics of interest to psychologists could be considered to be socially sensitive and findings could have implications far beyond the focus of a particular piece of research.

The BPS Code of Human Research Ethics (2010) outlines a set of general ethical principles that apply to all research contexts with human participants. These are a set of four moral principles that are intended to inform the decision-making of researchers, so that the activities of these psychologists reflect the underpinning values of professional psychology. The four principles are outlined in Table 16 below. Each one has a 'value statement', which is further elaborated as a set of standards.

Ethical principle	Value statement
Respect for the Autonomy and Dignity of Persons	'Adherence to the concept of moral rights is an essential component of respect for the dignity of persons. Rights to privacy, self-determination, personal liberty and natural justice are of particular importance to psychologists, and they have a responsibility to protect and promote these rights in their research activities. As such, psychologists have a responsibility to develop and follow procedures for valid consent, confidentiality, anonymity, fair treatment and due process that are consistent with those rights.'
Scientific Value	'Research should be designed, reviewed and conducted in a way that ensures its quality, integrity and contribution to the development of knowledge and understanding. Research that is judged within a research community to be poorly designed or conducted wastes resources and devalues the contribution of the participants. At worst it can lead to misleading information being promulgated and can have the potential to cause harm.'
Social Responsibility	'The discipline of psychology, both as a science and a profession, exists within the context of human society. Accordingly, a shared collective duty for the welfare of human and non-human beings, both within the societies in which psychology researchers live and work, and beyond them, must be acknowledged by those conducting the research.'
Maximising Benefit and Minimising Harm	'In accordance with Ethics Principle 3: Responsibility of the Code of Ethics and Conduct, psychologists should consider all research from the standpoint of the research participants, with the aim of avoiding potential risks to psychological well-being, mental health, personal values, or dignity.'

Table 16 A summary of the four BPS Ethical Principles and their associated 'statement of values'

Each value statement is further elaborated as ethical standards (i.e. the things that psychologists should do in practice to uphold the ethical principles). Some of these are discussed below.

Deception

Deception refers to deliberately withholding information from participants, for example concealing the real purpose of a study; something that the Code says should be avoided. This presents researchers with a conundrum. Presenting participants with all the information about a study may produce demand characteristics that could invalidate the findings, and strict adherence to this standard would mean that a great deal of useful and valuable psychological research would not be done.

In practice, it is accepted that some degree of deception may be necessary in psychological research. For instance, it might be acceptable to withhold information from participants when it is assumed that being deceived would not have affected their willingness to take part. Participants should not be misled if they are likely to object to this when later debriefed. Debriefing refers to the process conveying the real purpose of research and ensuring that individuals leave the study unaffected by their participation. If participants do subsequently object then it must be clear to them that they have the right to withdraw from the study at that point and withhold their data.

Consent

This refers to participants agreeing to take part in the study without excessive encouragement or threat. Consent should be sought from participants so that each explicitly agrees to participate knowing the aims and objectives of the research. This is called informed consent. This of course raises similar concerns to those discussed in the context of deception – how exactly do you gain full informed consent without invalidating the research with confounding demand characteristics.

As with deception, this issue is often dealt with by retrospective consent – seeking consent from participants with full disclosure of the aims of the research after they have taken part. Sometimes researchers adopt a policy of prior general consent, where participants agree to take part in a study knowing that it involves some degree of deception. A further option for researchers is to assume presumptive consent, which suggests that if other people have taken part in similar research without a problem then it can be presumed that other participants would have no objection.

The extent to which these are satisfactory solutions to the problems caused by a requirement for consent is debatable and to some extent depends on the aims of the research. For example, it is possible that knowing you are going to be deceived (prior general consent) produces the demand characteristics as much as knowing what the research is about to start with.

Protection of participants

Researchers have a responsibility to ensure that no physical or psychological harm comes to participants taking part in research. In terms of physical harm, participants should not be exposed to risk any greater than they would face in everyday life. For example, if the study is looking at the influence on vitamin supplements on school learning then the risks of taking the vitamins should be no greater when taking part in the study than if supplements were taken outside the research context. Psychological harm is a more vague concept but no less important. This involves preventing participants from embarrassment, stress, or any event that might affect self-esteem.

Basically, participants should leave having taken part in research in the same state as they entered. If psychologists detect at any time during the research that participants are being harmed, or could potentially come to harm, then they must consider terminating the research. This even includes situations where participants say that they are alright or want to continue.

Application of ethical guidelines

Ethical issues in research are not always conveniently black or white. As stated previously, it would be almost impossible to carry out research without some degree of deception. In order to decide whether researchers should be allowed to breach ethical guidelines, a kind of cost–benefit analysis is carried out. This may be by the researchers, an ethics committee that oversees research, or (usually) by both. Essentially, this involves weighing up the likely benefits of a piece of research against the likely costs to the participants. Benefits may include the advantages of such new knowledge and the advancement in understanding offered by it. Costs, on the other hand, might include harm or embarrassment to participants or the social sensitivity of findings. To some extent such analyses always involve an element of opinion and subjectivity, but these are minimized by scrutiny of research proposals by committees rather than individuals, and having very clear rules of conduct of behaviour for researchers.

Most potential ethical issues can be easily predicted and thus dealt with. For example, researchers should seek some form of consent from participants before the study commences. How this is managed depends on the nature of the research. Regardless of how researchers proceed with the issue of consent, it is essential that participants fully understand the implications of giving consent. It should also be stated by researchers that participants have the right to withdraw at any time any data gathered as a result of their participation. Finally, opportunities should also be provided for a full debrief so that any unforeseen negative effects of participation are dealt with. This is especially important when researchers have identified in advance potential risks of physical or psychological harm.

The role of peer review in the scientific process

Having conducted research, psychologists then need to disseminate (spread) it. As many experts as possible should have access to the research so that it is publicly read, evaluated and commented upon by other scientists. This is an integral part of science – the publication and scrutiny of research so that it is validated and added to the body of knowledge.

Once the study is written up as a report by the researchers, it is submitted for publication to a journal. Journals are publications that appear several times a year and contain collections of reports in particular areas of psychology. There are many different journals, and like-minded psychologists all over the world have access to these to keep themselves up to date with current research and thinking.

Reports are not automatically published in journals; they go through a peer review process. Each journal has an editorial board that selects reports for their relevance and quality. These are sent out to other specialists in the field for review. The report is carefully read and is returned by the anonymous reviewers with comments. These comments could suggest it is accepted for publication, or revised before publication. They often recommend that the research is rejected for publication. Many more studies are conducted and written up than are ever published, and this, it is argued, is central to science. Peer review acts as a quality control mechanism, ensuring that only the highest quality scientific research gets put into the scientific and public domains.

Fig. 10 Examples of psychology journals

Peer review is not without its critics, however. Some argue that work that is consistent with existing theory is much more likely to be accepted for publication than research that is 'left field'. Peer review is also subject to bias. A reviewer may have strongly held views at odds with those expressed in the reports. This may influence their views on the quality of the research and thus their recommendations. Finally, there is the 'file drawer' problem. Peer review strongly favours reports that support rather than reject the hypothesis. Therefore, researchers who find that their results support the null are unlikely to try to get their research published. This could lead to misunderstandings, as, for example, one study supporting a theory is published, but a further ten do not ever get seen.

The implications of psychological research for the economy

Other professions have identified their economic value. For example, the Law Society estimates that UK legal services is a market worth over £26 billion, employing over 300,000 people and contributing at least £3 billion to the UK balance of trade. Doing the same for psychology is much more difficult, however. Psychology is more spread out as a profession, and it is almost impossible to judge the economic impact of psychological research that may have been conducted decades earlier – it can contribute in ways difficult to comprehend to the body of knowledge underlying current theory and research. That psychology does indeed make a significant economic impact is indicated by the fact that UK university psychology departments currently receive in excess of £50 million annually in research grants. One criterion for receiving a research grant is the impact that the research has, including its economic impact. However, a great deal of psychological research takes place outside of university, in hospitals, businesses and government departments, and often occurs without contribution from research councils.

The problem is that any economic value placed on psychological research inevitably underestimates its true social value. One could reasonably argue that it is impossible to put a value on improving the quality of life of someone with anxiety, or assisting individuals who cope with constant chronic pain. When such conditions have direct economic impact however, for example because of an inability to work, then it may be possible to calculate an economic benefit. It has been argued that investment in psychotherapy could have considerable positive economic benefits. For example, it is estimated that 40 per cent of people claiming an incapacity benefit are doing so on the grounds of anxiety and depression. The cost of a course of psychotherapy is about equal to one month's lost tax and benefit payment. The clear implication is that investment in psychological services and the research that underpins these services has the potential to make major contributions to the UK economy.

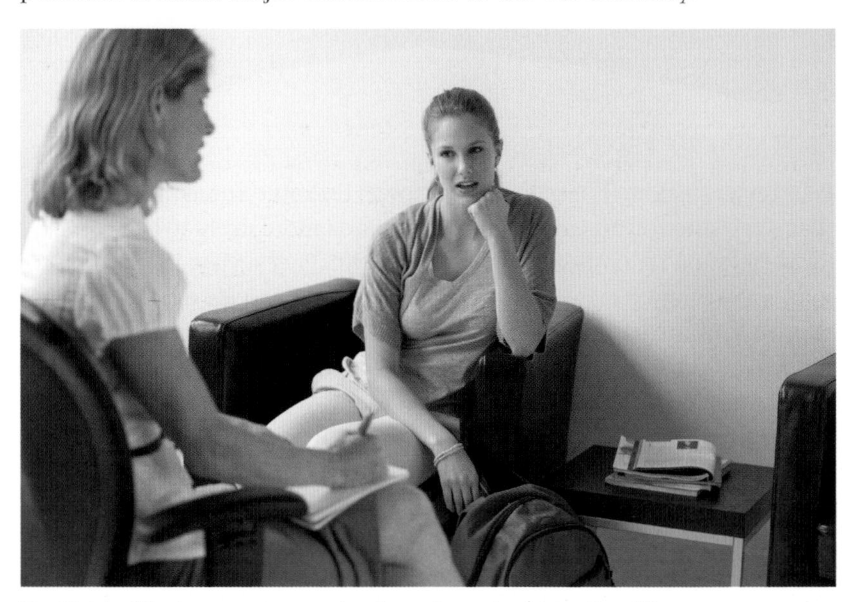

Fig. 11 It is difficult to put an economic value on improving the quality of life

One of the most important goals of psychology is to provide solutions to pressing social problems, such as those associated with violence, drug abuse, senility, or mental health. The economic benefits of such applied research would be much more readily calculable. Most psychological research is not directly applied in this way, however; it is carried out due to curiosity about human nature and animal behaviour. This is not to say that such research has no wider social value and economic value. The value of research outcomes are not always immediately clear, but can have applications and benefits unforeseen at the time of the research. For example, a health worker interested in improving dietary habits might make use of psychological research findings that suggest that restricting access to something actually makes it more attractive. The economic benefits of psychological research in this case are down to the way that psychological knowledge has been applied.

While it is virtually impossible to accurately calculate the economic impact of psychology, its growth in universities, its increased application in business and service industries, and the continuing expansion of psychological services in the health sector suggest that overall psychological research has a positive economic impact.

Reliability

The term **reliability** is used to describe the consistency of a study or some measuring device within a study. If a study can be replicated (repeated with similar results), it is said to be reliable. This idea of replicability is a key feature of science. It should be possible to draw the same conclusions from studies that are repeated time after time, and measuring devices should produce the same results if used in the same way over and over. Without the measuring devices within a study being reliable, the study overall cannot be reliable. If the study was published for other psychologists to read about and comment on, then it would be on the basis that we are confident enough that, if someone else carried out our study exactly the way we did, they would get the same outcomes. If others replicate our study exactly but get different results, then there is a problem with the reliability of our study.

Key term

Reliability: refers to consistency of a measure or a study, e.g. if the same results are achieved on another occasion there is said to be reliability.

External reliability: the extent to which a study can be replicated.

Test–retest reliability: when a test or measure is repeated and gives similar results.

Inter-observer reliability: the consistency in the records of two or more observers.

External reliability

When we talk about a test/measure within a study producing similar results if replicated, we are referring to its **external reliability** – the results are consistent. The external reliability of a study is assessed by a method called **test–retest reliability**. This is where a study or a test is repeated several times. For example, if we have devised a way to test very long-term memory for an experiment then we could reasonably assume that if the test were any good we could simply repeat it under similar circumstances and get very similar results. If this were not the case then we could not possibly trust the conclusions of the study – they would be based on very shaky evidence.

To demonstrate test–retest reliability, a correlation between the separate sets of scores could be carried out. Finding a strong positive correlation (so that scores would increase and/or decrease in similar ways) would indicate good reliability and increase confidence in the study and its conclusions. However, there are practical problems with test–retest reliability. For example, results may be influenced by extraneous variables that were not identified and properly controlled either on the first trial or subsequent trials. This might be seen when it is not possible to retest using the same participants, so that significant individual differences influence results.

Ensuring external reliability is important in observational studies. It is vital that an observer is consistent in the way that an observational checklist is used in practice. This can be checked using test–retest reliability methods. For example, an observer could make observations from the same recording on several separate occasions. If there is a strong correlation between the observations then the observer may be observing reliably.

An additional problem arises when there is more than one observer. It is important in these circumstances that observers record events in the same way; to not do so would mean that observations would be inconsistent and therefore lack reliability. This observer reliability can be assessed using **inter-observer reliability**. The observation records of the same event made by all the observers in the study would be compared. A strong positive correlation in scores would mean that the observations are being made reliably.

Internal reliability

It is important that the measuring instrument used in research has internal consistency; that is, it is constructed in a way that makes it a reliable tool. We can rely on mechanical devices to do what is expected of them, for example stop watches to record time consistently, or a computer program to deliver the same stimuli to all participants. However, a great deal of psychological research relies on such things as questionnaires and tests to measure things like personality or attitude. In these cases it is important that there is consistency within a test so that all items within the test measure the same construct, for example that a measure of some aspect of personality is measuring this throughout the test. One way of ensuring this is the **split-half reliability method**, whereby performance on one half of the test is compared to performance on the other half of the test. For example, if a personality test has 40 items then the score on the first 20 items would be compared to the scores on the second 20 items. A strong positive correlation would indicate **internal reliability** of the test.

Key terms

Split-half reliability: internal reliability is assessed by comparing scores on one half of a test with scores on the other half.

Internal reliability: the consistency within tests and other measures.

Validity: if something does what it claims to do it has validity.

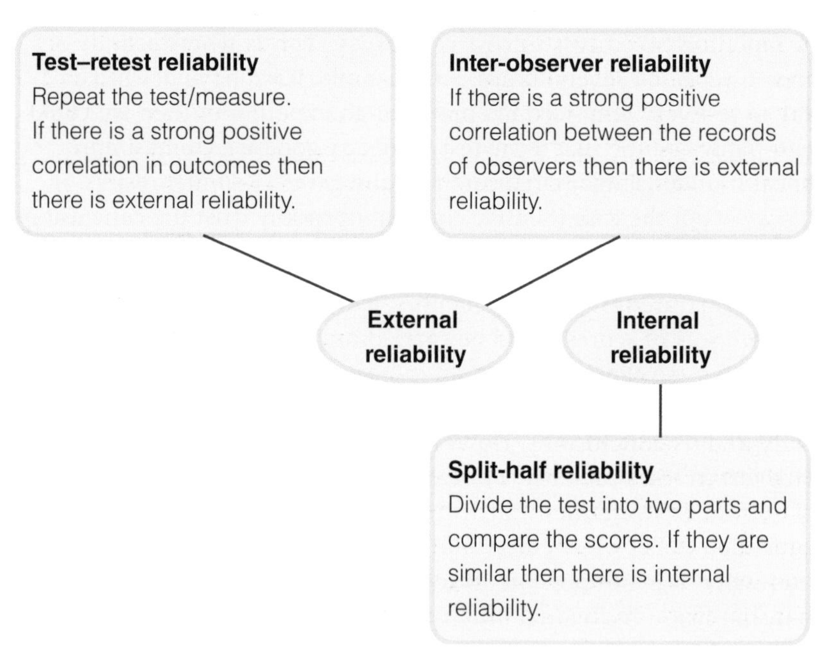

Fig. 12 Ways of assessing reliability

Validity

The term **validity** is used to refer to the extent that something does what it claims to be doing. This could be some tool created to measure something, like a questionnaire to measure personality. The question is, how sure can a researcher be that this questionnaire is truly assessing personality? If there is confidence that it really does do what it says it is doing, then it could be said to be a valid measure of personality. It could also be used to refer to broader concepts, for example whether a study into very long-term memory is really investigating very long-term memory as distinct from long-term memory. If this really is the case, then the study can be said to have validity, in that it really is doing what it says it is doing. Like reliability, validity is an issue that fundamentally affects trust in research – do we trust the data to represent what it claims to, and to what extent can we trust conclusions about behaviour drawn from the study? It is essential therefore that researchers take steps to ensure that their research has validity.

Internal validity

Internal validity refers to tests or measures used in research doing what they claim to do. Internal validity is essential in order to give confidence in the findings and conclusions. For example, if an experiment does not have internal validity then we cannot be sure that the results are only due to the manipulation of the independent variable. It could be that the results are due to something about the test used, demand characteristics, or investigator effects. There must be a sense that the research is doing what it claims to, that it is valid research.

Psychologists use a number of techniques to ensure internal validity. One is to ensure research has **face validity**. A simple and straightforward type of validity, this refers to the extent the research looks (on the face of it) to be doing what it claims to be doing. This might involve one or more expert individuals assessing the design and the measures used in a study to see that they are appropriate to the aims of the study. Of course, this only means that the study or measures in the study *look* as though they are doing what they are intended to – it is not a guarantee that they will, and this is especially the case when the study or measure is of something novel and previously untested.

Another approach to assessing internal validity is to look for **concurrent validity**. This is where the measures in one study (where validity is not known) are compared to measures in another, previously validated study. A strong positive correlation between the two would suggest that the new measure has validity. For example, we may have designed a new and quick way of measuring intelligence. To check for concurrent validity we would compare intelligence test scores on the new test with scores on a well-established intelligence test – if they are very similar then we might argue that our new test has validity. This way of assessing validity is commonly used when psychologists develop new aptitude and ability tests. However, the problem with it is that outcome is only as good as the test to which the new test is compared. If the 'benchmark' test is flawed in some way, then the new test (even if there is a strong positive correlation) would likely contain the same flaws. It can also involve a fair degree of subjective opinion, something that good scientific research always attempts to minimize.

External validity

Research needs to be generalizable beyond the context in which it was carried out. A researcher might be impressed by the results gathered in a tightly controlled laboratory setting on a wet and windy Wednesday evening, but do they apply across people, situations and times? If they do, then they can be said to have external validity.

When research findings can be generalized to settings other than the original research setting, then we say that it has **ecological validity**.

Key terms

Face validity: the extent to which research looks as though it is doing what it claims to.

Concurrent validity: the extent to which a new measure compares to a previously validated measure.

Ecological validity: the extent to which findings can be generalized to other people, situations and times.

This is an important consideration, especially with methods that are highly controlled and less naturalistic, such as laboratory experiments. Researchers do not set out intending that their research will apply only to the sample tested and in the context of the testing. The goal of scientific psychological research after all is to generalize in some way to the population from which the sample was drawn and to give insights into behaviour in general. An example of this in psychology is the series of experiments into obedience to authority carried out by Milgram and his colleagues in the 1960s (see page 85). When they conducted the experiments in different settings, for example in a university or a run-down office, similar results were found, suggesting ecological validity.

Key term

Temporal validity: the extent to which research findings hold true over time.

Another way of assessing the external validity of research is to see the extent to which it stands the 'test of time'. If a study is replicated after a period of time and the same or similar results are found then it is said to have **temporal validity**. Whether the period of time between the original study and replication demonstrates temporal validity depends to some degree on the claims of the original study. For example, if it claims something universal about human behaviour (something that is and always will apply), one would reasonably expect to be able to demonstrate this behaviour at any point in the future. The famous Asch studies into conformity (see page 74) could be said to lack temporal validity in that attempts to replicate his original findings have largely failed. It is argued that the high degree of conformity in his study was a reflection of the high rates of social conformity in 1950s USA.

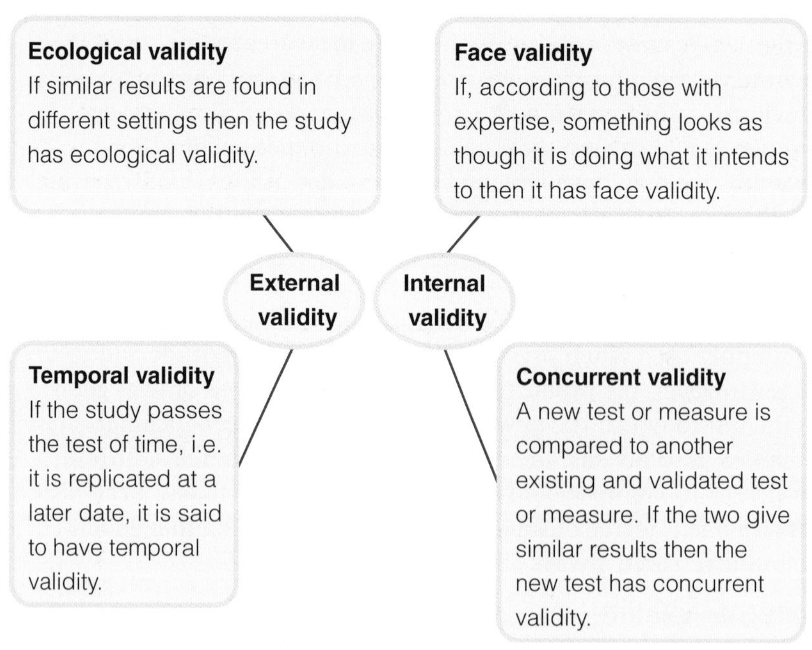

Ecological validity
If similar results are found in different settings then the study has ecological validity.
Face validity
If, according to those with expertise, something looks as though it is doing what it intends to then it has face validity.
External validity
Internal validity
Temporal validity
If the study passes the test of time, i.e. it is replicated at a later date, it is said to have temporal validity.
Concurrent validity
A new test or measure is compared to another existing and validated test or measure. If the two give similar results then the new test has concurrent validity.

Fig. 13 Ways of assessing validity

Features of science

There is no absolutely agreed definition of what psychology is. Some psychologists see it as the study of behaviour, others as the study of human behaviour and mental processes, others still as the study of mental phenomena and processes. What the vast majority of psychologists do agree on, however, is that psychology is a science. As a discipline that attempts to describe, understand, predict, control, and change behaviour, psychology relies heavily on the scientific method.

Objectivity and the empirical method

The scientific approach emphasizes the importance of empirical evidence. This means that evidence is gained through objective observation, experimentation, and measurement of behaviour. Objectivity is the key element here. It means that events are not distorted by emotions and prejudices and are recorded as they actually happen.

Replicability

Replication is essential to scientific research. Findings that cannot be repeated with the same or similar results will not be accepted by the scientific community. Replicability gives confidence that the results are valid and reliable and add to scientific knowledge.

Theory construction and hypothesis testing, and falsifiability

The scientific process begins with an observation of a problem. Maybe this came from academic sources (for example, something seen in published research), it can come from experience (for example, the psychologist has seen something that has piqued their curiosity), or it came from something that needs to be solved (for example, young people starving themselves). This leads to the development of a hypothesis – a testable statement that makes a specific prediction. The next step is to design a study and gather evidence to test this hypothesis. As a result the hypothesis is either accepted or rejected in favour of the null. Further observations are made, and hypotheses proposed and tested. As a result of all of this hypothesis testing, a theory is developed. If data contradicts the theory it will have to be adjusted and further hypotheses will need to be tested. If data continually supports the theory it becomes a law.

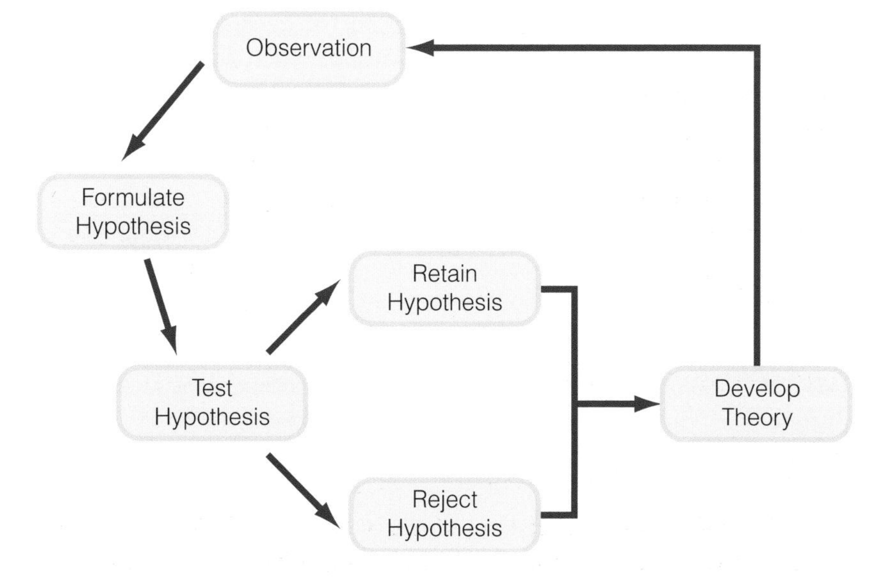

Fig. 14 Hypothesis and theory formation

Key term

Falsifiability: refers to the idea that a theory has only been properly scrutinized when attempts have been made to prove it false.

The philosopher Karl Popper called this process the hypothetico-deductive method. It is based on the idea of **falsifiability** – that a theory has only undergone appropriate scientific scrutiny when researchers have attempted to prove that it is false. By this, he means that research should attempt to falsify the null hypothesis, as we cannot 'prove' the hypothesis. The logic behind this is deceptively simple. Popper used the analogy of the scientist who only ever sees white swans. From this observation he proposes the theory that all swans are white. Observations of any number of white swans will only ever support this theory. We cannot conclusively affirm a hypothesis. However, by seeing just one black swan we can conclusively negate it. So it is with science – no amount of evidence can completely prove that a theory is right, but it takes just one piece of evidence to prove a theory wrong. Thus, for Popper, the scientific method is all about testing the null – it is tested and either accepted, or rejected in favour of an alternative hypothesis. Theories that defy attempts to prove them wrong, over time, become scientific laws. These 'laws' remain in place until there is a 'paradigm shift'.

Paradigms and paradigm shifts

A paradigm is a general theory or law that is accepted by the majority of scientists in that particular field of study. Paradigms are not fixed and unchanging. With time, evidence will accumulate that suggests that the paradigm is less adequate than it was. Eventually, enough evidence will accumulate so that the current paradigm is replaced by another paradigm.

According to the philosopher Thomas Kuhn, science develops through three distinct stages: pre-science, normal science and revolutionary science.

Pre-science

- During pre-science there are a variety of theories that attempt to explain a phenomenon, but there is no generally accepted theory or paradigm.

Normal science

- A paradigm has emerged that has generally accepted core assumptions. This paradigm dominates the science and influences the types of questions scientists ask. Over a period of time, however, evidence appears that contradicts this dominant paradigm.

Revolutionary science

- The accumulation of evidence against the existing paradigm is such that it is questioned and alternative theories are put forward, until eventually a new paradigm is accepted. This is called a paradigm shift. This shift is not sudden, nor does it occur without division and difference of opinion between scientists. Many scientists will resist change and continue to support the old paradigm for as long as they can.

Fig. 15 Kuhn's three distinct stages for the development of science

As a new science, many argue that psychology has no generally accepted paradigm and is still in a period of pre-science, therefore a paradigm has yet to emerge. Others point out that paradigm shifts have already occurred in psychology, for example the shift in the focus of psychology away from behaviourist to cognitive views of behaviour in the 1960s (see pages 214–215). It has also been suggested that psychology is a discipline fragmented in ways that other disciplines are not, so the likelihood of a paradigm emerging in psychology is remote. For example, a biopsychologist, a humanistic psychologist, and a social psychologist might all be interested in the same behaviour, but their perspectives are so radically different that it is hard to imagine a common paradigm emerging.

Reporting psychological investigations

Having conducted the research the final task for the psychologists is to write it up as a report for publication. Once published, other psychologists will be able to read and comment on the research, and use it to guide their own thinking about the subject matter. It is in this way that findings are communicated and the research contributes to psychology as a science.

While there are some variations, all published research follows the same basic convention in terms of its style and structure. It is usually written in a scientific style and divided up into sections, each of which describes something specific about the research. These are summarized in Table 17 in the order in which they appear in a report.

Section	Purpose
Title	Gives a clear indication of the focus of the study.
Abstract	Provides a brief summary of the theoretical background, aims, method, findings, and conclusions.
Introduction	Presents the relevant background literature and provides a rationale for the current study.
Method	Describes in detail how the study was carried out – the design, selection of participants, materials, and the procedure.
Results	Summarizes the findings, including any descriptive and inferential statistics.
Discussion	Reviews the findings in the light of existing research presented in the introduction.
References	All sources used by the researchers are written strictly according to conventions.

Table 17 A brief summary of report sections

Title

This needs to be concise but still convey the main focus of the study. As a rule of thumb, the title should include the main variables under investigation.

Abstract

Although placed at the start of the report, the abstract is the last thing written. In about 200 words, it includes details of the study aims, methods, design, findings, and conclusions. It provides a short summary for researchers who, when doing a literature search for their own research interests, might need to look at hundreds of reports. Reading lots of abstracts is much more efficient than reading entire reports, which usually run into thousands of words.

Introduction

This section introduces the background of the study. It provides a context and will contain reviews of past research relevant to the present study. It should be structured in such a way that it leads the reader logically to the aims and hypotheses of the study.

Method

This section includes details of the methodology and describes how the investigation was carried out. It is important that this section has sufficient detail to allow other researchers reading the report to replicate the study. For clarity, the method section is often divided into four sections:

- Design: this is where design decisions are explained, for example if the study is an experiment it would detail the control measure, experimental design, and conditions.
- Participants: key information about participants is described, such as age, gender, etc., and details of the sampling technique.
- Materials: the material and/or apparatus used to carry out the research is detailed. This might include how questionnaires were constructed, or what kind of software was used.
- Procedure: this section describes how the study was carried out. It should include details of instructions and how materials were used.

Results

The findings of the study are reported in this section. This would normally include descriptive statistics, such as measures of central tendency and dispersion displayed in a table, and graphs. It might also include results of inferential analysis, along with a statement of whether or not the hypothesis is supported.

Discussion

This section is where the results are discussed, which includes explanations for the findings in the context of the background research presented in the introduction. It would also include a critical assessment of the study, outlining any shortcomings in the design and conduct of the study – basically, anything that might affect its validity. Any practical or theoretical implications would also be discussed here.

References

All the research cited in the report must be alphabetically listed in this section. This allows psychologists reading the report to find the same sources. A particular convention is used for writing references, usually the Harvard (author-date) system.

Data handling and analysis

The distinction between quantitative and qualitative data

There are two types of data collected in psychological research. One type is called **quantitative data**. This is numerical data, which can be used in inferential analysis. Experimental studies gather quantitative data, as can other methods such as questionnaires and observations. By contrast, qualitative data is not numerical. This might take the form of quotes or themes that reflect thoughts and feelings of participants. Qualitative data is gathered in self-report methods such as interviews and questions. It is also the kind of data typically generated by thematic analysis. Qualitative data can be converted into quantitative data, for example in an interview study responses could be categorized to produce quantitative data.

Quantitative data is generally considered to be more reliable and objective than qualitative data, and it can be analysed statistically to reveal trends, relationships, and differences. However, qualitative data gives much richer detail than numerical data. For example, although it is possible to express as a number the strength of feeling about something by using a scale (giving quantitative data), this tells us little about the origins of those feelings, such as motivation and intent. This is exactly the kind of information qualitative data provides. The issue then is not about which type of data is best, but what is the most appropriate data given the goals of the research.

Key term

Quantitative data: data that is in a numerical form.

Primary data: data collected from first-hand experience.

Secondary data: data collected from already published sources.

Primary and secondary data

All psychological research aims to gather information to convert into results that help to support the hypothesis. Depending on the source, this information is classified as either primary or secondary data.

Primary data is data collected from first-hand experience. The advantage of this is that it is data gathered for the purpose of addressing specific research hypotheses. It is collected first-hand and has not been altered in any way by other researchers. This increases its validity. For example, researchers interested in the effects of machine-induced workplace stress can gather primary data specifically related to this issue. While primary data has the advantage of this close focus, it is often time-consuming and expensive to obtain and analyse.

Secondary data is data that has already been published in some form. There are many sources of secondary data, for example government and public sector reports, websites, and books. The key advantage of secondary data is that it is often readily available and inexpensive to obtain. However, because the data is second-hand and has often already undergone some form of interpretation by other researchers, it may have inherent biases.

Whether or not researchers elect to use primary or secondary data depends on many things, including the aims and hypotheses and the resources available, such as budget and expertise.

Key terms

Meta-analysis: a technique for combining the findings of independent studies.

Measure of central tendency: a central or typical value of a set of values.

Mean: an arithmetic average of a set of scores calculated by dividing the sum of scores by the number of scores.

Meta-analysis

Meta-analysis is a research method where, rather than conducting new research, the primary data from other studies are re-analysed. That is, it uses secondary data. It enables what may be many studies with relatively small samples to be combined into a single study with a large sample size. The elements of primary data reported as results in published studies are selected and combined, producing quantitative metadata. This metadata can then be analyzed using descriptive and inferential techniques.

Meta-analysis is particularly useful in situations where a topic has been extensively researched. By combining data from as many of these studies as possible, it may be possible to identify common trends that are either not apparent or not convincing in single studies. However, the technique does present some significant challenges. For example, the criteria for including studies have to be very strict, which eliminates many studies. Since it deals with secondary data it relies on the primary research being of good quality, or at least flaws being readily identified so that it can be excluded from the metadata.

Descriptive statistics

As the name suggests, descriptive statistics describe and summarize the data that is collected in a study. There are a number of descriptive statistics used in psychology, including measures of central tendency and measures of dispersion.

Measures of central tendency

The term **measure of central tendency** is used to suggest that one number can be used to represent the general trend of a set of numbers. In other words, it represents the typical number, sometimes referred to as the 'average'. The term 'data set' is often used to describe a group of scores derived from a psychological study. For example, the following is a data set from an experiment on reaction times, and represents the number of times a button was pressed within half a second of being shown an object on a screen:

5 3 6 7 7 4 8 5 4 4 5 3 4 8 17

This data set can be represented by three measures of central tendency, or averages.

Mean

The **mean** is sometimes referred to as the arithmetic average. It is calculated by adding together all the scores in a data set and dividing this number by the total number of scores.

For example, with our data set from the memory experiment we would first add together all the numbers:

$5 + 3 + 6 + 7 + 7 + 4 + 8 + 5 + 4 + 4 + 5 + 3 + 4 + 8 + 17 = 90$

Secondly, we would divide the total (90) by the number of scores (15):

Mean = 90 ÷ 15 = 6

The mean score of the set of data is 6.

Median

The **median** is the middle number of a set of scores after they have been put in numerical order.

So, with the data set from the memory experiment, the first step would be to put the scores in numerical order:

3 3 4 4 4 4 5 5 5 6 7 7 8 8 17

The median is literally the middle number. As this data set has an odd number this is very easy locate – the median score is 5. If there is an even number in the data set then the two middle numbers would be added together and divided by 2 to give the median, for example: 3 3 4 4 4 5 6 7 7 8 8 17. The two middle numbers are 5 and 6. 5 + 6 = 11. 11 ÷ 2 = 5.5. The median of this set of data is 5.5.

Mode

The **mode** is the most frequently occurring number in a data set. It is easier to identify when the numbers are put in numerical order, but with large data sets it is often a good idea to do a frequency count, that is, a tally chart of how often each number appears.

3 3 4 4 4 4 5 5 5 6 7 7 8 8 17

As can be clearly seen, the mode of this data set is 4, as this number occurs more frequently than any other number.

Advantages and disadvantages of measures of central tendency

The data set of memory scores gave us the following measures of central tendency:

Mean = 6

Median = 5

Mode = 4

Here we have three different measures of central tendency from the same set of numbers. The mean is higher because every number is taken into account in its calculation; therefore it is skewed by the one extreme score. Both the median and mode are unaffected by this extreme score. So which measure of central tendency is best? The answer to this is not as clear as it might appear. Some researchers argue that the mean is always the best measure of central tendency to use because it considers every number in a data set. Other researchers suggest that extreme scores create a mean that does not truly represent the data set (and the more extreme the score the more the mean is skewed), and so we should use the median or mode, which are less likely to be affected in this way. An additional problem with

Key term

Median: the middle value of a set of scores.

Mode: the most frequently occurring value in a set of scores.

the mean is that it is often a decimal fraction, and this can make the mean seem meaningless. For example, the average number of children per family in the UK is 2.6. Can you really have .6 of a child? In practice, measures of central tendency are used in conjunction with a measure of dispersion (described in the next section). As we will see, measures of dispersion are one way of indicating how representative a measure of central tendency is of the data set.

Measure of central tendency	Strengths	Limitations
Mean	• It takes all scores into account so is the most sensitive measure.	• Easily distorted by extreme scores, making it unrepresentative. The median might be more representative in this case. • Can give a peculiar measure that cannot represent reality, e.g. 2.6 children.
Median	• More representative than the mean, especially with small data sets. • Unaffected by extreme scores in one direction, e.g. one extremely high or one extremely low score.	• Less representative when the data set is polarized, i.e. has both one extremely high and one extremely low score.
Mode	• Unaffected by extreme scores. • Most useful with large data sets.	• Unreliable for use with small data sets as small changes to scores can result in it being multimodal, i.e. there being more than one mode.

Table 18 Strengths and limitations of the three measures of central tendency

Measures of dispersion

Key terms

Measures of dispersion: values which give an indication of how spread out a set of scores are.

Range: a measure of dispersion that is the difference between the highest and lowest score in a data set.

In addition to knowing the average score, it is usually also useful to know the spread of a set of scores, that is, its variability or dispersion. As was seen in the discussion of measures of central tendency, it is possible to calculate three different scores for the same data set. It would be useful to have a description of data that also includes some indication of how spread out a data set is, as this would tell us something about how representative our measure of central tendency actually is. For example, if we have two sets of scores, each giving us a mean of 24, we would have no idea which is the most representative set, if we did not know how spread out the scores are around the mean. The set that has the lowest spread (more numbers resembling it) would be the most representative (the best) set. There are a number of ways of calculating **measures of dispersion**, but only two will be considered here.

Range

The **range** is normally used when the median is the measure of central tendency of choice. It is a measure of spread calculated by subtracting the lowest score in a data set from the highest score and adding 1. For example:

5 3 6 7 7 4 8 5 4 4 5 3 4 8 17

The lowest number is 3 and the highest number is 17. To calculate the range:

17 – 3 + 1 = 15. The range of this data set is 15.

It is clear from this that the calculation of the range ignores the other thirteen numbers in the data set, so is a rather coarse figure as it is not considering what is happening in these other numbers.

Standard deviation

The **standard deviation** is a sophisticated measure of dispersion, as it takes into account all numbers in a data set in its calculation. In effect, it is the mean distance of scores from the mean of a set of scores. This means that the larger the calculated standard deviation (or sd), the more spread a set of score are about the mean and therefore the less representative the mean is of this set of scores. The example will help to clarify this.

Key term

Standard deviation: a measure of dispersion that shows how much each score in a data set deviates on average from the mean of that data set.

There is a formula used to calculate the standard deviation. You might sometimes see sd replaced with σ or a single s. It means the same thing.

$$sd = \sqrt{\frac{\Sigma(X - \bar{X})^2}{n - 1}}$$

The standard deviation is much easier to calculate than this formula might suggest.

The mean for the following data set was previously calculated as 6 (note: the mean is often symbolized by an x with a bar above it: $\bar{x}$).

Score (x)	$x - \bar{x}$	$(x - \bar{x})^2$
5	–1	1
3	–3	9
6	0	0
7	1	1
7	1	1
4	–3	9
8	2	4
5	–1	1
4	–2	4
4	–2	4
5	–1	1
3	–3	9
4	–2	4
8	2	4
17	11	121

To explain the process: first we listed our scores (x) as a column. Then we took each score away from the mean, for example for the first number $5 - 6 = -1$. Don't worry about minus numbers, because the next step is to square all the subtractions you just calculated, which eliminates the negative sign. So we have $5 - 6 = -1$, and $-1^2 = 1$; $3 - 6 = -3$, and $-3^2 = 9$, and so on.

Having completed all these calculations, we then need to use the formula. The first step is to replace the formula under the square root sign with the relevant numbers. This is very straightforward. $\Sigma(x - \bar{x})^2$ simply means to add up all the numbers under the column headed $\Sigma(x - \bar{x})^2$. (Σ simply means 'sum of', or 'add up'.) In our sum this adds up to 173. $n - 1$ is nothing more than the number of scores minus 1. In this case $n - 1 = 14$. We now have all the numbers under the square root, and all that remains is to divide $\Sigma(x - \bar{x})^2$ (which is 173) by $n - 1$ (which is 14). $173 \div 14 = 12.36$. The final step is to calculate the square root of 12.36, which gives us an sd of 3.5.

As long as the data came from a sample drawn at random from the population, the standard deviation can be used to make inferences about the population. $\Sigma(x - \bar{x})^2$ is divided by $n - 1$ in this case, as in the example above. However, if the sample is not drawn at random from the population $\Sigma(x - \bar{x})^2$ it is divided by n.

Measure of dispersion	Strengths	Limitations
Range	• Easy to calculate and give an indication. • Useful when the median is being used as an average, as the range uses the top and bottom of a set and the median is the middle number.	• Easily distorted by extreme scores. • Only uses two numbers no matter how large the data set so is a basic indication of spread at best. • It gives no indication of the spread of scores within a data set.
Standard deviation	• Uses all scores in a data set in its calculation. • It gives a sensitive measure of how all scores are dispersed around the mean. • It is a powerful statistic with applications elsewhere, e.g. in conjunction with normal distributions.	• More difficult to calculate than the range. • As it uses the mean it is distorted by extreme scores.

Table 19 Strengths and limitations of two measures of dispersion

ACTIVITY 8: MEASURES OF CENTRAL TENDENCY AND DISPERSION

The following data sets were gathered in a study looking at driver error and stress:

A: 8, 6, 14, 9, 13, 8, 9, 8, 7, 7, 10

B: 22, 12, 14, 21, 20, 14, 14, 18, 16, 17, 17

(a) Calculate the mean, median and mode of each.

(b) Calculate the standard deviation for each data set. Which mean is most representative of its data set?

Percentages and their calculation

'Per cent' simply means 'per 100'. So, when we say that 20 per cent of students achieved a grade A in a recent test, what we are really saying is that if there were 100 students 20 of them got a grade A. Of course, it is highly unlikely that we will have a nice convenient 100 people in our sample, so we need a way to convert scores to percentages. Let's say that 5 students in a class of 25 get a grade A. What percentage of the class does this represent? We use the following formula:

$$\frac{5}{25} \times 100 = 20$$

So, 20 per cent of the class got a grade A.

Percentages are useful because they enable scores to be compared. For example, it is not possible to tell whether a student who scored 60 out of 70 in their history test did better or worse in her psychology test where she scored 52 out of 60. Converting both scores to percentages allows us to compare them:

$$\frac{100}{70} \times 60 = 85.71\%$$

$$\frac{100}{60} \times 52 = 86.67\%$$

There's not much in it, but she did slightly better in psychology.

Percentages can also be expressed as decimal fractions, something that is quite common in psychology. For example, if 50 per cent of participants answered 'no' to questionnaire item 3, 50 per cent is half, which can also be expressed as 0.5. If 28 per cent of participants answered 'yes' to questionnaire item 4, this can also be expressed as 0.28. Percentages are most often expressed as decimal fractions in psychology when considering probability. You can read more about this on page 67.

Presentation and display of quantitative data

Although statistical analysis is at the core of the scientific method, it is also important to present findings in visually meaningful ways.

Graphs

Graphs help to show patterns in the data; in effect, they are describing the data in a visual way. Histograms, line graphs, and bar charts all show how variables differ in some way. Scattergrams on the other hand give a visual representation of how variables are related.

Histogram

A **histogram** is used to present data that is continuous and occurs as a frequency. For example, the histogram below shows the number of aggressive acts by children at different ages (in months), as observed during school play periods. Notice that the 'number of times' aggressive behaviour is observed is recorded on the vertical (x) axis, and the horizontal (y) axis has a continuous variable count of age in months (each bar representing 6 months).

Key term

Histogram: a graph used to present data that is continuous and occurs as a frequency.

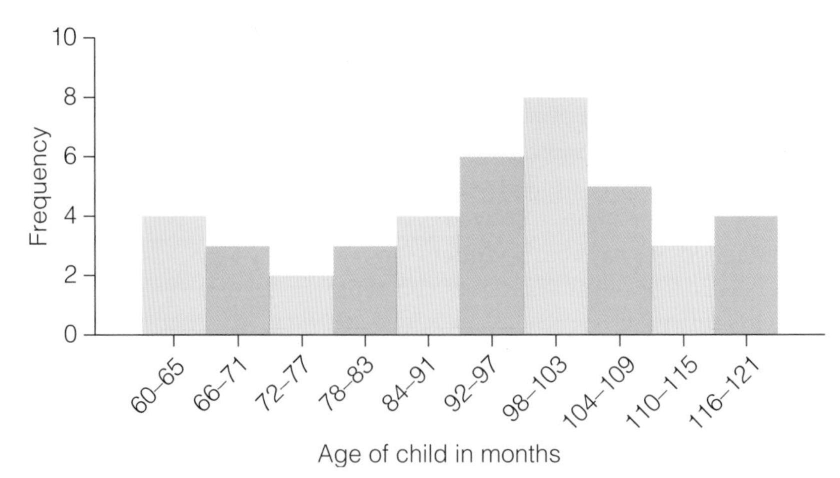

Fig. 16 An example of a histogram showing the number of aggressive acts initiated by children of different ages (in months) during a single period of school break

Line graph

A line graph, as the name suggests, uses lines on a graph to illustrate the results. A line graph can be used as an alternative to a histogram, in which case it would be called a frequency polygon. Instead of bars, a straight line would join the mid-point of each bar. The main advantage of the line graph is that it can give a clear view of how two or more sets of data compare. This is not always easy to see on a histogram.

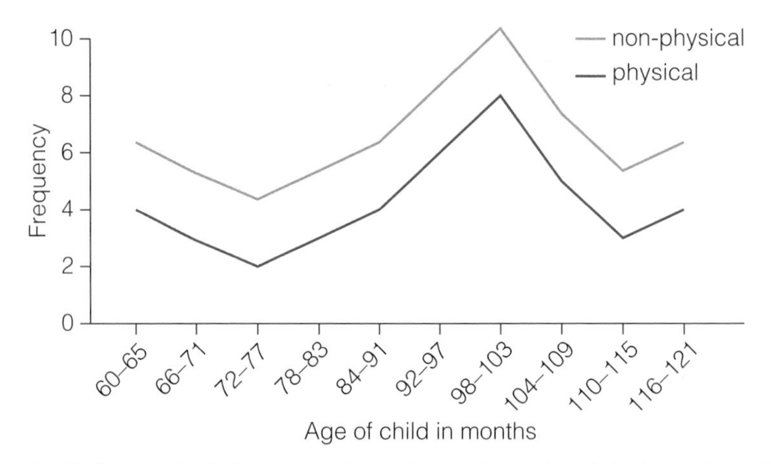

Fig. 17 An example of a frequency polygon showing the number of physical and non-physical acts of aggression initiated by children of different ages (in months) during a single period of school break

A line graph is also often used to illustrate the findings of experiments. It is particularly useful for showing the results of experiments that have more complex designs, for example when there are two or more independent variables. They can give an effective visualization not only of how the results of manipulating several independent variables differ, but also how they might be interacting. See Figure 18 for an example of a line graph used in the context of an experiment.

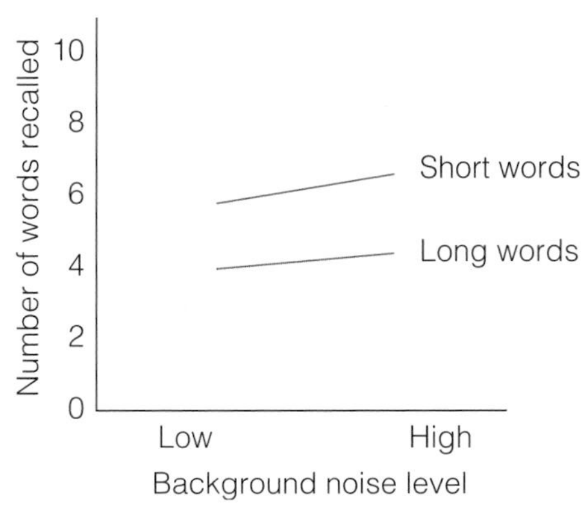

Fig. 18 An example of a line graph used to show the results from an experiment

Bar charts

Bar charts are used when the data is in discrete categories, rather than a continuous variable as with histograms and line graphs. The bars are always of the same width and separated by a gap to show that they are not continuous. A bar chart is useful for displaying two or more sets of data together, as in the example in Figure 19. A bar chart should be used when the data measured are on an ordinal or nominal scale (see page 62 for more about ordinal and nominal scales).

Note that a bar chart should not be used to plot individual participant scores, that is, each bar representing each participant. Although you might argue that the scores are discrete, the graph is not doing what it should do – summarizing the data. If you want to plot participant scores then it is more appropriate to summarize them as measures of central tendency, for example a mean of scores. While this might give what appears to be a very simple graph, this is not a bad thing. A good graph visualizes and clarifies, so as a rule the simpler the better.

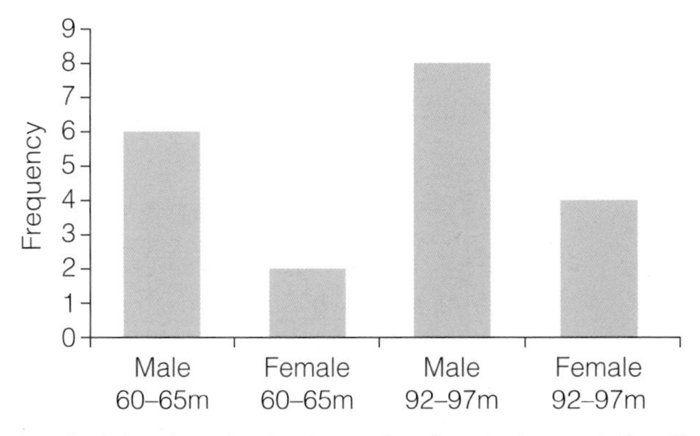

Fig. 19 An example of a bar chart showing the number of aggressive acts initiated by male and female children of ages 60–65 months and 92–97 months

It is usual when using a graph such as a bar chart to illustrate data from an experiment to put the independent variable along the horizontal axis and the dependent variable along the vertical axis.

ACTIVITY 9: GRAPHS

Draw bar charts representing the distribution of eye colours. First, record as many people's eye colour as possible. Remember to follow ethical guidelines for research. Once you have gathered as much data as possible, plot it on a bar chart. Remember to label the axis properly and to give your graph a title.

(a) Draw a graph showing distribution of eye colours regardless of the sex of the participant.
(b) Draw a graph showing the distribution of eye colour for males and females.
(c) What does each graph show about the distribution of eye colours?
(d) What ethical issues did you identify and how did you deal with these?

Scattergrams

As discussed on the section on correlation (see page 22), scattergrams are used to show relationships between variables. Two scores are used to plot scattergrams: one score will be variable (y) on the vertical axis and the other variable (x) on the horizontal axis. To add plots to a scattergram simply locate the y score on the y-axis and the associated x score on the x-axis. Follow each along its horizontal or vertical path to where the two scores intersect – this is the plot, often indicated with an 'x'.

Once all the pairs of scores have been plotted the scattergram gives some indication of both the direction and strength of the correlation. The scattergram is an illustration of the correlation; however, the correlation itself is determined by the correlation coefficient (see page 24). This is important – while sometimes it gives a clear indication of the nature of the correlation it is often not clear from the scattergram whether the correlation is significant.

When one variable increases or decreases as the other variable increases or decreases, we say we have a positive correlation. A perfect positive correlation (a coefficient of +1) would look like the one in Figure 20. A slightly less than perfect correlation might look like the one in Figure 21. Figure 22 shows another example of a positive correlation, this time with a smaller coefficient.

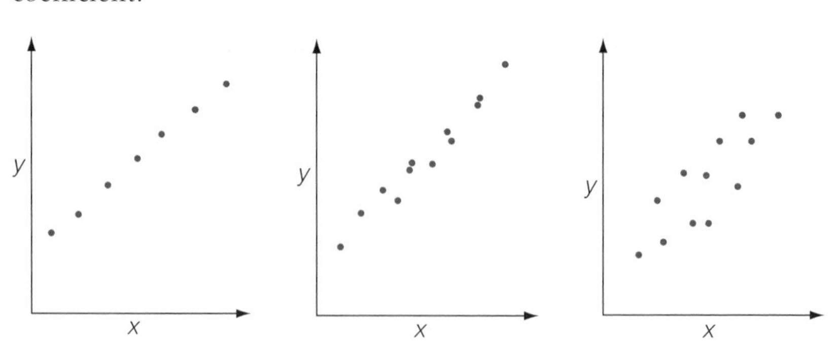

Fig. 20 A perfect positive correlation

Fig. 21 A less than perfect positive correlation

Fig. 22 A positive correlation

When one variable increases as the other variable decreases, we say we have a negative correlation. A perfect negative correlation (a coefficient of −1) would look like the one in Figure 23. A slightly less than perfect negative correlation might look like the one in Figure 24. Figure 25 shows another example of a negative correlation, this time with a smaller coefficient.

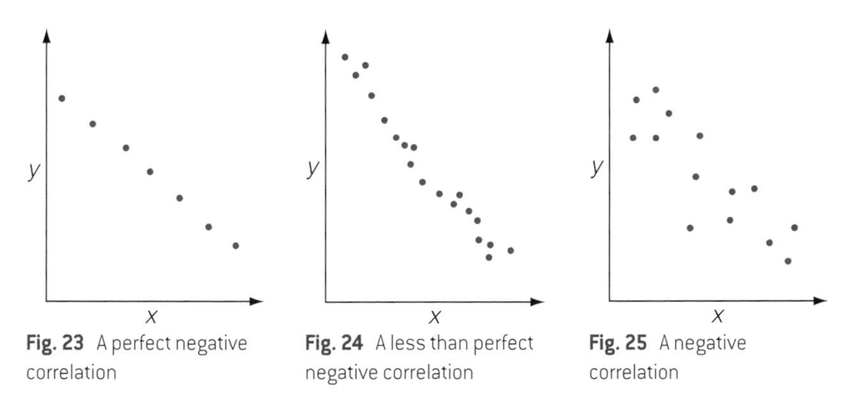

Fig. 23 A perfect negative correlation

Fig. 24 A less than perfect negative correlation

Fig. 25 A negative correlation

It is often the case that no relationship is found between two variables. This is called a zero correlation, and a scattergram might look something like Figure 26. It is worth remembering, however, that a scattergram can sometimes look like this when the correlation coefficient says there is a significant correlation. Figure 27 shows what are called curvilinear correlations. A coefficient for a curvilinear correlation might be close to zero, suggesting that there is no correlation between two variables, when there clearly is. A curvilinear correlation shows that two variables are positively correlated up to a point and then become negatively correlated, or vice versa. For example, you might find a positive correlation between performance and anxiety, but after a certain point the anxiety stops having a positive effect and begins having a negative one. Here, the plots on a scattergram may give you a shape something like an inverted U. The coefficient calculated from measures of anxiety and performance on a task would probably suggest zero correlation (the positive relationship being cancelled out by the negative), but there is an important relationship between anxiety and performance being shown by the scattergram. This is why coefficients and scattergrams go together – you do not do one without the other, and vice versa.

ACTIVITY 10: SCATTERGRAMS

Plot the following data sets as scattergrams. Don't forget to label the x and y axes, and draw them to an appropriate scale. Once plotted, decide what kind of correlation each one indicates.

1.

y	x
3	2
2	3
6	7
3	5
5	4
8	7
1	1
6	6

2.

y	x
5	1
2	1
2	5
5	7
7	4
4	3
1	3
8	3

3.

y	x
7	1
6	2
1	7
4	4
5	3
2	6
4	3
6	1

4.

y	x
5	5
1	8
3	2
4	6
2	6
5	3
1	1
4	2

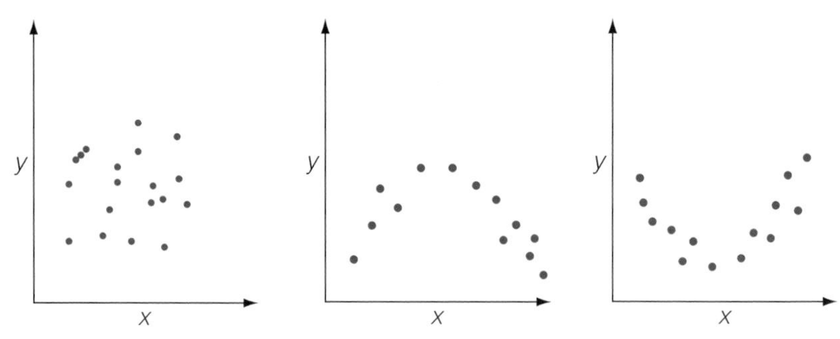

Fig. 26 A zero correlation **Fig. 27** Curvilinear correlations

Tables

Another way of summarizing data is to use tables. As with graphs, histograms, bar charts, and line graphs, tables should summarize participant scores, not represent them individually. This means that you will need to calculate the appropriate measures of central tendency and dispersion and present these on a clearly labelled table, as in the example in Table 20. Tables should be constructed and labelled in such a way that makes them straightforward to read and gives the data some meaning.

	Experimental condition	
	Control	Experimental
Mean	32	24
Standard deviation	3	4

Table 20 Example of a table showing the mean and standard deviation for the control and experimental conditions of the experiment

Distributions

Sometimes researchers gather data that tells us about how often something occurs. This is known as frequency data. It is this kind of data that would be plotted on a histogram or a bar chart, where the vertical axis is labelled 'Frequency'. The data will form some kind of pattern that may be seen on the graph – this is called its distribution. Others will occur grouped together at the top, bottom or middle. Data can be seen to be distributed in many kinds of ways. For example, some scores or numbers will occur throughout the possible range, from high to low. Others will occur grouped together at the top, bottom or middle of the range of scores. Each distribution has its own name and associated mathematical properties, but the three most important distributions are described below.

Normal distribution

When the mean, median and mode of a distribution are the same (or very similar) you get a very particular shape when it is plotted as a histogram. Most scores would occur around the middle (mean) with fewer being clustered as they occur above and below the mean. If a curved line is drawn through the mid-point of each bar the graph would look something like Figure 28.

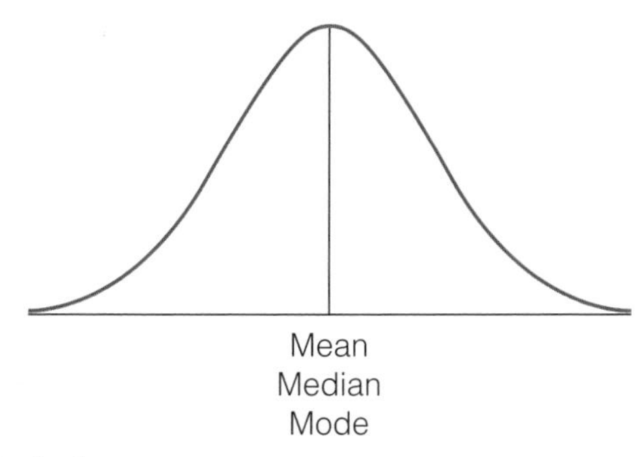

Fig. 28 A normal distribution

This distribution is called the normal distribution. Notice that the mean, median and mode lie at the midpoint of the graph and that the graph is symmetrical about these averages. The normal curve, as it is often referred to, has some very important mathematical properties that makes it a very useful distribution to psychologists.

Skewed distributions

Some distributions have most scores falling below the mean. When plotted on a graph this distribution looks something like Figure 29. This is called a positively skewed distribution.

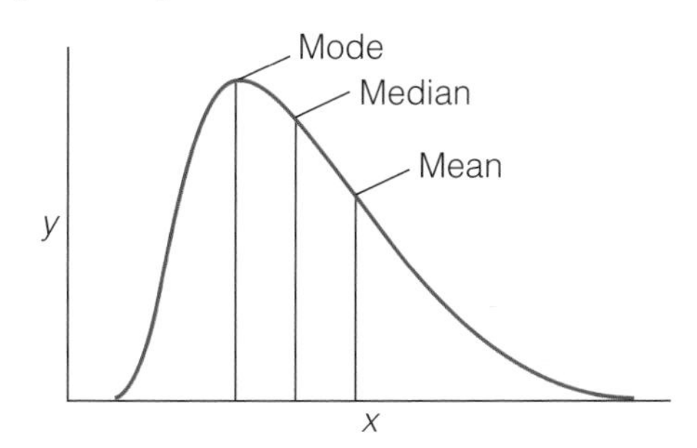

Fig. 29 A positively skewed distribution

Another type of distribution is where scores fall mainly above the mean. This is called a negatively skewed distribution, and data plotted on a graph would look something like Figure 30.

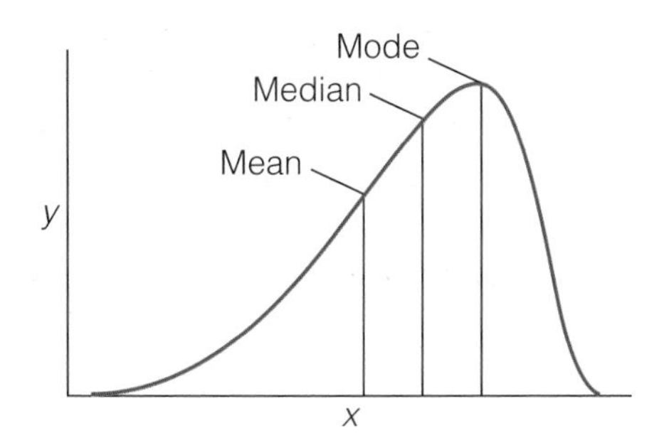

Fig. 30 A negatively skewed distribution

One thing to note with skewed distributions is that they show that the mean is not a very representative score – most scores are either above (i.e. bigger than) or below (i.e. smaller than) the mean. This means that mean should not be used as the sole measure of tendency when distributions are skewed.

Levels of measurement

Numbers can be used in different ways. Sometimes they are used to indicate quantity, such as when we find we have six red socks and five blue socks. Here the numbers contribute to the categorizing of the socks. Another time, numbers might be used to indicate a point on some scale, for example when we feel more strongly about one thing than another or when we compare examination grades. It could also be that we use numbers in more exact ways so that they have very precise properties, for example 20cm is exactly twice as long as 10cm, or a soft-boiled egg takes two minutes less to cook than a hard-boiled egg.

Because numbers can have different meanings depending on how they are used, it is very important to understand what kind of numbers we are gathering from research as data. The way that numbers are used dictates what can be done with them. It will determine to some extent the kind of analysis that can be done on the data and hence the conclusions we can draw from research findings. Each kind of number is said to have a level of measurement. Each level of measurement has a set of characteristics that set rules about the kind of arithmetic that can be done with it.

Nominal level of measurement

Numbers with **nominal level of measurement** are used to classify and categorize things. For example, we could survey the eye colour of 100 students and categorize them accordingly as either blue, brown, green, or other. In doing this we have placed our findings into one of four categories – the data is nominal.

This level of measurement tells us very little about the phenomena it represents. The most meaningful thing it can give information about is quantity. We could, for example, conclude that more people have blues eyes than have green eyes. We have not recorded the degree of blueness so that we can say on a scale that some eyes are bluer than others. We are left with simple comparisons between categories.

Key terms

Nominal level of measurement: a measurement where data is simply categorized and calculations are meaningless, e.g. Rugby Union jerseys are numbered 1 to 15, but the latter is not 15 times greater than the former.

Ordinal level of measurement: a measurement where the order matters but not the difference between values, e.g. on a scale of boredom, 8 is more boring than 6, which is more boring than 4, but the difference between 8 and 6 may not be the same as that between 6 and 4.

Ordinal level of measurement

Rather than simply categorizing data, the **ordinal level of measurement** gives some indication of how data relate to each other. As the name suggests, numbers with an ordinal level of measurement have a position in some kind of rank, ordering, or scale. For example, say we ask participants to indicate on a scale how anxious they feel about a forthcoming exam:

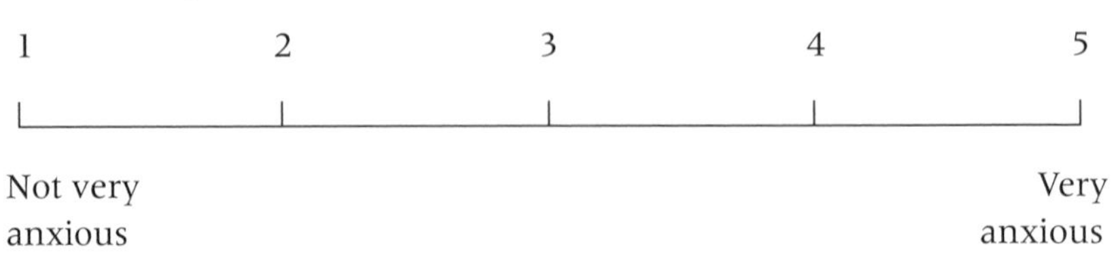

Fig. 31 An example of ordinal level of measurement

A participant who circles 1 is indicating not very much anxiety. We could say that this person is feeling a lot less anxious than another person who indicates 4. This, the ordinal data, is telling us where one piece of data lies in relation to another. Clearly, this tells us more than nominal data does. We could even convert this ordinal data to nominal data by categorizing responses as the number of 1s, number of 2s, etc. However, there are limitations to what ordinal data can tell us and hence what kind of analysis we can do with this kind of data. This can be demonstrated using the anxiety scale. Two participants might circle 1 and another participant might circle 2. We can say that two participants rated themselves the same but we do not know if this rating has the same meaning for each participant – it might mean more or less for one participant than another. Also, one participant indicates a 2 and although this is one higher than the other two participants we cannot say what this represents. What does it mean to rate one higher? If it were a measure on a ruler then we could say absolutely that 3cm is 1cm longer than 2cm. We cannot do the same with ordinal levels of measurement, however, and this is their major limitation. There is no exact distance between points on an ordinal scale. All we can do with ordinal numbers is describe them as bigger than, less than, or equal to. We cannot attribute any further value to them.

Interval level of measurement

Interval data is like ordinal data in that it involves data that can be ordered. Crucially, however, there are equal intervals between points on a scale. Because of this it is possible to carry out meaningful arithmetic. The zero point on interval scales is arbitrary. For example, the Celsius scale of temperature is interval because the distances on the scale are equal (you can take away 30 °C from 40 °C) and the zero point is not an absolute zero. Someone decided where 0 °C should be – it is possible to get colder than 0 °C.

Key term

Interval level of measurement: a measurement where the difference between two values is meaningful, e.g. the difference between 5°C and 10°C is the same as that between 15°C and 20°C.

Inferential testing

Key terms

Inferential tests: tests of significance that tell us the probability that the results of the analysis could have occurred by chance.

Significance: when the result of analysis is significant it means that you can say with some degree of confidence that the results are not due to chance.

The ultimate goal of psychological research is to collect data and analyse the results. Statistics are used to describe, summarize, and make sense of the data, such as graphs, percentages, distributions, measures of central tendency, and dispersion. Although these techniques describe data, they do not necessarily permit researchers to draw sound conclusions about the results of the study. For this, researchers need to use statistical tests that will allow them to infer things about what the data mean. Thus, these tests are usually referred to as **inferential tests**.

The data gathered by researchers is generally not complete, in that they only constitute usually a small percentage of all the data available – they came from a sample of the population and not the entire population itself. If the sample is a good one that is, it is truly representative, then inferential tests enable researchers to make generalizations about the population from which it was drawn.

Inferential tests take many forms according to the nature of the study and the type of data gathered. However, they all have in common the notion of **significance**. 'Significant' in the context of inferential analysis simply refers to confidence that the result is not due to chance. When psychologists find a significant result then what they are saying is that they are confident that they do not have chance findings.

The sign test

The idea of significance can be seen most clearly in the context of an experiment. Let's imagine that we have conducted a study because we are interested in finding out whether students who revise in noisy settings (e.g. loud music) are disadvantaged by this (i.e. do worse in exams). After careful consideration and planning we have ended up with a repeated measures design experiment where participants attempt to learn a list of words in silence (the control condition) and then attempt to learn another list of words with background noise (a random hammering sound, the experimental condition). Given what we know of psychological research into this area, our directional hypothesis is that recall of word lists will be greater in the silent condition than in the noise condition. We collect the following data:

Control	Experimental
11	9
8	8
6	8
11	6
10	10
9	7
8	8
10	9
7	8
8	6

Fig. 32

We might look at this data set and from an 'eyeball test' decide that recall is indeed affected by noise. From this we might conclude that revising in noisy surroundings is bad for you and offer this as advice to all revising students. But how sure are you that the difference in performance between the two conditions is sufficiently big that it is significant (i.e. if you repeated the study again in all probability you would get the same or similar outcome)? An inferential test would tell us the probability that the difference in the two sets of scores occurred by chance.

So, we decide to do an inferential test, and choose to do something called a sign test (the section on choosing statistical tests on page 68 will explain how we came to this decision).

Participant	Control	Experimental	Step 1
1	11	9	–
2	8	8	0
3	6	8	+
4	11	6	–
5	10	10	0
6	9	7	–
7	8	8	0
8	10	9	–
9	7	8	+
10	8	6	–

Fig. 33

Step 1: Subtract each participant value in the 'experimental' column from the participant value in the 'control' column, recording its sign. If the two scores are equal, insert a 0.

For example, with Participant 1, 9 – 11 is –2, so record the minus sign in the Step 1 column; for Participant 2, 8 – 8 is 0, so insert 0; for Participant 3, 8 – 6 is +2, so insert +.

Step 2: Count the number of times the less frequent sign occurs. This gives us S.

For example, the plus signs are the least frequent sign. They occur twice, so $S = 2$.

Step 3: Count the total number of pluses and minuses. This gives us N. (Do not include 0 in this count).

For example, there are seven signs, so $N = 7$.

Step 4: Decide if the hypothesis is one-tailed or two-tailed (there is no need here to go into the 'what' and 'why' detail of one- and two-tailed tests – just remember that a directional hypothesis is one-tailed and a non-directional hypothesis is two-tailed).

Step 5: You now need to use a table of critical values for the sign test – a section of one is reproduced in Table 21. *N* means the number of pluses and minus scores (there are 2 pluses and 5 minuses giving an *N* of 7). Go down the *N* column until you come to the number 7 and stop. From this point you need to go across to the column headed 0.05 for either a one-tailed or a two-tailed test. In this case, the hypothesis is directional so it is a one-tailed test. The number (or *critical value*) at the intersection of $N = 7$ and 0.05 for a one-tailed test is 0. The rule on the table says that *S* must be equal to or less than the critical value to be significant. $S = 2$, so it is greater than the critical value of 0, so the result is not significant.

Step 6: State the conclusion. As the result is not significant we cannot reject the null hypothesis – there is no significant difference in recall of words in noisy and silent conditions. Note that if we cannot support the hypothesis (i.e. the result is not significant) then we must retain the null hypothesis.

	Level of significance for one-tailed test				
	0.5	0.025	0.01	0.005	0.005
	Level of significance for two-tailed test				
N	0.10	0.05	0.02	0.01	0.001
5	0	–	–	–	–
6	0	0	–	–	–
7	0	0	0	–	–
8	1	0	0	0	–
9	1	1	0	0	–
10	1	1	0	0	–
11	2	1	1	0	0
12	2	2	1	1	0
13	3	2	1	1	0
14	3	2	2	1	0
15	3	3	2	2	1
16	4	3	2	2	1
17	4	4	3	2	1
18	5	4	3	3	1
19	5	4	4	3	2
20	5	5	4	3	2

Table 21 Table showing the critical values of *S* for the sign test. *S* must be equal to or greater than the stated critical value to be significant.

Probability and significance

The end result of all inferential tests is a figure that indicates the probability of the results being due to chance. In the case of this experiment, the figure describes the probability that the difference between the two sets of data is due to chance.

Probability is usually abbreviated p, and is used to indicate that the probability is less than, greater than, or equal to 0.05. A probability of 0.05 is usually used by psychologists as a cut-off point for significance. If there is a less than 0.05 likelihood that the difference occurred by chance, it is assumed that the result did not occur by chance and therefore it represents a significant result. Another way of thinking about this is to imagine doing the same experiment in exactly the same way 100 times. As long as we get the same or similar result at least 95 times then we are satisfied that, in all probability, there is a real difference between the two conditions. The five or fewer times we do not find what we expect is just bad luck – things happen by chance and we have to accept an element of this in psychological research. If we find a significant result we can accept the hypothesis and reject the null hypothesis.

If there is a greater than 0.05 likelihood that the difference occurred by chance then it is assumed that the result is due to chance and therefore is not significant. With a non-significant result we cannot be sure enough that the results did not occur by chance; therefore we must reject the hypothesis and accept the null hypothesis.

Expression	Interpretation	Meaning
$p < 0.05$	The probability that the difference occurred by chance is less than 0.05 (one in twenty, or 5 per cent).	The result is significant.
$p = 0.05$	The probability that the difference occurred by chance is equal to 0.05 (one in twenty, or 5 per cent).	The result is significant.
$p > 0.05$	The probability that the difference occurred by chance is greater than 0.05 (one in twenty, or 5 per cent).	The result is not significant.

Table 22

Sometimes, inferential tests tell us that the null hypothesis can be rejected with greater confidence than 0.05. If analysis indicates that the null can be rejected at the 0.01 level or greater, the result is said to be highly significant. For example, at the 0.01 level we can be 99 per cent confident, and at the 0.001 level we can be 99.9 per cent confident.

ACTIVITY 11: DO A SIGN TEST

A psychologist gave participants a memory test using acoustically similar words (Condition A) and later gave the same participants a memory test using acoustically dissimilar words (Condition B). The data are shown below:

Condition A: 8 9 7 6 6 7 7 8 8 5

Condition B: 6 7 7 5 5 6 6 8 9 5

(a) Write a directional hypothesis for this study.
(b) Use a sign test to analyse the data.
(c) Explain whether the result is significant or not.

Type I and Type II errors

> **Key term**
>
> **Type I error**: rejecting the null hypothesis and accepting the hypothesis even though findings are due to chance.
>
> **Type II error**: retaining the null hypothesis even though the hypothesis is correct.

Whilst interpreting the result of a statistical test might seem straightforward, it is possible to make two kinds of error:

- **Type I error**: we reject the null hypothesis and accept the hypothesis, even though findings are due to chance. Also known as a false positive.
- **Type II error**: we might retain the null hypothesis even though the hypothesis is correct. Also known as a false negative.

In effect, a Type I error is caused by making it too easy to support the hypothesis. For example, if we work to a 10 per cent significance level ($p = 0.1$) then we are saying that we only need to be 90 per cent confident in our results for them to be significant. This is a much easier 'target' to hit statistically and therefore we are more likely to accept the hypothesis. Indeed, the likelihood of Type 1 errors can be reduced by making the significance level more stringent. For example, we could make the minimum significance level 1 per cent, which would give us 99 per cent confidence in our results. The risk here, however, is that in making the significance level too stringent we would be increasing the likelihood of a Type II error. A 1 per cent level is a harder 'target' to hit so we are more likely to say the results are due to chance.

The 5 per cent significance level is used by psychologists because it minimizes the likelihood of making both Type I and Type II errors. Five per cent lies nicely between 10 per cent (likely Type I error) and 1 per cent (possible Type II error).

There are times when a psychologist might want a more stringent confidence level, and hence run the risk of a Type II error. For instance, if the result of a study is likely to be controversial in some way researchers might want to make sure that they are not making a Type I error (falsely accepting the hypothesis). It is better to be safe (saying that your results are due to chance) than sorry (making controversial claims that are not really justified).

It is unusual to claim significance with confidence levels below 0.05, for example 0.1. The risk of making a Type I error is too great. In some circumstances a 10 per cent significance level might be acceptable in speculative research as evidence that further research is justified, to try to achieve the minimum 5 per cent level.

Choosing the correct statistical test

Inferential tests are designed to be used for very specific purposes – you can't just randomly select a test that you fancy using. It is important to understand which test to use under which circumstances – using the wrong test will give a statistical outcome which is entirely meaningless. Choosing the right statistical test to use involves asking three questions. You will not be able to select the right test unless you understand (and can correctly answer) these questions, as follows.

1. What kind of data do I have?

Some statistical tests make certain assumptions about data and some statistical tests do not. Tests that do are called parametric tests, whilst tests that make no assumptions about data are called non-parametric tests. These assumptions place restrictions on the use of parametric tests for analysing data. One assumption is that the data comes from a sample drawn from a normally distributed population (see the earlier discussion on normal distribution, page 60). A second assumption is that there is homogeneity of variance in the data. What this means is that the spread of scores in the two data sets is similar (see earlier discussion of measures of dispersion, page 52).

Parametric tests, however, are robust enough to be relatively unaffected by breaking these assumptions. For example, the population might be quite normally distributed, or the spread of scores in the conditions might not be quite equally spread. It might even be that we are not certain about either of these at all, but think that our data might meet these assumptions.

However, the third assumption must be met – the data has to have interval level of measurement. This is because parametric tests involve sophisticated arithmetic operations (addition, subtraction, division, etc.). As explained in the section on levels of measurement (see page 62), nominal and ordinal data are rather crude measurements which do not allow us to do much more than say that one thing is larger than, smaller than, or equal to, something else. What this means, then, is that we can use level of measurement as the key indicator of whether data is parametric. If this particular assumption is met, then we will assume the data is parametric.

It is essential, therefore, that the level of measurement of the data is accurately identified:

- If the data is categorized into groups in some way (such as people with small, medium, or large feet), then the data is nominal.
- If the data is ordered in some way (such as ranks, or points on a scale), then the data is ordinal.
- If the data derives from a measurement of equal intervals (such as the number of test questions answered correctly), then the data is interval.

2. Am I looking for a difference or a relationship between variables?

Some research looks to see if there is a difference between behaviours in two conditions (experiments), and some research seeks to uncover relationships in data (correlations).

3. What is my experimental design?

When the study is an experiment then you must know its design:

- If different participants are used in each condition, it is an independent groups design.

- If the same participants are used in each condition, it is a repeated measures design.
- If different participants are used in each condition, but they are matched in some way, it is a matched pairs design.

Once you have answered these questions correctly you can use the flow chart in Figure 34 to select the right statistical test to use.

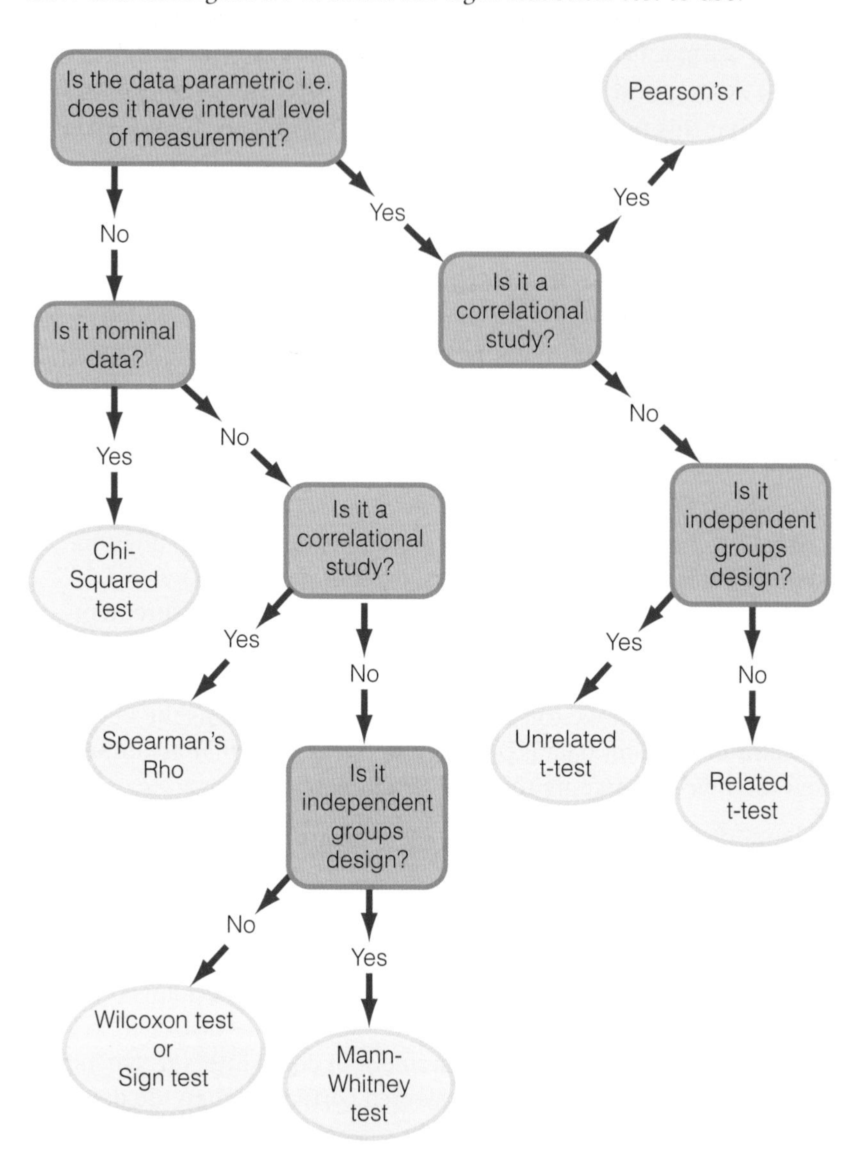

Fig. 34 Flow chart showing the selection of the correct statistical test

EXAMPLE EXAM QUESTION

A psychologist was interested in discovering whether continuously learning and revising throughout an A Level course was a more effective strategy than binge-learning and revising shortly before an exam at the end of an A Level course.

She selected a sample of students from a large sixth form centre. She assessed their learning style with a questionnaire shortly after an A Level examination and, based on their responses, classified them as either 'binge' or 'continuous' learners. She then looked to see if there was a difference in exam marks between the two groups.

(Continuous) Group A	(Binge) Group B
63	48
55	61
61	55
61	60
74	63
73	66
63	45
69	45
68	60
70	48

(a) What kind of experiment did the psychologist conduct? Explain your answer. [3 marks]

(b) Write a hypothesis for this study. State whether your hypothesis is directional or non-directional. [3 marks]

(c) What would be the appropriate statistical test to use in this study? Explain your choice. [4 marks]

(d) Explain how the psychologist might have selected her sample. [3 marks]

Exam hint

You are expected to know about different kinds of experiment, and question (a) tests your understanding by not only asking you to recognize the type of experiment but also to explain your thinking. One way of doing this is by a process of elimination, e.g. does it meet the criteria for a laboratory experiment? If 'yes', you have your answer. If 'no', compare it to the features of a field experiment, and if this does not 'fit', then compare it to a natural experiment, etc. By doing it this way you are also answering the 'explain' part of the question.

Part 1: Introductory topics in Psychology

Chapter 1: Social influence

Introduction

This chapter is concerned with social psychology. Social psychologists are interested in the social world and the interactions between people. Some interactions are with strangers on the journey to school or college, some are with casual acquaintances at college, and others are with our close friends, families, and partners. Social psychologists are interested in the processes that take place when people are in groups or crowds. Recent developments show that an increasing proportion of these processes are mediated through technologies of various kinds.

Much of the time we assume that our choices and actions are freely chosen: for example, the music we listen to, the clothes we wear, and our choices of A Level subjects. We do not think about the strong and sometimes hidden influence others may have upon us. While most people can identify situations in which parents, teachers or employers have influenced or coerced them into acting in certain ways, many like to believe that their behaviour is freely chosen, and that they think and act as they want to most of the time. The study of social influence examines to what extent actions and thoughts can be influenced by people around us, and the social roles in which people are placed. In this section we will consider the study of conformity and obedience (two important kinds of social influence), and how people resist pressure from others to behave in certain ways.

As you work through this topic, you will notice that many of the research studies included here were carried out in the middle to late twentieth century. Forty or fifty years ago, there were very different ideas about how participants could be treated in research studies. This is because psychologists have become much more aware of the need to treat research participants with respect and to ask for their fully informed consent to take part in research. Experiments involving conformity and obedience can be difficult to carry out in an ethical framework, as they often require participants to be naive in order to observe genuine behaviour. We will examine how greater ethical awareness has shaped research into social influence by looking at more recent studies of conformity and obedience in this chapter.

What is covered in Social influence?

Types of conformity

What is conformity?

Key term

Conformity: the tendency to change what we do (behaviour), think or say (attitudes) in response to the influence of others. The pressure to conform can be real or imagined.

Conformity refers to the tendency to change our behaviour or attitudes (what we think) in order to fit in with other people. We can see many examples of conformity in everyday situations, from choosing the correct clothes for work or the school prom, to following the unwritten rules at a restaurant or an interview. In each of these situations, behaviour is adapted to fit in with social rules. The pressure to conform may be obvious or subtle, or even imagined.

We will begin by exploring a classic experiment by an American social psychologist, Solomon Asch. Asch (1951) set up a situation to see if people would conform when a clearly wrong answer was given to a simple question by other group members. We will use Asch's work to explore different types of conformity and the reasons why people sometimes conform to others. We will end this section by examining the work of Philip Zimbardo, who demonstrated the power of social roles in producing conformity in an influential role play carried out in 1971.

KEY STUDY: ASCH (1951)

Asch believed that conformity was a rational process in which people work out how to behave from other people's actions. He wished to assess what would happen when an individual was confronted with a group who were plainly wrong in their judgements, to see if the individual would change their view to agree with the majority.

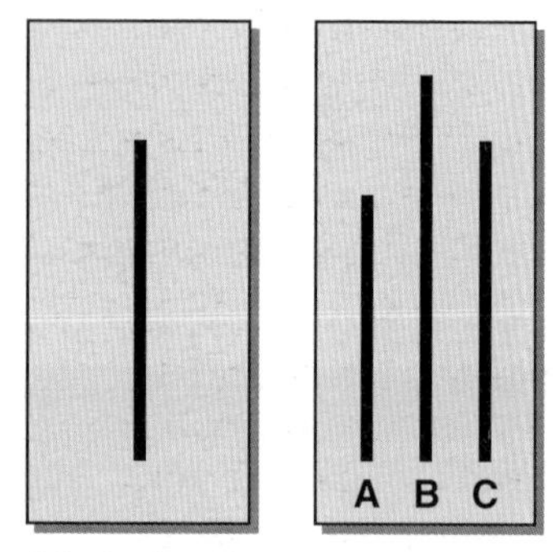

Fig. 1.1 The first of these cards shows the standard line and the second the three comparison lines. Which line, A, B or C, would you say matches the standard line?

Asch created an experimental paradigm to study responses to group pressure. He recruited 123 male students and asked them to take part in a 'task of visual perception'. They were placed in groups of seven to nine, and seated around a large table. The experimenter showed them two cards, one displaying a standard line and the other showing three comparison lines (see Fig. 1.1). Participants were asked to call out in turn which of the three comparison lines, A, B or C, matched the standard line in length, to which there was a clear, obvious answer. Each group carried out a total of 18 trials.

In order to manipulate group pressure, Asch ensured the group was made up of confederates who had been briefed to answer in a particular way. The confederates were instructed to give the same wrong answer in 12 out of the 18 trials (called critical trials). In six trials they gave the incorrect answer of a longer line and, in six trials, a shorter line was incorrectly identified. The real participant was seated second to last or last around the table so they were exposed to the same wrong answer repeatedly before giving their own view. As the trials progressed, participants became increasingly anxious and self-conscious regarding their answers and some reported feelings of stress.

Research methods link

Validity is covered on pages 42–44.

Asch counted how many times the naïve participants gave the same wrong answer as the confederates in the critical trials and referred to this as the overall conformity rate. This was 37 per cent, or just over one in three. Asch found large *individual differences* in conformity:

- Five per cent (1 out of 20) of the participants conformed on every critical trial. These could be seen as the most conformist.
- Twenty-five per cent (one-quarter) remained completely independent. They gave the correct answer on all 12 critical trials and chose to stick to their viewpoint despite considerable group pressure.

After the study, Asch asked the participants why they had answered as they did. The participants referred to a range of explanations for their conformity. Most knew that the rest of the group was wrong but conformed because they did not wish to stand out from the group. A small number wondered if their perceptions were inaccurate and doubted their eyes. We will return to consider the reasons why people conform a little later on and to examine why some people are able to remain independent.

THINKING SCIENTIFICALLY: THE 'CONTROL/VALIDITY' TRADE-OFF

Asch's study is a classic example of the experimental approach to social psychology. In this experiment, a complex social situation was reduced to its elements in a laboratory – the elements being an individual faced with group pressure who was then asked to make an individual decision. The situation was highly controlled in terms of the number of people present and the use of confederates to ensure that social pressure could be moulded. The laboratory setting gave Asch the chance to manipulate a range of independent variables including group size, task difficulty and unanimity. This allowed Asch to establish cause and effect – for example, in further studies a group of three confederates giving the wrong answer led more participants to conform than two confederates.

However, such a high level of control has a downside – a lack of validity. Participants were placed with groups of strangers in an artificial situation for the purpose of the experiment. In real life, conformity usually takes place when people are in groups with whom they have long-lasting ties – friends, colleagues or family members. In Asch's experiment, the answer to the question of line length was obvious. In real life, conformity often occurs where there is no 'correct' answer – when we are discussing our opinions on a film, computer game or type of music. Many of these interactions now take place online. Recent experimental studies of conformity make use of 'virtual' pressure exerted in an online environment. Later in this chapter you can read about conformity experiments carried out by Allan, Midjord, Martin and Gabbert (2011) and Rosander (2012), which have taken place online.

EXAMPLE EXAM QUESTION

Identify the dependent variable in Asch's experiment on conformity. How was this operationalized? (1 + 2 marks)

Exam hint

Spotting independent variables (IVs) and dependent variables (DVs)

The easy way to identify and understand IV and DV is to think about the IV as the cause and the DV as the effect. Operationalizing refers to explaining how a variable is measured. Ensure you operationalize variables in questions of this nature.

Factors affecting conformity

Size of the majority

Asch's experimental method allowed him to manipulate a variety of factors to see which influenced conformity rates. In one set of variations, Asch manipulated the size of the group of confederates carrying out the conformity trial by using 1, 2, 3, 4, 8, 10 and 15 in the group.

- Asch found that conformity was very low when there was one confederate and one real participant, with only 3 per cent of the real participants changing their view to that of the confederate.
- Two confederates against one participant produced a conformity rate of 13 per cent.
- When the group was increased to include three confederates and one real participant, conformity climbed to 33 per cent. It did not increase much beyond this regardless of group size.
- In some conditions, a large group of 15 confederates led to slightly lower levels of conformity, perhaps because participants became increasingly suspicious when confronted with such a large majority group!

Many replications of Asch's study have shown these findings to be robust. Conformity seems to be at its maximum with a three-to-five person majority (Stang, 1976). However, Latané and Wolf (1981) suggested that adding more numbers to a majority can increase conformity but in ever decreasing amounts – each additional voice in the majority adds a smaller increase in conformity.

Campbell and Fairey (1989) suggested that group size has different effects depending on the *type* of conformity task. In situations where the task relates to personal preference (e.g. liking a film or band), group size has a linear effect – more people leads to greater conformity. When the conformity task has a correct answer (e.g. an Asch-style experiment), the views of a couple of people are quite enough and increasing the size of the majority has little effect on conformity. This supports Asch's findings and shows an interaction between conformity task and the size of the group.

Unanimity

Key term

Unanimity: complete agreement from a group of people about an answer or viewpoint.

What happens when one of the confederates is replaced by another 'dissenter' who also disagrees with the answer given by the majority? Asch investigated the importance of **unanimity** by positioning a confederate just before the real participant around the table and instructing them to give the correct answer on the critical trials. He found that conformity dropped drastically to 5.5 per cent.

Asch identified two explanations for why this might occur:

1. The dissenter supports the participant, increasing the participant's confidence that they are correct.
2. The dissenter breaks the united front of the rest of the group.

Fig. 1.2 Any break in unanimity can help people to stick with their own views

Asch tested these explanations by using two conditions:

1. The dissenter gave the correct answer, providing support for the real participants.
2. The dissenter gave a different incorrect answer to the real participant, breaking the unanimity of the majority group.

Asch found that the two were equally effective in reducing conformity, implying that simply breaking the unanimity was the vital factor. The existence of a different viewpoint is enough to give participants confidence to pursue their own answer, regardless of whether the participant received support for their view or not. This led Asch to conclude that any breakdown in unanimity meant a reduction in conformity. We will return to these findings later in the chapter, when we examine the impact of social support on resisting the pressure to conform.

ACTIVITY 1.1

Design an experiment to see if there is a difference between correct and incorrect answers in reducing conformity. You should use an independent groups design (see page 10).

Task difficulty

The nature of the task is another influence on conformity. In difficult tasks, our confidence in our own judgement tends to drop. In Asch's original experiment, the task of judging line length was extremely easy. Asch manipulated this by making the difference in lengths much smaller and found an increase in conformity when the task was more difficult. This was also shown in a study by Rosander (2012), who investigated conformity in around 1000 members of various Internet communities (e.g. Facebook, Twitter, etc.). Participants were asked questions about general knowledge and logic. Half the participants were provided with incorrect answers via confederates (i.e. the standard conformity manipulation used by Asch). The results showed that conformity to incorrect answers increased with task difficulty.

The following recent experiment, using 'virtual' social pressure, illustrates how people make careful judgements about whether or not to conform based on the likelihood that their own or other people's views are correct.

KEY STUDY: ALLAN, MIDJORD, MARTIN AND GABBERT (2011)

'My memory is better than your memory – or is it?'

Allan et al. (2011) investigated conformity using a memory task. Participants were informed that they would be working in pairs with another virtual participant. They were instructed to memorise pictures of three household scenes: one picture was shown for half a minute, one for a full minute, and the third picture for two minutes.

- Half of the participants were told that their virtual partner would spend less time than them studying each picture.
- Half of the participants were told that their virtual partner would spend more time viewing the pictures.

Participants were then provided with descriptions of the pictures from their 'virtual partner' containing true or false elements. Conformity to the partner's response was most likely to happen when the picture had been viewed for 30 seconds, but only in the group who believed their virtual partner had studied the picture for longer. In this case, participants made their judgement to conform based on their knowledge of whose memory was more likely to be accurate. Allan et al.'s experiment shows how we adjust our behaviour based on the likelihood that we or other people are likely to make the correct judgement.

EXAMPLE EXAM QUESTION

Max and his friends are discussing the latest Grand Theft Auto computer game. Everyone agrees that it is great, but Max isn't so sure. Once he criticizes the game, Si also says the game isn't very good, but gives a different reason why.

Use your knowledge and research into unanimity to explain why Si expresses his views after Max. [4 marks]

Exam hint

This is an application question, so don't fall into the trap of describing research in too much detail. Pick out the most important elements of research which relate to this scenario.

Three types of conformity: compliance, identification, and internalization

Kelman (1958) argued that we can distinguish between three types of conformity. These can be seen as different levels, from superficial (compliance) to deep and permanent change (internalization) in attitudes or behaviour.

Identification

Identification is a deeper type of conformity, which takes place when the individual is exposed to the views of others and changes their view publicly and privately to fit in with them. In order to do this, the person identifies with the group and feels a sense of group membership. However, the change of belief or behaviour may be temporary. For example, Grace joins the army and changes her beliefs in order to fit in with the views held by others in the group and the overall army culture. She adopts the belief that you should support your colleagues even when they are wrong. However, she does not keep these views after she leaves the army.

Compliance

Compliance is the most superficial type of conformity, shown by most of the participants in Asch's experiment. Here the person conforms publicly (out loud) with the views or behaviours expressed by others in the group, but continues privately to disagree with the view that they express. For example, Sam agrees with his friends that a film was excellent whilst secretly not enjoying it very much.

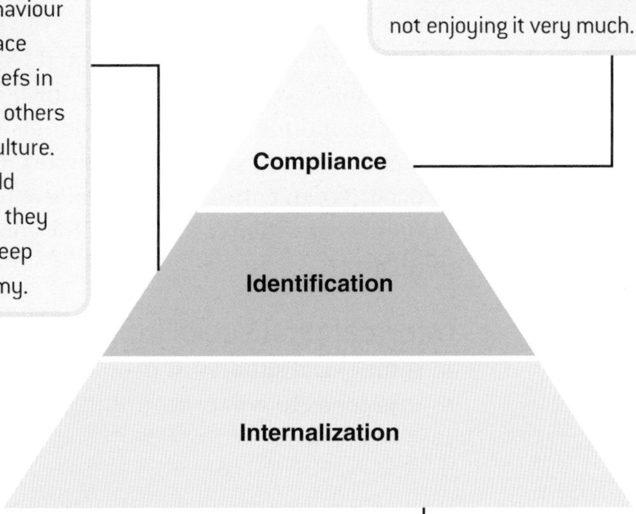

Compliance

Identification

Internalization

Internalization

Internalization is the deepest level of conformity and is also known as conversion. Some views are taken on at a deep and permanent level, and they become part of the person's own way of viewing the world. For example, Ollie becomes a vegetarian while sharing a flat with animal rights activists at university. He retains those views and continues to be a vegetarian for the rest of his life. People can internalize the views of a larger group (majority influence) or of a small group or individual (minority influence).

Fig. 1.3 The three types of conformity

These three types of conformity reflect the amount of change that has taken place to a person's views or actions, with internalization affecting the person's beliefs most deeply. They also reflect the reasons or motives for change, from superficial group acceptance (compliance) to a sense of belonging (identification) and conversion to a different viewpoint (internalization).

Key terms

Compliance: a superficial type of conformity in which people conform publicly but privately disagree.

Identification: a type of conformity in which people change their beliefs to fit in with a group, but the change may only be temporary.

Internalization: the deepest type of conformity in which people change their beliefs permanently, so the beliefs become part of their way of seeing the world.

ACTIVITY 1.2

Use online sources to find out about the experiments carried out by Kelman (1958) and Crutchfield (1955) on conformity. How do these experiments differ from Asch's?

Why do people conform?

The dual process dependency model (Deutsch and Gerard, 1955) identified two reasons for conformity – the desire to be accepted and the desire to be right. This model views conformity as a cognitive process in which the person weighs up the information given to them and their need for group approval:

Key terms

Normative social influence: conformity based on the desire to be liked and accepted.

Informational social influence: conformity based on the desire to do the right thing.

Normative social influence

Normative social influence occurs when the person conforms because of their need to be accepted by and belong to the group. This may be because belonging to the group is rewarding (think of the need to belong and be accepted by various groups at school) and groups have the power to punish or exclude people who do not fit in and toe the line. Individuals may personally and privately continue to disagree but conform on the surface. This is most likely to occur when conformity is shallow (compliance). Normative social influence was the reason given for conforming by most of Asch's participants.

Informational social influence

In some social situations, people may be unsure of how to behave, or unclear as to what they think or feel about an issue. In this case they conform and copy other people because they do not know what to do or say – the drive for conformity is the desire to do the right thing. This is **informational social influence**. If you are unsure how to behave, conformity is a sensible option: the majority viewpoint is likely to be right. If it is not, at least the individual will blend in with the group rather than standing out and feeling embarrassed. In Asch's experiment, a small minority of people doubted their own eyes and thus agreed with the confederates, showing informational social influence.

Criticisms of the dual process dependency model

The dual process dependency model has been criticized as it does not sufficiently acknowledge the importance of a sense of belonging to a group. Hogg and Turner (1987) carried out a series of experiments using a conformity task similar to Asch's 'line' experiment, but varying the composition of the group from strangers to groups of friends. Participants were placed in booths so they could hear other people's responses but could not see them. Hogg and Turner found that conformity to a wrong answer only occurred when people were among groups of friends. Other studies have extended these findings, indicating that conformity to group norms persists even when group members are not present. This shows how friends serve as a reference group, implying that conformity takes place due to group membership. We will examine this kind of conformity in the next section of the chapter.

EXAMPLE EXAM QUESTION

Samira has just started a new job at New Look. She notices that most of her new workmates tend to return a bit late from their lunch break. Samira doesn't want to get in trouble with the boss but she does want to get on with the rest of her team, so she starts coming back a few minutes late.

What type of conformity is shown by Samira? Explain your answer. (2 marks)

Use your knowledge of explanations of conformity to explain why Samira comes back late for work from her lunch break. (4 marks)

Exam hint

Tackling application questions

The key to application questions is selecting appropriate knowledge and applying it to the scenario. It is a good idea to start by underlining the 'hooks' or cues in the scenario. Here you are told how Samira changes her behaviour and provided with a reason why this occurs. You should structure your answer around these cues, applying your knowledge of the dual process model of conformity. Make sure you explain the links that you make between the theory and the scenario: this is key to accessing the highest marks for this kind of question.

See page 107 for sample student answers to this question, and examiner feedback.

ACTIVITY 1.3

Using Asch's data on size of majority, draw a graph to show the percentage of participants conforming in the presence of one, two and three confederates. Label your graph and give it a title.

KEY POINTS

- Asch (1951) found an overall conformity rate of 37 per cent, with substantial individual differences in participants.
- Kelman (1958) distinguished three levels of conformity: compliance (shallow), identification (intermediate) and internalization (deep).
- The dual process model suggests that people conform because of the need to belong (normative social influence) or the need to be right (informational social influence).
- A larger majority generally leads to higher levels of conformity, while a break in unanimity leads to a reduction in conformity. Conformity is more likely on difficult than on easy tasks.

Conformity to social roles as investigated by Zimbardo

We have seen that conformity can involve superficial agreement with others (compliance) and permanent changes to beliefs and behaviours (internalization). We are now going to look in more detail at the other type of conformity, identification, which occurs when an individual temporarily or permanently adopts the behaviours or values of a group.

Key term

Conformity to social roles: social roles such as a doctor, teacher or prison officer are associated with patterns of expected behaviours which people may adopt.

A famous study that set out to investigate conformity to social roles was carried out by Philip Zimbardo in 1971, and this study (like Milgram's, which you can read about on page 85) changed the face of social psychology. Working at Stanford University in the US, Zimbardo set up a mock prison in the basement of the university over the summer vacation. Zimbardo wished to see if the brutality found in many American prisons at the time was a consequence of the personality of the guards or identification with the social roles in which they were placed.

KEY STUDY: HANEY, BANKS AND ZIMBARDO (1971)

Zimbardo recruited 24 male students from volunteers, using a variety of psychological tests, to select those who appeared the most stable with no violent or antisocial tendencies. He randomly allocated each student the role of prisoner or guard. Prisoners were arrested at their homes early on Sunday morning, taken to the prison, searched, deloused and dressed in smock uniforms. They were referred to by number instead of by name. The guards were given uniforms, a 'night stick' or truncheon, and dark glasses. They were instructed to keep the prisoners under control but to use no physical violence.

Within a day the prisoners rebelled and ripped off their numbers. The guards responded by locking them in their cells and confiscating their blankets. As the experiment continued, the punishments imposed by the guards escalated. Prisoners were humiliated, deprived of sleep and made to carry out roll-call in the night. One, who went on hunger strike in protest at the treatment, was force-fed by the guards and locked in a dark cupboard measuring only around four feet in size. The prisoners rapidly became depressed and passive, with some showing serious stress-related reactions to the experience. The role play, which had been intended to run for two weeks, was called off after just six days.

Zimbardo's interpretation of the findings was that social roles have an extraordinary power over individuals, making even the most well-adjusted capable of extreme brutality towards others. Ordinary, stable individuals can abuse power and behave in violent and antisocial ways if placed in a social role where this is acceptable behaviour. Zimbardo's research has become notorious in social psychology due to the implications of the findings and the ethical debates it provoked. Critics have argued that although Zimbardo asked for consent from his participants, he became too involved to see clearly what was happening and should have called off the study even earlier, as the atmosphere in the prison amounted to a 'living hell'.

The Stanford Prison study has become infamous not just in social psychology but in popular culture as well, inspiring two feature films and a band, the Stanford Prison Experience. It has also been used to explain real life atrocities, such as the brutalization of prisoners in Abu Ghraib prison during the Iraq war.

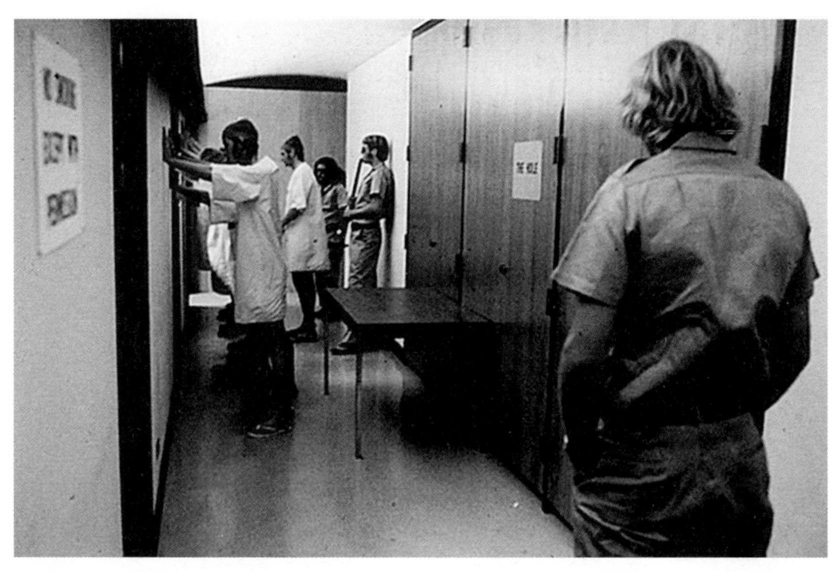

Fig. 1.4 The Zimbardo prison experiment

THINKING SCIENTIFICALLY: THE IMPORTANCE OF REPLICATION

More recent examinations of the Stanford Prison experiment cast doubt on the official 'story', suggesting that Zimbardo may have played a key role in encouraging the guards to behave in a sadistic manner toward the prisoners, and implying that demand characteristics came into play in the original study. It is worth noting that only about a third of the guards behaved sadistically, implying that there were more forces at play than simply the overwhelming power of the social role and the situation.

In 2002, a study based on Zimbardo's research was carried out in the UK by Stephen Reicher, a psychologist working at the University of St Andrew's, and Alex Haslam from the University of Exeter. The study was broadcast on UK television by the BBC, in a series called *The Experiment* (although it was not technically an experiment but a simulated role play). Volunteers responded to an advert in the national newspapers asking 'How well do you really know yourself?', and 15 males aged between 22 and 44 were selected from 500 applicants, following a battery of psychological tests. They were randomly allocated to roles of nine prisoners and six guards and placed in a purpose-built prison at Elstree Studios. The guards were unwilling to impose authority over the prisoners, who rapidly took charge of the prison. Following the breakdown of authority in the prison, both groups attempted to establish a fair and equal social system. When this failed, a small group of prisoners took power in the prison and the experiment was called off.

These findings are very different from those of Zimbardo 30 years earlier. Zimbardo (2006) himself has argued that there are substantial differences between the two studies, notably that most of the prisoners in Reicher and Haslam's study were much tougher and more streetwise in comparison to his own prisoners. In Reicher and Haslam's 'prison', all participants wore microphones and were constantly aware that they were being filmed, rather than being observed through hidden cameras as in Zimbardo's study. The findings also show how research can only really be understood within the social and cultural context that it takes place. Social roles in the twenty-first century are less clearly defined and authority is seen in a different light compared to the 1970s.

Fig. 1.5 A film still from *The Experiment*

KEY POINTS

- Conformity to social roles is shown in Zimbardo's prison study. Reicher and Haslam's 2002 replication indicates how social roles have changed since the 1970s.

Explanations for obedience

Key term

Obedience: following an order to carry out an action. Orders are usually given by people with power or authority.

In this topic, we are going to look at how psychologists have investigated **obedience**. Every day there are occasions when we are told to do things by other people. At school and at work we operate within a hierarchy in which teachers, supervisors and managers have power over us. Most of the instructions we are given are legitimate, although we may resent or disobey them if we do not want to carry them out. It is unlikely, however, that we will be given an order to do something that goes against our conscience or involves inflicting serious harm on another person.

Psychological interest in topics often relates to the social context, time and events that are taking place. This is true of research into obedience, which thrived after the Second World War. Much of this interest came from the reports of extreme obedience that had taken place in Nazi Germany and in the Vietnam War (1955–1975). When Stanley Milgram, a psychologist working at Yale University in the US in the early 1960s, set out to study obedience, the trial of a prominent Nazi, Adolf Eichmann, was taking place in Israel. What was most noticeable in this trial was the ordinariness of Eichmann, who presented as his defence that he was an ordinary man, simply obeying orders given to him by those in authority. Hannah Arendt later referred to this as 'the banality of evil' in her 1963 book about the trial of Eichmann.

It was within this context that Stanley Milgram set out to investigate obedience to authority in an infamous series of experiments at Yale University. Milgram had noted the reports of extreme obedience carried out during the Second World War and wondered to what extent ordinary, decent people could do extraordinary things. Milgram had been extremely impressed by Asch's work on conformity and his initial interest was in investigating how group pressure might lead an individual to act aggressively towards others. However, Milgram realized that he would need a control condition, with a single individual behaving aggressively towards another person as a baseline for comparison. It was the interest in this control condition that led Milgram to set up a situation in which individuals were ordered to act against a stranger in an inhumane way, and to see at what point they would refuse to obey the order (Russell, 2010).

KEY STUDY: MILGRAM (1963)

Milgram advertised for male volunteers by placing an advert in a local paper, which offered $4.50 (equivalent to around £25 today) as payment for taking part in a study of 'memory and learning'. Forty men from a range of occupations and backgrounds were selected and individual appointments were made to attend the laboratory at Yale University, a prestigious institution. When they arrived, they were greeted by an 'experimenter ', a 31-year-old teacher in a white coat, and introduced to a middle-aged man, 'Mr Wallace', whom they believed to be another participant. In reality Mr Wallace was a confederate of the experimenter.

The experimenter explained to both men that one participant was to be the teacher and the other the learner, and then they drew lots to allocate roles. These were rigged so that the real participant was always the teacher. Both teacher and learner were taken to a room that contained a shock generator. This had a series of switches ranging from 15V to 450V increasing in 15V increments. There were written labels on the generator including slight shock (15–60V), moderate shock (75–120V), strong shock (135–180V), intense shock (255–300V), danger of severe shock (375–420V) and finally "XXX" (435–450V).

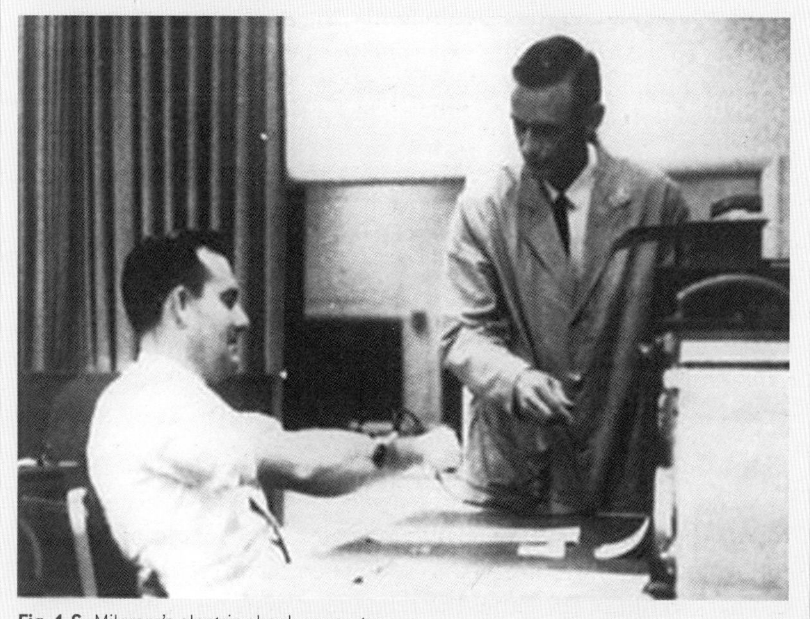

Fig. 1.6 Milgram's electric shock generator

The experimenter explained to the 'teacher' that it was his job to teach the 'learner' a series of word pairs and then test their recall. The learner was to indicate, by means of a switch, which words had originally been paired. If he answered correctly they would proceed to the next pair, but if he made an error, the teacher was instructed to administer an electric shock, starting at 15V and increasing by one increment each time. Both teacher and learner were taken to an adjacent room containing an electric chair. The teacher was given a sample electric shock to convince them the procedure was real, then the learner was strapped into the chair and electrodes were attached to his wrists and electrode paste applied to prevent burns. In response to an anxious enquiry from the learner about the danger of the shocks, the experimenter replied that 'the shocks may be painful but they are not dangerous'. Teacher and learner were then placed in separate rooms so the teacher was able to hear but not see the learner.

When the experiment started, the learner gave a predetermined set of responses to the test, with roughly three incorrect answers for every correct answer. As the shocks became higher, the learner's screams (which were pre-recorded) became more dramatic. At 180V he complained of a weak heart and at 300V he banged on the wall and demanded to be allowed to leave. At 315V he refused to answer and became silent. When the teacher objected to the procedure, the experimenter responded with a series of 'prods', which were standardized in order:

- 'Please continue' or 'Please go on'
- 'The experiment requires that you continue'
- 'It is absolutely essential that you continue'
- 'You have no other choice, you must go on'.

During the experiment, many of the participants showed signs of extreme tension. They shook, sweated and stuttered, with 14 out of the 40 having nervous laughing fits. Many of the participants repeatedly argued with the experimenter but continued to obey. Milgram found that all 40 participants went to 300V on the shock generator and 65 per cent administered the maximum shock of 450V.

This finding was as disturbing to Milgram as it was to other psychologists. Before Milgram carried out the study, he had asked a variety of groups, including psychiatrists and students, how many people they thought would obey completely. Psychiatrists had predicted that only 2.6 per cent of participants would continue to administer a very strong shock of up to 240V.

Most discussions of Milgram's work focus on the obedient participants, but it is important to note the extent of disobedience in Milgram's study. Despite the pressure put on the participants and the prestigious nature of the university, 35 per cent of participants (14/40) managed to resist the pressure put upon them and backed out of the experiment between 300 and 450V.

Research methods link

You can remind yourself about the differences between internal and external validity by looking at page 43.

THINKING SCIENTIFICALLY: MILGRAM (1963): EXPLORING VALIDITY

As you have read in the section on research methods, we can distinguish between internal and external validity. Orne and Holland (1968) argued that Milgram's research lacked internal validity, suggesting that the participants did not believe the shocks were real. They pointed out that participants should have questioned why there was a need for a 'teacher ' at all – after all, the experimenter could have simply administered the shocks himself if the experiment was really about punishment and learning. If participants did not believe the shocks were genuine, the experiment would not provide an adequate measure of obedience.

Milgram answered these criticisms by stating that participants were given a sample shock to convince them the shocks were real before the experiment began. He also referred to the behaviour shown by participants in the film footage of the experiment. This showed the intense signs of stress experienced by some participants as they trembled, sweated, stuttered, and occasionally burst into laughter. Milgram argued that this clearly showed the extent of stress indicating that they were fooled by the experimental set-up. Orne and Holland argued in return that the participants behaved this way to please the experimenter, effectively showing demand characteristics.

Orne and Holland also argued that Milgram's research lacked external validity as the task of administering electric shocks to strangers is not one that would be likely to occur in real life. This criticism was also made by Aronson and Carlsmith (1988), who argued that Milgram's research was high in internal validity but lower in external validity. Aronson and Carlsmith argued that the most important challenge for social psychologists is balancing the need for control in experiments against the need for realistic settings.

Obedience in the field

Following Milgram's experiments, there was an explosion of interest in obedience. The ongoing debate about external validity led some social psychologists to investigate obedience in natural settings using field experiments. As people are generally unaware they are taking part in a field experiment, this minimizes the likelihood of demand characteristics. Hofling et al. (1966) looked at nurses' responses to an order from a 'bogus' doctor. An experimenter phoned 22 nurses, who were working alone on wards at different hospitals, and introduced himself as 'Dr Smith' (there was no real Dr Smith working at any of the hospitals). The researcher instructed each nurse to check the drug cupboard for a drug called 'Astroten'. When they had done this, he ordered them to administer 20 milligrams of the drug to a patient on the ward. This order broke several hospital rules:

- Nurses should not take orders over the phone but should wait for the doctor to visit the ward and sign the prescription.
- Nurses should not take orders from an unknown doctor.
- The dosage instructed was twice the maximum dosage on the bottle.
- The drug (being fictional) was not on the ward list.

Hofling was interested to see if the nurses would obey an order given by an authority figure when it went against hospital rules. Despite the clear contradiction of the rules, 21 out of the 22 nurses studied were prepared to obey and went to collect the drug to administer it to the patient. They were stopped on the way to administer the drug by a confederate, and debriefed. At this point, many nurses stated that an order of that nature was not unusual and that obedience was expected.

Research methods link

You can remind yourself about the strengths and weaknesses of field experiments by looking at page 10.

Fig. 1.7 Hofling et al. tested nurses' responses to 'bogus' instructions

Despite the natural setting, Rank and Jacobson (1977) criticized Hofling's research for lacking ecological validity. As this was a field experiment, the nurses studied were unlikely to respond with demand characteristics due to their not knowing that the experiment was taking place. However, Rank and Jacobson argued that there were a number of threats to ecological validity in Hofling's study:

- The use of the drug 'Astroten'. This drug was fictional and it was unlikely that experienced nurses would come across a drug they had not heard of.
- The order coming from the unknown 'Dr Smith'. Even in a large hospital, nurses would be likely to work regularly on a specific ward and be familiar by name and in person with the consultants covering the ward.
- The nurses were phoned when they were alone on the ward. Again this would be unlikely to happen. In a real situation, nurses would be working with one or more colleagues and would be able to discuss an order with their workmates.

Taking this into account, Rank and Jacobson replicated Hofling's study in 1978, making three changes. The fictional drug was replaced with a real drug, Valium, which the nurses were familiar with. A genuine doctor who worked on the ward gave the order by phone and nurses were able to consult with colleagues working on the ward. Under these conditions, those prepared to obey the order fell to a minimal one out of 18. These findings imply that there is a need to be cautious when interpreting the results of Hofling's original research.

Ethics in social influence research

Research methods link

You can remind yourself about the ethical guidelines that are used to regulate research by looking at pages 35–36.

Milgram's study was roundly criticized for raising serious ethical issues. Baumrind (1964) levelled a number of charges at Milgram's research. Milgram failed to ask his participants for informed consent and he coerced them into continuing with the experiment, making it very difficult for them to withdraw. They were put in an extremely stressful situation in which they believed that they may have seriously injured or killed another person. This may have resulted in temporary or permanent psychological harm.

Milgram responded to these charges with his own defence, although his death in 1983 meant that he was unable to contribute to the continuing debate regarding the ethics of his research after this date.

- With reference to consent, Milgram argued that he *had* attempted to gain presumptive consent before the study by asking the psychological community to predict the findings of the study. Most suggested that only one or two in a hundred would go as far as 450V, implying that the experiment should be allowed to go ahead. Milgram argued that critics of his research would not have given such strong opposition if this had been the actual result. In effect, what people object to is not what Milgram did, but what he found – that ordinary, decent people can behave inhumanely towards others.

- In response to coercion, Milgram argued that each person who took part in his experiment was able to accept authority or to reject it and that although it was difficult to withdraw, it was possible. In fact, 35 per cent of the participants were able to stop the experiment and refuse to continue to give the shocks.
- With reference to psychological harm, Milgram argued that his participants were provided with a thorough debriefing at the end of the experiment. They were told that the shocks were not real and were reintroduced to the unharmed 'learner'. Milgram also took steps in the immediate debriefing to ensure that participants' feelings about their behaviour were minimized. Obedient participants were told that their behaviour was normal and that many others had also obeyed. Disobedient participants were told that their behaviour was desirable. In this way, Milgram attempted to make all participants feel better about their actions.

In the aftermath of the experiment, Milgram sent out a questionnaire to over 1000 people who had taken part in his studies (he carried out many variations on his original study; see page 91). Of them, 92 per cent responded. Milgram found that:

- 84 per cent were either glad or very glad to have taken part
- 15 per cent were neither glad nor sorry to have taken part
- 1.3 per cent were either 'sorry' or 'very sorry' to have taken part
- 74 per cent had learned something of personal importance.

Milgram also argued that he had shown concern for his participants in the longer term. In order to assess potential psychological damage, they were visited and interviewed by an independent psychiatrist one year after the experiment, who found no evidence of psychological harm.

Studying obedience within an ethical framework

As we have seen, Milgram and Hofling deceived their participants about the nature of the experiments. However, without this deception it would have been very difficult, if not impossible, to study obedience – if participants had known that the study was focused on obedience, they would have been unlikely to act in a realistic way.

In the years following Milgram's research, ethical guidelines were introduced by the British Psychological Society (BPS) and the American Psychological Association (APA). These guidelines state that participants in research should be protected from harm and deception should only be used if absolutely necessary. How then should psychologists investigate obedience?

Methods have been developed that allow psychologists to explore obedience within an acceptable ethical framework. Burger (2009) carried out a face-to-face 'Milgram-style' experiment with the shock level set at 150V. This shock level ensured that participants did not feel that they had caused serious damage to the learner, protecting them from stress and psychological harm. Burger utilized Milgram's original procedures and prompts and found that 12 out of 40 teachers withdrew by 150V, whereas the remaining 28 administered the 150V shock – figures that are strikingly similar to Milgram's. In this version of the experiment, stress to participants was reduced as the shock level was mild. It is worth noting that Burger's method still involved deception.

Another approach involves using a virtual environment to study obedience. This method ensures that participants know they are not inflicting harm on a real person, removing much of the risk of psychological damage. Slater et al. (2006) asked participants to play the role of teacher, interacting with a virtual learner and to administer electric shocks at wrong answers. This method enabled Slater to experiment with other technologies, for example requiring teachers to communicate with the virtual 'learner' via text message. In this 'text' variation of the experiment, all participants went to the highest level on the shock generator. These findings have important implications for cyber-bullying.

Exam hint

Choose two distinct issues (e.g. right to withdraw and debriefing), rather than issues which overlap (e.g. deception and informed consent). Ensure you relate them explicitly to Milgram's research.

EXAMPLE EXAM QUESTION

Explain two ethical issues in Milgram's research into obedience. [3 + 3 marks]

Situational variables affecting obedience: proximity, location, and uniform

In order to further explore the factors that influence obedience, Milgram replicated his experiment, carrying out 18 studies in total with over 1000 participants. In these variations he systematically modified the proximity (closeness) of the learner to the teacher, the location of the experiment and the impact of a uniform on obedience. Each of these factors gave increased understanding of when and why people obey orders.

Proximity

Milgram noticed that the proximity of the teacher and learner affected obedience. In the original version of the experiment, the teacher was unable to see the learner as they were in separate rooms, but could hear his screams. In a series of variations, Milgram altered the proximity of teacher and learner as follows:

- Milgram removed the experimenter from the room and instructed him to give the teacher orders over the phone. Many more participants resisted the authority of the experimenter, with only 20 per cent going to the full 450V.
- Milgram brought the learner into closer proximity, placing him in the same room as the teacher where he could be seen and heard. Obedience levels dropped.
- In a variation referred to as 'touch proximity', the teacher and learner were in the same room and in order for the learner to receive the shocks, he had to place his hand voluntarily on a shock plate. When he refused to do this, the teacher was instructed to force his hand down onto the shock plate. Under this condition, a staggering 30 per cent of participants still continued to 450V.

Slater's (2006) study in a virtual environment included a condition in which participants were instructed to shock the learner via text

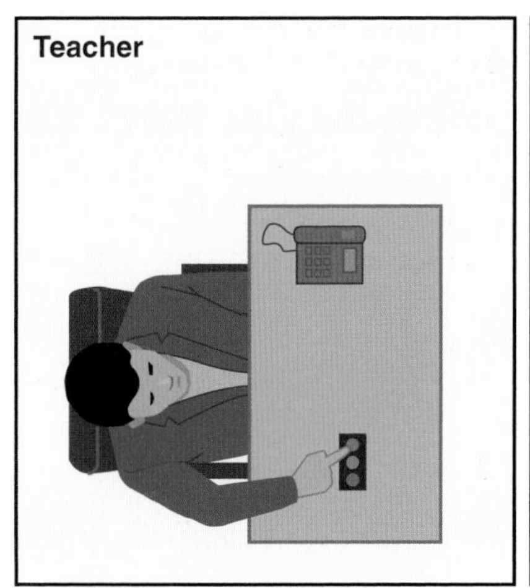

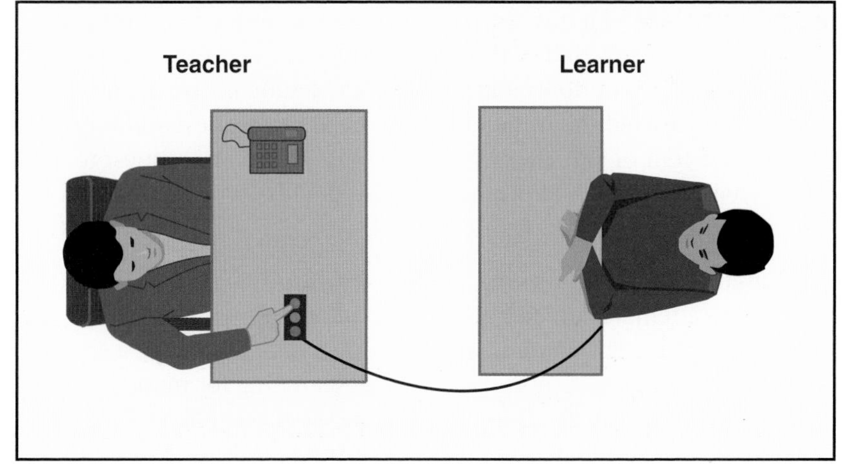

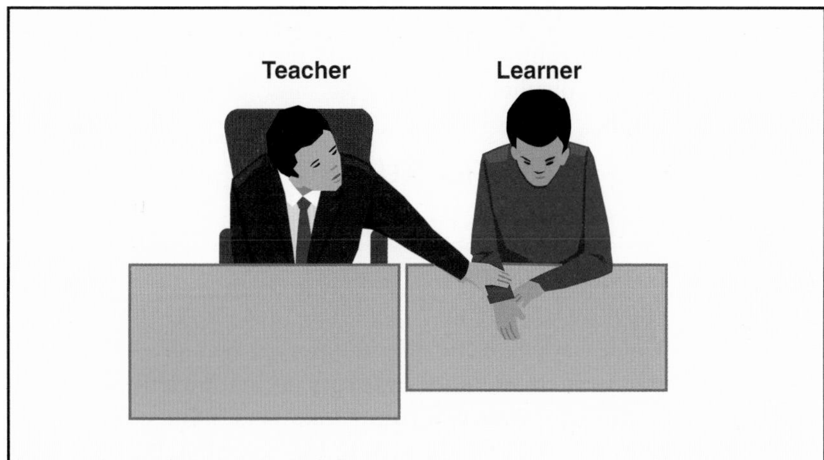

Fig. 1.8 Three variations in the Milgram experiment

message. The decrease in proximity produced through use of a mobile phone led to the highest levels of obedience in all participants.

Location

One factor that Milgram thought may have contributed to the high levels of obedience was the setting of the experiment, Yale University. In order to see if obedience was caused by the prestige of the setting, Milgram packed up his shock generator and moved his experiment into a seedy office above a shop. Calling himself 'Research Associates

Ltd' he advertised for participants in the paper and replicated the study exactly. Under this condition he found a significant drop in obedience. Forty-eight per cent of his participants in this setting continued to 450V on the shock generator. This led Milgram to conclude that the high status of Yale University was one factor that contributed to high levels of obedience.

Uniform

Milgram standardised his experimental variations, ensuring that the experimenter wore a white lab coat that helped to establish the authority of the experimental situation. Other social psychologists have investigated the impact of a uniform on obedience. Bickman (1974) carried out a field experiment in New York in which he asked passers-by to carry out unusual orders – picking up rubbish, standing on the other side of a bus-stop sign or lending money to a stranger for a parking meter. Half of the time the experimenter was dressed in a security guard's uniform and the rest of the time in street clothes. Bickman measured the number who obeyed the request and found that 92 per cent of participants would comply with the request to lend money when he was uniformed, compared with 49 per cent when he was wearing street clothing.

Bushman (1988) used Bickman's method of studying obedience, this time using a female confederate dressed in one of two ways – uniform or smart clothes. The confederate ordered passers-by to give a small amount of change to a motorist who was searching for money at a parking meter. Bushman found that 70 per cent complied when she was uniformed, compared with 58 per cent when dressed in smart clothing. Whilst the difference is less impressive than that found by Bickman, both studies show how a uniform provides a symbol of authority, increasing obedience.

Legitimacy of authority and the agentic state

Legitimacy of authority

An important factor in obedience is legitimate authority. This refers to the amount of social power held by the person who gives the instruction. Most human and, indeed, many animal societies are ordered in a hierarchical way, with some members of the group having power over those beneath them in the hierarchy. Power may be associated with social roles (for example, police officer, teacher, doctor) or with social status (gang members). From early childhood, social interactions in the family and at school teaches us that we are more acceptable if we obey those who have authority over us. We may obey people with authority because we trust them, or because they have the power to punish or harm us.

The importance of legitimate authority was shown in Milgram's experimental variations. Obedience was high (65 per cent) when the experiment took place at the prestigious Yale University, but dropped when the setting was altered to an office in downtown New York

(48 per cent). The change of setting effectively reduced the power and authority of the experimenter. It is reasonable to assume that the change of setting also influenced the degree of trust participants felt in the experimenter.

Legitimate authority can be signified by the use of a uniform (e.g. doctor, police officer). In Bickman's 1974 field experiment, 92 per cent of pedestrians obeyed an order to give a stranger money for a parking meter when the researcher was dressed as a security guard, compared to only 49 per cent when the same man was dressed in civilian clothing. In this experiment, the authority figure was immediately recognizable by the uniform. Similarly, Hofling's 1966 field experiment (see page 87) illustrates the importance of legitimate authority held by doctors. During the debriefing, many of the nurses argued that an order of this nature from a doctor was not unusual and that obedience was expected. This can be explained by the degree of power and trust invested at that time in hospital doctors.

The agentic state

In order for an authority figure to be obeyed, it is important that they are prepared to take the responsibility for their subordinates' actions. The importance of this is shown in film evidence and transcripts of Milgram's experiment. Many of his participants had serious reservations about continuing to administer shocks and asked the experimenter if they were personally responsible. When participants were told that the full responsibility was the experimenter's, they continued to obey. If the experimenter had replied that the participant was personally responsible, it is likely that the outcome of this experiment would have been very different.

Milgram explained the importance of responsibility through agency theory. He argued that people operate in two different ways in social situations:

- When they act as autonomous individuals they are aware of the consequences of their actions and choose voluntarily to behave in particular ways.
- In an **agentic state**, the person sees themselves as the agent or subordinate of others. They carry out their orders but do not feel personally responsible for the actions they take.
- The change from an autonomous to an agentic state is known as the **agentic shift**.

The concept of the agentic state is shown in the following extract from a war crimes trial. Lieutenant William Calley was tried for his part in the My Lai massacre of South Vietnamese villagers in March 1968.

Q: Did you learn anything in those classes of what actually the Geneva Convention covered as far as rules and regulations of warfare are concerned?

A: No, sir. Laws and rules of warfare, sir.

Q: Did you receive any training in any of those places which had to do with obedience to orders?

A: Yes, sir.

Key terms

Agentic state: a state in which an individual carries out the orders of another person, acting as their agent with little personal responsibility.

Agentic shift: the switch from operating as an autonomous individual to acting as an agent for another person, usually an authority figure.

Q: What were the nature of the – what were you informed were the principles involved in that field?

A: That all orders were to be assumed legal, that the soldier's job was to carry out any order given to him to the best of his ability.

Q: Did you tell your doctor or inform him anything about what might occur if you disobeyed an order by a senior officer?

A: You could be court-martialled for refusing an order and refusing an order in the face of the enemy, you could be sent to death, sir.

Q: Well, let me ask you this: what I am talking and asking is whether or not you were given any instructions on the necessity for – or whether you were required in any way, shape or form to make a determination of the legality or illegality of an order?

A: No, sir. I was never told that I had the choice, sir.

Q: If you had a doubt about the order, what were you supposed to do?

A: If I had – questioned an order, I was supposed to carry the order out and then come back and make my complaint.

This extract demonstrates the agentic state in stark reality. The soldier does not see himself as an individual but as an agent of a senior officer.

Exam hint

When asked to apply your knowledge of reasons for obedience to a scenario, you could refer to Milgram's variations to illustrate your arguments. For example, in this scenario you could refer to research on the power of a uniform.

EXAMPLE EXAM QUESTION

You are travelling in the quiet coach of a train. A young man boards the train, sits opposite and turns on his tablet to watch a film. You politely ask him to turn the sound down and he ignores you. The train guard passes through the coach to check tickets and makes the same request. The young man obeys the guard immediately.

Use your knowledge of explanations of obedience to suggest why the train guard is obeyed. (4 marks)

ACTIVITY 1.4

David Mandel has suggested that Milgram's work provides an 'obedience alibi' for war crimes. Find out about Mandel's critique using Internet sources.

Dispositional explanation for obedience: the Authoritarian Personality

Key term

Authoritarian personality: a person who has extreme respect for authority and who is very obedient to those who have power over them. They may be hostile to those of lower rank.

Other psychologists have attempted to establish whether certain types of people are more likely to be obedient than others. Theodor Adorno was a psychologist working in the US in the late 1940s and early 1950s, along with a group of European psychologists who had fled Nazi persecution in Europe. Adorno argued that the key to understanding extreme obedience and racial prejudice lay in early childhood experiences, when personality is formed. He argued that people with an '**authoritarian personality**' have a tendency to be extremely obedient.

Adorno studied over 2000 American students from mainly white, middle-class backgrounds. He interviewed them about their political views and their early childhood experiences. He also used projective tests (see Fig. 1.9), neutral stimuli such as pictures that could be used

Fig. 1.9 The Rorschach test, an example of a projective test

to gain access to people's thoughts, to assess whether or not they were racially prejudiced. Adorno found that people who had been brought up by strict parents who used harsh, physical punishments when they were children often grew up to be very obedient. Under these conditions, children quickly learn to obey and develop a strong respect for authority. Adorno drew on Freud's ideas about the unconscious mind to build his explanation, arguing that harsh and physical punishment led to the child feeling hostile and angry towards their parents. This hostility was uncomfortable for the child and created feelings of conflict, so it might be repressed or locked away into the unconscious mind. The child then displaces these hostile feelings on to others, often of a different racial group, which then become an alternative target for their hostility.

Link

You can read more about Freud's ideas about the unconscious mind in the psychodynamic approach on page 216.

From his research, Adorno developed a number of scales to measure aspects of behaviour and attitudes, including ethnocentricism (the preference for one's own racial group), anti-Semitism (prejudice against Jewish people) and, most famously, the potential for fascism, which has become known as the 'F scale'. The F scale measures the 'authoritarian personality'.

Conventionalism	Obedience and respect for authority are the most important virtues children should learn.
Authoritarian aggression	Sex crimes such as rape and attacks on children deserve more than imprisonment: such criminals ought to be publicly whipped or worse.
Power and toughness	People can be divided into two distinct classes: the strong and the weak.

Table 1.1 Sample items from Adorno's F scale, adapted from Psychology*: The Science of Mind and Behaviour* by Richard Gross, copyright © 2001 Richard Gross, reproduced by permission of Hodder Education.

Although the role of personality and individual differences was played down in Milgram's experiment, Elms and Milgram (cited in Miller, 1986) carried out interviews with a subsample of those who had taken part in Milgram's first four experiments. They found that those who were fully obedient and went to 450V scored higher on tests of authoritarianism and lower on scales of social responsibility than those who defied the experimenter, supporting Adorno's claims. We will be exploring personality differences in disobedience in the next topic.

ACTIVITY 1.5

Nonesuch Secondary School encourages sixth form students to act as lunchtime supervisors for a small payment. Many sixth formers complain that the younger students lack respect for them and do not see them as legitimate authority figures. Using your knowledge of research into obedience, explain different ways that the school could increase the authority of sixth form supervisors.

KEY POINTS

- Milgram carried out a series of experiments exploring obedience using over 1000 participants. In the original experiment, 65 per cent of participants administered the strongest shock of 450V.
- Milgram's experiments were criticized for the ethical issues raised, including protection from psychological harm. These experiments led to the development of ethical guidelines and principles.
- Proximity, location and uniform influenced levels of obedience.
- Obedience is highest where orders are issued by people in power who hold legitimate authority.
- In an agentic state, the individual acts as an 'agent' for a person or organization.
- Authoritarian personalities have a strong respect for authority and are most likely to show high levels of obedience.

Explanations of resistance to social influence, including social support and locus of control

Explanations of resistance to social influence

Research studies carried out by Asch, Zimbardo, Hofling and Milgram have shown how many people conform or obey when put under pressure. However, in each of these studies, some individuals resisted the pressure put on them and retained their independence.

- In Asch's 1951 experiment, 24 per cent of people did not conform to the confederates' estimates of line length at any point.

- In Milgram's 1963 experiment, 35 per cent of the 40 male participants disobeyed the experimenter by refusing to give the full 450V shocks.
- In Hofling's field experiment, one nurse out of 22 refused to administer the drug 'Astroten' to a patient.
- In Zimbardo's prison study, around two-thirds of the guards resisted the pressure to behave sadistically towards the prisoners.

What factors lead people to resist social pressure? Obedience and disobedience are opposing sides of the same coin, influenced by both external (situational) and internal (personality) factors. An important external factor is the presence of others who are also resisting the pressure to conform or obey, providing **social support**. An internal (personality) factor which seems to be important is an internal **locus of control**.

Key terms

Social support: support from other people who are also defying the pressure to conform or obey.

Locus of control: refers to the sense of control people have over the successes, failures and events in their lives.

SOCIAL INFLUENCE

Social support

Most of us will have noticed that it is easier to ignore orders or break rules as a group. One factor that leads individuals to resist the pressure to conform or obey is support from others. Social support can increase an individual's confidence that their own view or position is correct. Alternatively, the presence of other defiant people means that disobedient behaviour stands out less than if the individual acted alone, effectively providing an alternative, if small, 'group'.

Fig. 1.10 Women protesting against nuclear weapons at Greenham Common, 1982. Social support makes protest easier.

Many studies show how social pressure can be resisted with the support of other people. In one variation of Milgram's obedience experiment, teachers were paired with two confederates who either refused to administer the shocks to the learner or obeyed the orders. The presence of two disobedient confederates had a dramatic effect, lowering complete obedience to 10 per cent of participants. In contrast, the presence of two obedient confederates raised the level of complete obedience (i.e. administering 450V) to 92.5 per cent. This demonstrates how support from others increased the participant's ability to resist the pressure put upon them to administer the shocks.

A similar finding was obtained in Asch's variation in which unanimity was manipulated (see page 76). When the condition included a dissenter who gave a different answer to the line length question, conformity dropped to 5.5 per cent. As we noted earlier, social support was equally effective when the confederate provided the correct answer or a different incorrect answer.

KEY STUDY: GAMSON, FIREMAN AND RYTINA (1982)

Gamson et al. wished to set up a situation in which participants were encouraged to rebel against an unjust authority. The researchers placed an advertisement in the local newspapers in a town in Michigan, USA, asking for volunteers to take part in a paid group discussion on 'standards of behaviour in the community'. Those who responded were asked to attend a group discussion at a local Holiday Inn. When they arrived they were put into groups of nine and met by a consultant from a fictional human relations company called Manufacturers Human Relations Consultants (MHRC). The consultant explained that MHRC was conducting research for an oil company, which was taking legal action against a petrol station manager. They argued that the manager had been sacked because his lifestyle was offensive to the local community. In contrast, the manager argued that he had been sacked for speaking out on local television against high petrol prices.

Participants were asked to take part in a group discussion about the sacking, and this was filmed. As the discussion unfolded, it became apparent that the participants' own views were irrelevant and that MHRC wanted them to argue in favour of the sacking. At a number of points during the discussion, the cameraman stopped filming and instructed different members of the group to argue in favour of the oil company's decision to sack the manager. Finally, the participants were asked to sign a consent form allowing the film to be shown in a court case.

Rebellion against authority in this context involved challenging two well-established social norms in the situation, the norm of obedience and the norm of commitment, both of which participants had engaged in by agreeing to take part in the study. Of the 33 groups tested by Gamson, 32 rebelled in some way during the group discussion. The participants established a strong group identity in which the members agreed that the demands of the authority were unreasonable. This could be seen by the way in which they addressed the MHRC coordinator, saying that 'we don't want to go on record, even pretending that we agree with what we're saying. We don't. All three of us feel the same way' (cited in Smith and Mackie, 2000, page 409). In 25 out of the 33 groups, the majority of group members refused to sign the consent form allowing the film to be used in court. Nine groups even threatened legal action against MHRC.

THINKING SCIENTIFICALLY: ANALYSIS OF GAMSON: THE PROBLEM OF CAUSE AND EFFECT

Unlike the experiments conducted by Asch and Milgram, Gamson's research had a high level of realism. The participants were unaware that they were participating in a psychological study and were unlikely to respond to demand characteristics. However, Gamson's study was a controlled observation rather than an experiment. Without manipulation of an independent variable, it is impossible to establish a cause-and-effect relationship between presence of a group and disobedience.

One interpretation of the study is that the presence of a group allowed an alternative consensus of the correct way to behave. However, the rebellion could also have been influenced by the potentially serious consequences of lying on film in court. Both of these are likely to have contributed to the high levels of disobedience shown. Further experimental work would be needed to establish which of these played the most important role.

Locus of control

The concept of locus of control was put forward by Rotter in 1966. Rotter argued that we can measure an individual's sense of personal control over events in their life using a scale. At one end of the scale are those who largely believe that they can influence events in their life and who feel that their actions are their own choice and responsibility. This is an internal locus of control. At the other end of the scale are those who believe that outside factors such as luck, fate or 'the stars' influence their daily lives and decisions. This is an external locus of control. The individual with an internal locus of control who receives a promotion at work is likely to feel this is due to their own hard work, whereas the person with an external locus of control may think their boss was simply in a good mood that day or it was their lucky day. Most people score somewhere in the middle of the locus of control scale with few individuals having strong scores at either end.

Research methods link

Rotter's scale is a self report technique. You can remind yourself of this method by looking at pages 18–19.

A strong internal locus of control plays an important role in resisting orders to obey. Elms and Milgram (1974, cited in Miller, 1986) investigated the background of those participants who were classed as disobedient participants in the first four of Milgram's experiments. Each participant was followed up and interviewed. Elms and Milgram found that disobedient participants had a high internal locus of control and also scored highly on a social responsibility scale. Similar findings were obtained from studies examining those who defied social pressure in Nazi Germany. Oliner and Oliner (1988, cited in Blass, 1991) interviewed two groups of non-Jewish people who had lived through the Holocaust in Nazi Germany. They compared 406 people who had protected and rescued Jews from the Nazis with 126 who had not done this. Oliner and Oliner found that the 'rescuers' had scores demonstrating an internal locus of control and also scored higher on measures of social responsibility. From these studies, it appears that locus of control and social responsibility are both important factors in an individual's ability to disobey orders or to defy social norms.

Studies of locus of control and conformity have been less conclusive. Williams and Warchal (1981) studied 30 university students who were given a range of conformity tasks based on Asch's experimental paradigm. Each student was also assessed using Rotter's locus of control scale. Williams found that those who conformed the most were significantly less assertive but did not score differently on the locus of control scale, implying that assertion may be more important than locus of control to conformity. However, Avtgis (1998) re-examined a series of studies on locus of control and conformity, and found that those who scored higher on external locus of control were more easily persuaded and likely to conform than those with a low score. The average correlation between the locus of control and conformity was 0.37, which was statistically significant. This suggests that there are genuinely higher rates of conformity in 'externals' than 'internals'.

Research methods link

Correlation co-efficients are covered on page 24.

Item	Agree very much	Agree somewhat	Agree slightly	Disagree slightly	Disagree somewhat	Disagree very much
By taking an active part in political or social affairs people can control world events.						
Who gets to be the boss depends on who was lucky enough to be in the right place.						
The world is run by a few people in power and there is not much the little guy can do about it.						
What happens to me is my own doing.						
Most people don't realize the extent to which their lives are controlled by accidental happenings.						

Table 1.2 Sample items from Rotter's (1966) locus of control scale (adapted from *BPS Manual of Psychology Practicals*)

Exam hint

Selecting material:
You have learned about two explanations for resisting social pressure in this section of the course. Identify which is referred to in the scenario opposite to ensure you select the most relevant material.

EXAMPLE EXAM QUESTION

You are waiting in your car in a queue of traffic at some traffic lights. The lights have not changed for several minutes and you wonder if they are stuck on red. Eventually, the car at the front of the queue moves forward, crossing the red light, and the line of cars follows.

Use your knowledge of explanations of resisting social influence to explain why the other drivers cross the red traffic light. (4 marks)

KEY POINTS

- Support from others can help people to resist social pressure to conform or obey.
- An internal locus of control is associated with greater resistance to social pressure.

Minority influence including reference to consistency, commitment, and flexibility

Asch's study examined the impact of social pressure from a larger group towards an individual. This type of social pressure is referred to as majority influence. Another type of conformity occurs when a single person or a small group changes the views of a larger group, effectively converting others to their position. This is known as **minority influence**.

There are many examples of minority influence taking place throughout history. Galileo was one of the first to suggest that the earth travelled around the sun rather than the other way round – this idea was seen as highly controversial at the time. At the start of the twentieth century, a group of women who became known as suffragettes challenged the British law that women could not vote and, through consistent protest, changed the laws to enable equal voting rights for men and women. In 2013, gay rights campaigners finally won the right to civil marriages for gay couples in the UK.

Key term

Minority influence: occurs when an individual or small group of people influence a larger group to change their attitudes or behaviour towards an issue.

SOCIAL INFLUENCE

KEY STUDY: MOSCOVICI, LAGE AND NAFFRECHOUX (1969)

Serge Moscovici and colleagues carried out an experiment using a modified version of Asch's paradigm. Groups of six were each made up of four participants who were naive to the experiment and two confederates who were instructed to give incorrect answers. The task used by Moscovici et al. was a colour perception task in which the groups were shown a series of 36 slides of different shades of blue and asked to state aloud the colour of the slide.

- In condition one, the two confederates acted as a *consistent* minority, calling all 36 slides green.
- In condition two, the confederates acted as an *inconsistent* minority, calling 24 out of 36 of the slides green.
- The control condition consisted of six genuine participants with no confederates.

Moscovici et al. measured the number of genuine participants who adopted the minority position and called any of the slides green. In condition one, just over 8 per cent of the genuine participants moved to adopt the minority position. In the second (inconsistent) condition, the move to the minority position was around 1.25 per cent. In the control condition, no participants referred to the slides as green, indicating there was no ambiguity about the colour of the slides.

In a variation of the experiment, Moscovici et al. tested the real participants' colour perception privately after the experiment (i.e. with no social pressure), asking them to identify when gradations of coloured slides changed from blue to green (see Fig. 1.11). Those who had been exposed to the minority view that the slides were green identified the ambiguous slides as green at an earlier stage than those who hadn't.

Fig. 1.11 When does blue become green?

THINKING SCIENTIFICALLY: MINORITY INFLUENCE IN EVERYDAY LIFE

As we have already explored in relation to Asch and Milgram, experiments of this nature have been roundly criticized for lacking ecological validity: the colour perception task is unlikely to occur in daily life and the decision to conform has few consequences. More recent studies have considered how minority influence occurs in a more realistic, everyday setting. Juries consist of 12 randomly selected adults who come to a group decision regarding the innocence or guilt of a defendant. In most juries there is disagreement, creating naturally occurring minority and majority groups, which provide a fertile ground for studying social influence. As there are ethical difficulties in studying real-life juries, social psychologists construct mock juries for the purpose of exploring minority influence.

Clark (1999) carried out a series of studies based on the 1957 film *12 Angry Men*, in which a single juror (played by Henry Fonda) believes that a defendant is innocent of killing his father and sets out to convince the other 11 members of the jury that the young man is innocent. Participants were asked to play the role of jurors and to make up their minds about the guilt or innocence of the young man.

Clark supplied his participants with a four-page booklet containing evidence suggesting the defendant was guilty. He varied whether or not the students were given information about Henry Fonda's defence and the counter-arguments that supported the claim of innocence. He found that a minority juror led people to change their minds only when they could provide arguments against the evidence for guilt.

Consistency, commitment and flexibility

Moscovici's work identified a number of elements of behavioural style that make minorities persuasive or influential, including consistency, commitment and flexibility. The most important of these appears to be consistency. In a consistent minority, everyone gives the same message. Why is this important? According to Hogg and Vaughan (2002), a consistent minority disrupts the established norm, producing doubt and uncertainty in the minds of the majority.

Consistency demonstrates commitment to an alternative, viable viewpoint. Another important feature of minority influence is flexibility. A minority group that appears rigid and refuses to accept any other views is likely to be seen as dogmatic. However, there is a fine line to tread here, as minorities run the risk of being viewed as inconsistent if they are too flexible. For maximum impact, the minority should be consistent with regard to their argument or position, but should also appear open-minded and reasonable (Mugny, 1982).

Conformity: putting it all together

When a group of people disagree on an issue, there is usually a majority and a minority. How do we know whether a dissenting individual will convert the majority to their view, or give in to the pressure imposed by the majority group? Moscovici's conversion theory (1980) describes the different ways in which majority and minority influence occur. According to conversion theory:

- Majorities exert their influence by making people *compare* their views with that of the majority group ('I think X but you think Y'). Most people would prefer to belong to the majority group with its superior social status, so they comply with the majority position without really thinking about it too much. Majority influence occurs during exposure to the majority viewpoint (i.e. it is immediate) and often involves little thought.
- In contrast, minorities exert their influence through *validation* processes. The different view put forward leads people to think deeply about the message. As there may be social costs attached to adopting a minority viewpoint (such as stigma or discrimination), attitude change tends to be private and occurs after exposure to the minority viewpoint (i.e. it is delayed). However, it is likely to involve conversion, a profound modification of beliefs. Over time there is public acceptance of the minority position.

KEY POINTS

- Minority influence occurs when an individual or small group converts the majority to their viewpoint.
- Minorities are most persuasive when they are consistent, committed and flexible.

The role of social influence processes in social change

Most research into minority influence focuses on the effects of minorities on individuals (i.e. changing people's attitudes). We have seen how minorities can change the views of majority groups when they are consistent, committed and flexible. In the final topic of this chapter we will examine the important role played by minority groups in producing **social change**.

Key term

Social change: changes in attitudes, behaviour and/or laws which take place on a large scale and affect society.

Fig. 1.12 Social change is 'almost invariably [brought] about by minority influence' (Prislin and Filson, 2009)

One social change that has occurred in the UK is the acceptance of homosexual relationships. In 1983, the British Social Attitudes Survey found that over 60 per cent of adults who described themselves as 'non-religious' disapproved of same-sex relationships, thinking they were 'wrong'. By 2010, this figure had dropped to around 20 per cent. For Catholics, the respective time period showed a decrease from 70 per cent disapproval of gay relationships down to 37.5 per cent in 2010.

This change in attitudes has been mirrored by legal change. Up until 1967, homosexual activity was a crime that could lead to prosecution and imprisonment. It was also considered a deviance that required psychological treatment. The first stage towards equality was the decriminalization of homosexuality in the Sexual Offences Act of 1967. Other milestones included the UK Civil Partnership Act (2004), which allowed gay couples to enter relationships recognized in law. The Civil Marriages Act (2013) allowed gay couples to enter marriages with the same legal benefits as heterosexual couples. These dramatic changes were achieved using a range of tactics, including protest marches, media campaigns and legal battles.

Prislin and Filson (2009) note that while some minority groups aim to change social structures, others campaign for *tolerance* for their way of life and for the right to live without persecution or discrimination, seeking to 'expand the scope of acceptable positions'.

Social change is often accompanied by social cryptomnesia. This term refers to the acceptance of values promoted by the minority (e.g. women's right to vote) accompanied by an apparent forgetting (hence amnesia) of the crucial role played by the minority group. Therefore, the changes achieved by minority groups are accepted but the group is not given credit for producing these changes, allowing a rejection of the general 'position' of feminist. This is similar to the sleeper effect in persuasion. By this process, minority groups do not receive credit for their successes and may still be viewed negatively or discriminated against.

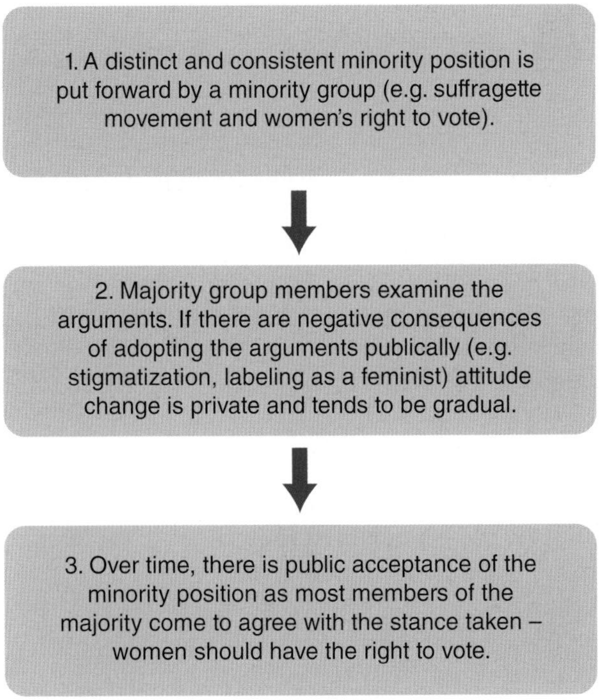

1. A distinct and consistent minority position is put forward by a minority group (e.g. suffragette movement and women's right to vote).

2. Majority group members examine the arguments. If there are negative consequences of adopting the arguments publically (e.g. stigmatization, labeling as a feminist) attitude change is private and tends to be gradual.

3. Over time, there is public acceptance of the minority position as most members of the majority come to agree with the stance taken – women should have the right to vote.

Fig. 1.13 Moscovici's conversion theory (1980) shows us how social change occurs

Prislin and Filson explored the differences between conversion and tolerance in a series of studies in 2009, concluding that these very different types of social change have different consequences. Groups that increase tolerance for their position are more accepting of social changes than those that aim for conversion, and take the view that 'those who are not with us are against us'.

ACTIVITY 1.6

Find out about the three Edmund Pettus Bridge marches (1965) in Montgomery, Alabama. What methods were used by black rights campaigners to draw attention to racial inequality? Why was the Edmund Pettus Bridge so significant in the black rights struggle and what did the marches achieve?

KEY POINTS

- Social changes refers to large scale changes in behaviours and/or attitudes.
- Some minority groups seek tolerance for their way of life rather than conversion.

PRACTICAL ACTIVITY

Try it yourself

This activity focuses on the relationship between locus of control and obedience. Previous research by Elms and Milgram (1974) and Oliner and Oliner (1988) suggested that individuals with an internal locus of control are less likely to obey orders than those with an external locus of control. Locus of control is naturally occurring; hence we cannot manipulate this as an independent variable. For this reason, we will use a correlational method to assess whether there is a relationship between the two variables.

In order to assess a relationship, you need some method of measuring your chosen variables – locus of control and obedience. The locus of control scale has been refined and validated; therefore you should use Rotter's scale. You can find various versions on the Internet. The original scale has 29 items, six of which are distracters, giving a maximum score of 23. A high score indicates an external locus of control and a low score indicates an internal locus of control. You can also find a shortened version of the scale with 13 items. Either would be fine to use.

To measure obedience, devise a list of ten situations in which people are given an instruction that they can obey or disobey (e.g. turn down music in the school library, pick up litter in the park, wear different shoes to work). In order to create a simple measurement for each of these you could award a score of 1 for obey and zero for disobey, making a maximum score of 10. It would be a good idea to pilot your scale and, if necessary, amend it. A more complex method is to use a scale of 1– 5 for each situation, as show below:

definitely obey	probably obey	neutral	probably disobey	definitely disobey
5	4	3	2	1

Before collecting your data you should consider ethical issues around consent and debriefing. You will need to decide which scale should be given to your participants first. You should also devise a set of standardized instructions. You will need a sample of ten or more people if you wish to carry out inferential statistics on your results. Ask your participants to complete both scales and record their scores.

When you have collected the data, plot your results using a scattergram to provide an instant picture of the relationship. You can also carry out a statistical test to assess if the relationship between the two variables is significant.

Exam focus

Read through the following example exam question, example student answers, and examiner comments. Then, have a go at answering the question yourself!

EXAMPLE EXAM QUESTION, TAKEN FROM PAGE 81

Samira has just started a new job at New Look. She notices that most of her new workmates tend to return a bit late from their lunch break. Samira doesn't want to get in trouble with the boss but she does want to get on with the rest of her team, so she starts coming back a few minutes late.

What type of conformity is shown by Samira? Explain your answer. (2 marks)

Use your knowledge of explanations of conformity to explain why Samira comes back late for work from her lunch break. (4 marks)

Kat's answer

Samira shows the type of conformity that is called compliance. She doesn't agree with the behaviour of her workmates, but she goes along with them even though she thinks it is wrong.

Examiner comment: Kat correctly identifies the type of conformity as compliance, and explains her answer with the definition of compliance (going along with others on the surface but privately disagreeing). The first part of the answer gains **2/2 marks**.

Samira has just started her job so she wants to fit in with her new work mates – it can be difficult when people leave you out. Because she wants to fit in this kind of conformity is normative social influence. It isn't informational social influence because Kat isn't doing the right thing.

Examiner comment: In the second part of the answer, Kat shows a basic understanding of the reasons for conformity and she accurately identifies Samira's motive as normative social influence. However, the answer lacks focus and includes irrelevant information ('it can be difficult when people leave you out'). The last point about informational social influence is muddled, and there is no reference to relevant theory (i.e. the dual process model). The second part of this answer gains **2/4 marks**.

Jack's answer

Samira is conforming by coming back late from her lunch break. This type of conformity is known as compliance: Samira conforms on the surface by behaving like her workmates, but there is no evidence that she thinks it is the right thing to do.

Examiner comment: This answer is accurate, and so it gains **2/2 marks**. However, it provides more detail than is needed for a 2 mark answer.

The dual process model put forward by Deutsch and Gerard identified two reasons for conformity — to fit in with others and to do the right thing. The type of conformity shown by Samira is normative social influence which refers to conforming to fit in — Samira 'wants to get on with her workmates', showing that acceptance from others is the reason for Samira coming back late.

Examiner comment: Jack's answer here is succinct, but well-informed, and well-focused. He refers to relevant theory (dual process model), and links this explicitly to the scenario with a quote. **4/4 marks.**

Part 1: Introductory topics in Psychology

Chapter 2: Memory

Introduction

Memory is such a basic human function that we tend to take it completely for granted. An apparently simple task, such as bringing to mind your friend's phone number, requires a very complex process. You have to know what a phone is and how numbers relate to these machines; you have to select and retrieve the correct number sequence from many such sequences stored in your memory; you may retrieve this number as a mental image (you picture the number in your mind), and/or as an auditory image (you may say the numbers aloud in your mind). If you want to use this number you then need to retrieve stored knowledge about how to use a phone and enact the correct pattern of movements so that you hold it correctly and press the appropriate buttons. And you may do all of this automatically without any conscious awareness or effort. As complicated as this sounds, it is a simplified description of what really goes on! Clearly, even the simplest act of memory is a very complex process.

With the development of computers in the 1950s, psychologists became more interested in **cognition**. This term basically refers to thinking, and encompasses all our mental abilities, such as reasoning, perceiving, communicating, problem solving, creating, and remembering. Those who study these mental processes and how they influence behaviour are called cognitive psychologists. Computers provided a metaphor for how humans might also process information. This approach, whereby the operations going on inside our heads are compared to the various functions of computers, is referred to as the information processing approach. Indeed, many of the terms used in cognitive psychology are borrowed directly from computer science.

In this chapter we will be looking at what cognitive psychologists have discovered about the structure of human memory, how new information is acquired, how it is stored, how it is recalled from memory, and why, sometimes, our memory lets us down and we forget information. We will also look at one very important practical application of memory research: improving our understanding of the reliability and accuracy of the testimony of individuals who have witnessed crimes.

What is covered in Memory?

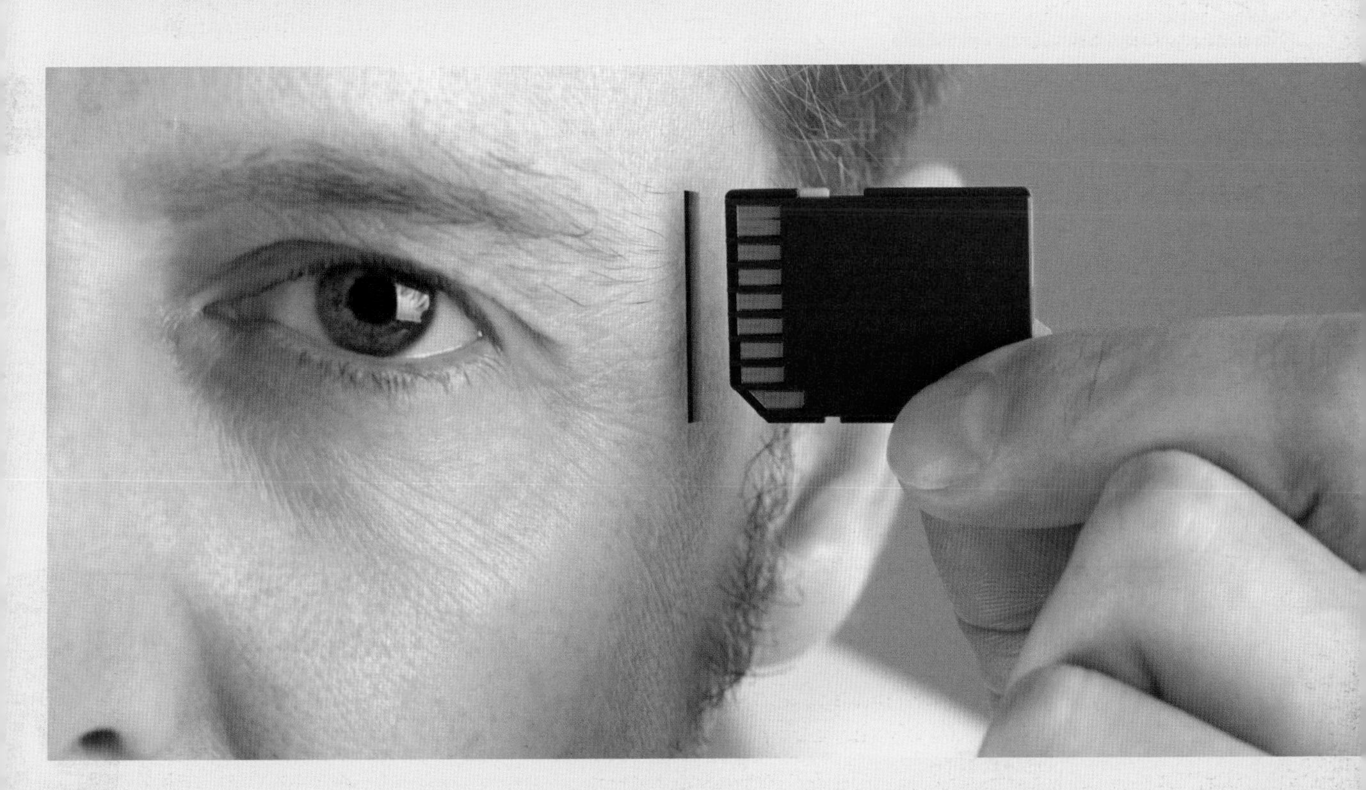

Models of memory

Many of the things of interest to cognitive psychologists are not directly observable. For example, whilst we directly experience the results of our memory – we remember what we went to the supermarket for, we use the functions on our mobile phones effortlessly – we cannot see how our memory system is organized to enable such complex behaviours. What cognitive psychologists do in these circumstances is to develop models of how things might work.

Models provide a very useful way of viewing things that we actually cannot see. A basic model is constructed after careful consideration of existing evidence, and then further research is conducted to test the assumptions of this model. As a result of this testing the model is either supported, updated, or even discarded in favour of one that better fits the evidence. This can be seen in the development of our understanding of the structure of memory. The multi-store model of memory was a development from an earlier idea that there was a primary memory for temporary conscious thoughts and a secondary memory for more permanent storage of thoughts. As our understanding of the complexity of human memory increases, so our models of memory change to accommodate these complexities. For instance, over time, deficiencies in the multi-store model saw new models developed, including the working memory model, an alternative to the multi-store model's short-term memory store. We will look at two of the most influential models of memory next – the multi-store model and the working memory model.

The multi-store model of memory

The multi-store model of memory is the most well-known and influential model of memory, proposed by Atkinson and Shiffrin in 1968. They saw memory as a flow of information through a system divided into a series of interacting memory stores (see Fig. 2.1). Each store has a different purpose, and each varies in terms of its **coding**, **capacity** and **duration**.

Key terms

Coding: changing the format of information for use in memory (also referred to as encoding).

Capacity: the amount of information that can be held in memory.

Duration: the length of time information remains in memory.

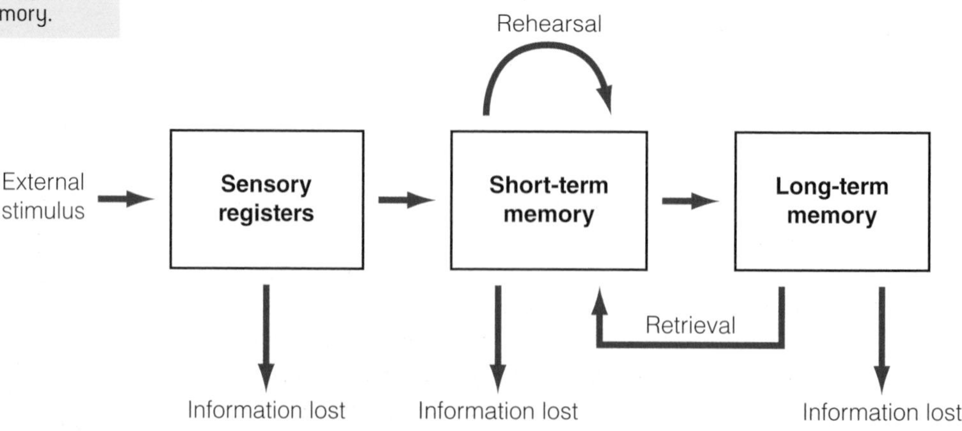

Fig. 2.1 The multi-store model of memory

EXAMPLE EXAM QUESTION

Outline the main features of the multi-store model of memory. (4 marks)

Exam hint

It is a really good idea to learn the diagram for the multi-store model. You can draw this in your answer, and it is a great aid to memory. There are enough features in the diagram to get full marks for a description, but don't just focus on the structure – be sure to mention processes too, for example rehearsal.

Sensory registers

Information enters the system from the environment through our senses. Everything we hear, see, touch, taste and smell enters sensory memory. There are actually several stores in sensory memory, called **sensory registers**. Each register deals with information from a particular sense, for example there is the iconic register (vision), the echoic register (sound) and the haptic register (touch). These are *passive* stores, in that we cannot control what enters sensory memory, nor can we consciously control their functioning. The sensory registers are constantly bombarded with information, far more than the later memory stages can handle, so it has a mechanism for selecting the relevant sensory information and discarding the rest. This is called *attention*. Whilst sensory registers have a relatively large capacity, information is stored only briefly and in a relatively unprocessed form (i.e. there is limited encoding). Research has shown that sensory information that does not receive attention has a duration of a few seconds at most. Information that is the focus of attention is transferred to the next memory store.

Key term

Sensory register: a store of sensory information that lasts no more than a few seconds.

Iconic register

'Icon' is another word for image or picture. The iconic register therefore refers to our memory for visual information. It has received the most research interest not only because it is relatively straightforward to investigate, but also because it is through vision that we receive most of our sensory information about the world. It has been claimed that the purpose of the iconic store is to allow us to integrate and make sense of the mass of visual sensations we receive so that our perception is of a smooth and continuous visual experience. You can use an analogy of a cartoon film to understand this. Cartoons are constructed of a large number of slightly varying still images. The scene would make no sense by looking at each still in turn, but when presented in quick succession we perceive a continuous moving scene. We do not see a jerky sequence of movements nor the blank space that must occur between stills – at least not in good quality cartoons! Our iconic register works in a similar way, ensuring that our visual experience is not a jumbled set of disconnected images.

ACTIVITY 2.1

Take a torch into a very dark room. If you move your arm fast enough you can actually create visual images of letters. These letters are not physically out there. They are formed because sensory memory holds onto visual information, or an *icon*, for a brief period after the visual image has gone. The image (light) has moved in space so we are remembering all the previous locations of the light. You will notice that the letter you trace will disappear very quickly. In fact, you might have to concentrate quite hard to see it at all. This reflects the very limited duration of information in iconic memory.

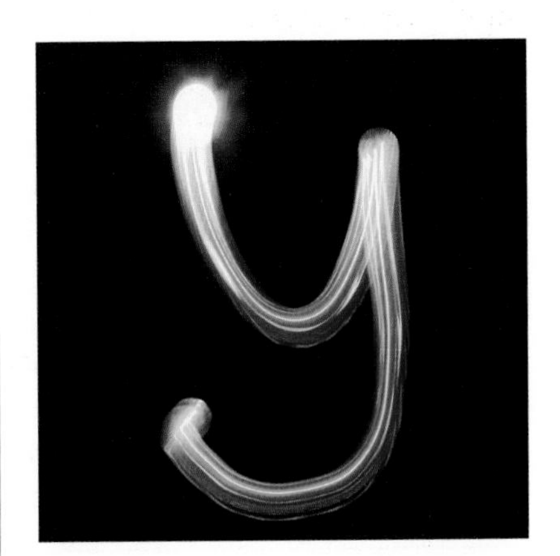

Fig. 2.2 This image is created by waving a torch in a dark room. You could create your own easily enough.

KEY STUDY: SPERLING'S EXPERIMENTS INTO ICONIC MEMORY

Atkinson and Shiffrin based their assumptions about iconic memory on the findings of previous research, in particular that of Sperling (1960). In his experiment, Sperling very briefly displayed to his participants visual arrays containing three rows of letters (see Fig. 2.3). He found that participants could only recall four or five of the letters from the 50 millisecond (0.05 second) arrays, but reported being aware of more letters that they could not report. Sperling assumed that, because visual information was only available for a very short time, it faded in memory before participants could recall it. Sperling conducted a further experiment to investigate this, using what he called a partial report procedure. He trained participants to recognize three tones – a high tone related to letters on the top row of the display, a medium tone related to the middle row, and a low tone related to the bottom row. Once participants had learned this, Sperling once again presented them with a series of displays for 50 milliseconds each, this time along with a tone, cueing participants to a particular row. He found that participants recalled on average 75% of the letters in the cued rows, a much better percentage than for the whole array.

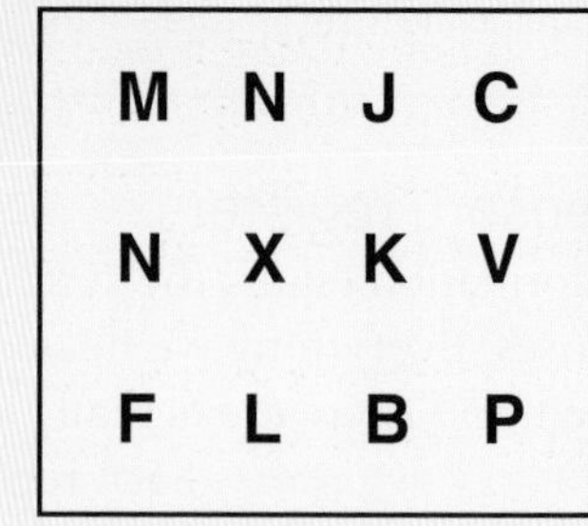

Fig. 2.3 An example of the Sperling visual array

According to Sperling this improved performance because a row contained fewer items than the whole display, therefore there was less decay of information from memory before participants had to recall it. Recall was not 100% however, even though participants only had to remember a small amount of information immediately after being shown it. Sperling saw this as evidence that not only does iconic memory have a very limited capacity, but that information decays and is lost very rapidly.

Research methods link

You can read more about the advantages and disadvantages of laboratory experiments on page 10.

THINKING SCIENTIFICALLY: THE COSTS OF HIGH CONTROL

Sperling's study is an example of a laboratory experiment. The advantage of a laboratory experiment like this is that there is a high level of control, allowing other researchers to *replicate* the findings (as indeed they have). Whilst this gives the results greater *reliability*, it comes at a cost. Such experiments use stimuli and environments that are quite artificial, in that they do not accurately reflect how we use memory in everyday circumstances. Some psychologists argue that this reduces the validity of the findings. This is an example of what frequently happens with tightly controlled psychological experiments – greater reliability comes at the cost of reduced *validity*.

Echoic memory

Echoic memory is the sensory register for auditory information. Research by Darwen et al. (1972) and others suggests that the length of time information is stored in echoic memory is about three seconds. This is much longer than the 0.5 seconds that information in iconic memory lasts. According to Cowan (1984), echoic memories last longer because of the important role language (and thus the sound of language) plays in communicating with others and understanding the world around us.

Darwen et al. (1972) conducted a study similar to Sperling's, but using auditory rather than visual stimuli. Participants were presented with spoken recordings of letter and number lists. The lists were presented over headphones so that it seemed to participants that one list came from the left, one from the right, and a third from behind. After hearing the lists participants were given a cue to recall one of the three lists. The length of time from the presentation to the cue varied between 0 and four seconds. The cue should have made the task easier as then participants only had to recall a list from a particular direction. Darwen et al. found that as the time between presentation and cue increased, the recall performance of participants decreased. After a three-second delay, participants performed no better than they would have without cues.

Further testing showed that performance did not significantly improve when participants were cued to recall either letter or digit lists. To do this task successfully, some analysis of the meaning of the auditory information would have been needed (that is, participants would need to distinguish a letter from a number). This finding suggests that auditory information in echoic memory is simply held there momentarily in an unprocessed 'raw' form before it is transferred for further processing.

Short-term memory

Information that is selected from sensory memory by the attention system is transferred to **short-term memory (STM)**. This is a temporary holding area, and can be thought of as a kind of immediate memory – the part of the memory system that holds all the information an individual is consciously thinking about at any one time. Atkinson and Shiffrin identified a number of important characteristics of STM, including its limited capacity, short duration and acoustic encoding. Anyone who has used a telephone will be aware of these characteristics. When you look up a number you have to repeat (or rehearse) it until it is used, otherwise it 'disappears' (short duration). If the number is too long you end up remembering the latter numbers in the string but forgetting the earlier ones (limited capacity). You almost certainly verbalized the whole process too, repeating the numbers out loud or in your head (acoustic encoding).

Key term

Short-term memory (STM): a temporary memory store that holds limited amount of information for a short period of time.

ACTIVITY 2.2

Try working out these problems in your head – do not write anything down or use a calculator:

$4 + 9 =$
$6 + (17 \times 3) =$
$7 + 2 + (8 \times 46) =$

It is likely that you had no difficulty with the first problem; the second problem was a bit more challenging, but quite possible; the last problem almost certainly tested you beyond the limits of your STM.

This kind of activity demonstrates the limited capacity of STM and shows that we can only hold and manipulate a small number of items at any one time.

Capacity of STM

STM has limited storage space. This was an early discovery by Jacobs in 1887. He used a digit span technique, which involved presenting participants with sequences of letters or digits at half-second intervals that then had to be recalled in the correct order. He started by presenting three-item sequences, increasing the sequences by one item until participants were unable to recall the sequence correctly. He repeated this process over a number of trials until he established the average number of items that a participant could recall – this was their digit span. Jacobs found that the participants recalled on average between five and nine items.

However, the term 'item' is very vague. For example, Jacobs found that digits were recalled better than letters (9.3 items as opposed to 7.3 items). Miller (1956) suggested that while STM is indeed limited to 'seven plus or minus two', capacity is determined by the number of 'chunks' of information rather than the number of individual letters or numbers.

ACTIVITY 2.3

Read the following list of items quickly and once only, then cover them up and write them down in the same order as they appear.

1234 2016 1845 1963

How did you do? You may have found this difficult – the number of digits is beyond the normal short-term memory span of five to nine digits. Note that there are 16 individual digits (or items) in this list, but because they were grouped together to create more meaningful 'chunks' (they resemble dates), you were able to expand the capacity of STM.

Other researchers have questioned this assertion and criticized Miller's term 'chunk' for also being too vague. Simon (1974), for example, found that memory span as measured in chunks depends on the amount of information contained in the chunk. He investigated the ability of participants to recall one-syllable, two-syllable and three-syllable words, and two-word and eight-word phrases. He found that larger chunks resulted in reduced memory span, so that participants accurately recalled fewer large chunks (e.g. eight-word phrases) and more smaller chunks (e.g. two-word phrases). Clearly, it is not easy to put an absolute capacity limit on STM as you can on a hard drive or CD-ROM. Unlike digital devices, which have clearly defined basic units of information (e.g. a 'bit'), it is not at all clear what constitutes a basic unit of information in STM.

Researchers have uncovered a number of factors that affect the capacity of STM. According to Cowan (2000), performance on digit span tests is influenced by our long-term memory. For example, it has been found that when sequences of digits are repeated in a digit span test, recall is improved. So, if a participant is given a task where they have to recall immediately a series of seven-digit sequences (e.g. 5 – 8 – 3 – 4 – 6 – 8 – 2), they perform better on the sequences that are repeated during the task (e.g. they do better on subsequent recalls of 5 – 8 – 3 – 4 – 6 – 8 – 2 than on other sequences that are not repeated). Presumably, even though this is a short-term memory task, information is being stored in long-term memory and is used to improve recall of repeated sequences. In this sense, performance on tasks like digit span tests does not necessarily reflect 'pure' short-term memory at all. In addition, research has shown that performance on digit span tests improves if participants are required to read the sequences aloud. There are a number of possible reasons for this phenomenon, but Baddeley (1999) proposes that it occurs because, by reading aloud, information is stored briefly in the echoic store, which in turn strengthens the memory for that information.

Duration of STM

Atkinson and Shiffrin saw STM as a temporary store, holding information for only brief periods. Anything we need to retain for longer periods has to be transferred to long-term memory. According to Atkinson and Shiffrin, we hold information in STM by rehearsing (repeating) the information. Rehearsal keeps the information in STM by continually reinserting it into the STM rehearsal loop. This rehearsal also strengthens the memory so that it can be stored permanently in long-term memory. According to Craik and Tulving (1973), it is not the amount of rehearsal time in STM that determines long-term retention. Rather, it is how the information is rehearsed. They suggested that there were two kinds of rehearsal. With *maintenance rehearsal* a person keeps information in STM by continually repeating it. This does not lead to a transfer to long-term memory. This is achieved through *elaborative rehearsal*. Here, the information has to be processed in some way so as to make it meaningful. For example, you might remember a new telephone number because of its similarity to a number you already know. In this case, the new number has been integrated with existing knowledge.

Potentially (though, obviously, unrealistically) information can be retained permanently in STM by maintenance rehearsal. How long information is retained without rehearsal was famously investigated by Peterson and Peterson in 1959. They found that even a small amount of information is quickly forgotten when participants are prevented from rehearsal – after 18 seconds, recall of simple three letter stimuli fell to 5 per cent.

KEY STUDY: THE DURATION OF SHORT-TERM MEMORIES

Peterson and Peterson (1959) investigated the duration of information in STM. They presented participants with consonant trigrams (these are non-pronounceable three-letter sequences, such as LDH or CKX). On presentation of a trigram, participants were required to count backwards in threes from a specified number (e.g. 358, 355, 352 ..., etc.). This was to prevent participants rehearsing the trigrams by repeating them in their heads. Participants were asked to stop counting and to repeat the trigram after intervals of 3, 6, 9, 12, 15 or 18 seconds. This process was repeated several times using different trigrams with each presentation.

It was found that participants were able to recall about 80 per cent of the trigrams after a three-second interval, but became progressively worse as the intervals lengthened. After 18 seconds, participants could recall fewer than 10 per cent of the trigrams correctly. Peterson and Peterson concluded that information disappears (or decays) very rapidly from STM when rehearsal is prevented.

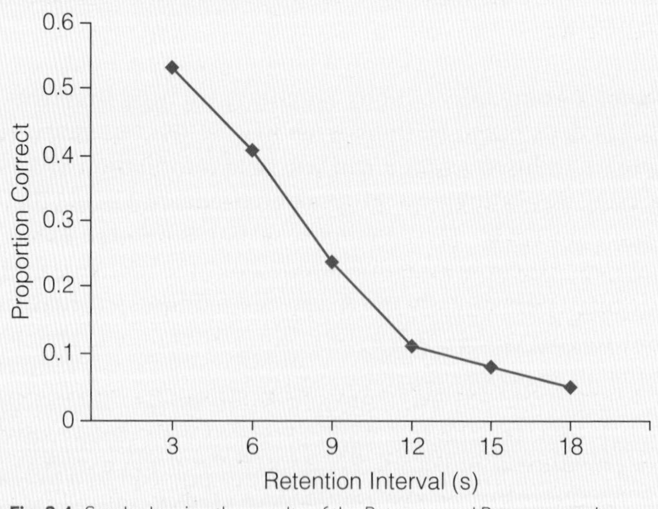

Fig. 2.4 Graph showing the results of the Peterson and Peterson study

THINKING SCIENTIFICALLY: INTERPRETING FINDINGS

The Peterson and Peterson study is a good example of how findings have to be *interpreted*, even from tightly controlled laboratory experiments such as this one. The experiment is lauded as objective and scientific, but a great deal of subjectivity is introduced when the findings of experiments need to be explained. While the findings are usually interpreted in terms of short duration in STM, they could be explained in a number of other ways. For instance, they might reflect capacity limitations rather than duration, with the counting task not allowing enough 'space' for the trigrams. It could even be that the experiment was so artificial, using a task that we are never likely to encounter in real life, that the findings tell us nothing useful about how memory really works.

This shows that we should always be cautious about accepting the findings of an experiment on face value – there are often several possible interpretations of findings, and the one presented may be just the one that suits current knowledge, or even the motivations or biases of the researcher, however unlikely this may be.

As discussed in relation to capacity in STM, the actual duration of short-term memories seems to depend on a range of factors. In addition to rehearsal, we can extend duration by our intention to recall the information later. This can be seen in the study by Sebrechts et al. (1989). They tested recall for sets of three familiar English nouns. In the condition where participants were not expecting to be asked to remember the words, correct recall fell to one per cent after only four seconds. Duration in STM can also be affected by the amount of information to be recalled. Murdock (1961) adopted the Peterson and Peterson technique but used either a single three-letter word such as 'cat', or a set of three unrelated words such as 'pen', 'hat' and 'lid'. When he used three words as the stimulus, he found the same pattern of decline in recall as in the original Peterson and Peterson study. However, when he used three letters (that formed a recognisable single word), recall was remarkably resistant to decay. Even though rehearsal had been prevented, accurate recall level was at about 90 per cent after 18 seconds. It seems, then, that the important factor is the number of chunks rather than the number of individual items.

Encoding in STM

When information arrives in the sensory registers, it is still in its original form, for example as a visual image or as a sound. The sensory store, as we saw earlier, has separate stores for different modalities. (A modality is a particular form of sensory experience such as vision, sound or touch.) Unlike sensory memory, Atkinson and Shiffrin saw STM as a single storage space that operated in the auditory (or acoustic) modality.

Research supporting this idea has come from studies into so-called *substitution* errors. These occur when people accidentally substitute a different item for a similar one on a list of items to be learned. The rationale for this is that people are likely to confuse items that sound alike if they are using an acoustic code, but should not make this error if they are using a visual code – why make a sound-based error when using the visual modality?

This was investigated in an experiment by Conrad (1964), who concluded that short-term memory encodes all information according to sound. He showed participants a random sequence of six consonants, projected very rapidly onto a screen. Some participants were shown consonants that were acoustically similar, that is, they sounded similar when vocalized (B, C, T, D ...). Other participants were shown consonants that were acoustically dissimilar (R, F, J ...). Immediately following the presentation, participants were asked to write the letters down in the order that they were shown. Since this task was well within the five-to-nine-item capacity of STM it should have been quite easy for participants. However, Conrad found that participants frequently made errors of recall. Participants found it more difficult to accurately recall sequences of consonants that sounded the same compared with sequences that sounded different. Where errors occurred they involved the substitution of a similar-sounding letter (e.g. a V for a D). Conrad concluded that while the consonant sequences had been presented visually, the participants had converted them to an acoustic code in STM. It was this encoding that resulted in difficulties distinguishing between consonants that sounded similar.

Conrad's conclusions were supported by Posner and Keele (1967). They showed participants pairs of letters (such as B–B, B–b, A–B) with a very brief time delay between the two letters. Participants were simply asked to say whether the two letters were the same or not. If STM encodes by sound, participants should be as quick responding to B–b as to B–B. However, if encoding is visual, participants should take slightly longer to respond to B–b because we would have to translate the different symbols into their appropriate letters. Posner and Keele found that participants did indeed take longer to respond to B–b than B–B if the delay between the two letters was less than 1.5 seconds, but took the same amount of time if the delay was longer than 1.5 seconds. They concluded that the letter pairs had been encoded visually in STM, but this was soon transformed from the visual to the acoustic modality.

However, other research has suggested that it is too simplistic to conclude that all encoding in STM is acoustic. For example, evidence suggests that semantic encoding is possible in STM. Semantic encoding is where the meaning of something is encoded, rather than its sight or sound, for instance. This is a process normally associated with long-term memory. Shulman (1970) presented participants with a series of word pairs and required them to indicate as fast as possible if one of the two words (the 'probe' word) was identical to the other, a homonym of the other (e.g. prey – pray), or a synonym of the other (e.g. leap – jump). He found a similar performance for all three probe types, leading him to conclude that semantic encoding is possible in STM.

EXAMPLE EXAM QUESTION

According to the multi-store model, short-term memory and long-term memory are separate components of memory. Use your knowledge of the multi-store model to evaluate this claim. [4 marks]

Exam hint

Read questions carefully so that you fully understand what they are asking you to do. You have a choice here – you can choose evidence that supports the multi-store model in this regard, or you can choose evidence that does not support this claim. It doesn't matter which you choose, just be clear about how they support or do not support the claim.

Long-term memory

For Atkinson and Shiffrin, a **long-term memory** (LTM) is anything that lasts longer than the duration of STM – basically information that lasts in memory anywhere from a couple of minutes to a lifetime. This is a limitless store of information, containing everything we know and have learned, such as yesterday's date, what a bird is, how to ride a bicycle, etc. Information that is held in STM for a period of time is likely to become part of our LTM. The store is *relatively permanent* however, rather than absolutely permanent – information that is entered into our long-term stores can easily be lost again.

Key term

Long-term memory: a permanent store where limitless amounts of information can be stored for long periods of time.

Capacity of LTM

It is probably impossible to say with any confidence what the capacity of LTM is, and science has not been able to provide us with a definite answer. It is generally accepted among researchers that LTM probably has no upper limit as to how much information it can store. While it is possible to lose things from LTM, this is through processes such as decay and interference. The loss does not occur because of capacity limitations.

Duration in LTM

The practical difficulties of measuring how long LTMs actually last means that few studies have been attempted. One well-known study that was attempted was by Bahrick et al. (1975). Participants aged up to 74 years were tested on their memory of their former classmates, demonstrating that memories can be accurate for a very long period of time.

ACTIVITY 2.4

Copy out the table below, and use what you have read about the multi-store model to complete it.

	Coding	Capacity	Duration
Sensory register			
Short-term memory			
Long-term memory			

Exam hint

This table is extremely useful for organizing your knowledge. You need to know about coding, capacity and duration of the three stores, and this table not only summarizes the essential information in one place, but also allows you to make comparisons between them.

KEY STUDY: VERY LONG-TERM MEMORY

Bahrick et al. (1975) attempted to explore the length of time memories can be retained. They tested the memory of 392 graduates of an American high school for their former classmates. They did this by testing their memories for other students in their yearbooks (a yearbook is a collection of photographs commemorating the school and given to students when they leave). They used various memory tests, including the recognition of classmates' pictures, matching names to pictures, and recalling names with no picture cue. Participants performed remarkably well up to about 34 years (90 per cent accuracy), and memory was good even for those participants who had left school 48 years previously (80 per cent accuracy). Predictably perhaps, performance was better on recognition tasks than on recall tasks – participants could pick out and recognize faces better than they could recall their classmates. For Bahrick et al., this was evidence for the durability of long-term memories.

Fig. 2.5 Bahrick et al. researched the durability of people's memories about their childhood classmates

THINKING SCIENTIFICALLY: THE COST OF HIGHER ECOLOGICAL VALIDITY

The Bahrick et al. study is an example of a field experiment. It was good in that it tested memory in a more natural way than a laboratory experiment normally would. However, the cost of higher ecological validity is often the loss of control. Were participants still in contact with people from their yearbook? How often did participants look through their own yearbooks? Was the dip in performance after 47 years due to the passage of time or to the effects of ageing on the brain? These and many other questions are unanswerable, meaning that we should be cautious about drawing firm conclusions from this study.

EXAMPLE EXAM QUESTION

Research suggests that coding in short-term memory differs from coding in long-term memory.

(a) Explain what is meant by coding. [2 marks]

(b) Outline how coding differs in short-term memory and long-term memory. [4 marks]

Exam hint

Some questions come in two or more parts. Make sure you read all parts of a question before beginning your answer. In (a), give a definition of coding you have learned. One mark will be given for an answer that is fundamentally correct but lacking in clarity. You will only get both marks for a clear definition. Take care in part (b) to avoid just saying how coding occurs in both stores. Make the point that what happens in one does not happen in the other.

As mentioned earlier, accurately measuring the duration of information in LTM is extremely problematic. It appears that the experimental techniques used to measure memory give different indications of its duration. Bahrick et al. (1975), for example, found that people seem to remember things from the distant past much better if they are given certain cues instead of being asked to recall from scratch (in their case, the cue was a photograph). The accuracy of their participants' memories was better when measured by recognition than by recall. It perhaps comes as no surprise to learn that the length of time information stays in LTM also depends on how well the information was learned in the first place. Bahrick and Hall (1991) tested long-term memory for algebra and geometry. People who had only taken maths courses up to secondary school level showed a steady decline in their recall accuracy over the years. However, students who had gone on to take a higher level course in maths showed greater levels of accurate recall as much as 55 years later.

Encoding in LTM

Research has consistently demonstrated that semantic encoding, that is, coding based on the meaning of information, is preferred in LTM. One of the first pieces of research to identify a preference for semantic encoding in LTM was conducted by Baddely (1966). He found that participants had difficulty remembering similar sounding words when tested immediately, but after 20 minutes had greater difficulty remembering words of the same meaning. Baddeley considered this good evidence for semantic encoding in LTM.

KEY STUDY: ENCODING IN STM AND LTM

Baddeley (1966) investigated the possibility that long-term and short-term memory process information in different ways. He constructed a pool of short, familiar words for each of four categories:

- acoustically similar words (e.g. mad, map, mat, cad, cap, cat)
- acoustically dissimilar words (e.g. pen, cow, pit, sup, day)
- semantically similar words (e.g. tall, high, broad, wide, big)
- semantically dissimilar words (e.g. foul, thin, late, safe, strong).

For each category, he presented a random sequence of five words and asked participants to write them down immediately after presentation in the order they were shown. He found that the words that sounded similar were much harder to remember than words in any of the other three categories. He concluded, like Conrad (1964), that STM codes acoustically.

Baddeley then modified this experiment to test LTM. He extended the length of the word lists from five words to ten and prevented the participants from rehearsing by interrupting them after each presentation. Each list was presented four times and then recall was tested after a 20-minute interval. Under these conditions, he found that acoustic similarity had no effect on recall but that participants had difficulty recalling words that were semantically similar (i.e. similar in meaning). Baddeley concluded from this that words similar in meaning interfered with each other, and so information in LTM is coded semantically and information in STM is coded acoustically.

THINKING SCIENTIFICALLY: THE IMPORTANCE OF CONTROL

One of the key features of an experiment is control. A subtle but important control used by Baddeley in his experiment was to ensure that the words in all four conditions were familiar words, so that no single list was easier to remember. By doing this, a potential confounding variable (word familiarity) was eliminated, and he could now be more confident that any change in performance between conditions must be due to the factor that differs between conditions – the independent variable.

Researchers are quick to point out however that while semantic encoding is its preferred method, this is not the only type of encoding in LTM. Everyday experience tells us that we readily recognize sounds such as police sirens and ringing telephones, suggesting that we also encode LTMs acoustically. Similar arguments could be made for the other modalities; that visual and haptic (touch) encoding in LTM is possible from our immediate recognition of what we see and touch.

Strengths and weaknesses of the multi-store model

The multi-store model has made an important contribution to memory research. The information-processing approach has enabled psychologists to construct models of memory that can be tested and further refined, massively improving our understanding of memory. Most modern researchers would agree that there is a basic distinction to be made between a short-term, temporary, limited-capacity store and a more robust and permanent long-term memory, and there is plenty of evidence to support this distinction.

Some of the strongest evidence for a distinction between STM and LTM comes from the study of people who have suffered brain damage. The loss of memory among such people is usually selective, that is, it affects one type of memory but not another. Shallice and Warrington (1970) reported the case of KF, a young man who sustained brain injuries after a motorcycle accident. He had an impaired STM working alongside a fully functioning LTM. He appeared to have an intact LTM in that he was able to learn new information and recall stored information. However, his STM had a much reduced capacity so that he was only able to store a couple of bits or chunks of information rather than the normal five to nine chunks.

KEY STUDY: BRAIN DAMAGE AND LOSS OF MEMORY

Milner (1966) reported on the famous case study of a young man known only by his initials, HM. He suffered from severe epilepsy and underwent brain surgery to alleviate this. This involved removing parts of his temporal lobes, including the hippocampus. While the operation helped his epilepsy it left him with severe memory problems. He was able to recall events in his early life but was unable to remember events for about ten years before the surgery and could not learn or retain new information. He could remember approximately six numbers in the order they had been presented, suggesting that his STM was relatively intact. However, he repeatedly read the same magazine without realizing that he had read it before, and was unable to recognize the psychologists who spent long periods with him. This suggests that HM had a normal STM, but that his LTM was now defective and that it was no longer possible for him to lay down new memories in it or, if he could, that he was unable to retrieve them.

THINKING SCIENTIFICALLY: THE VALUE OF CASE STUDIES

Case studies can be very useful when an experiment would be impossible for ethical or practical reasons. A great deal of what we now know about memory comes from studying the problems that individuals have with their memory following brain damage.

Another source of evidence comes from the study of people with Alzheimer's disease. This is a serious disorder of the brain, and early symptoms include severe memory impairment. Researchers have been interested in investigating some of the specialized chemicals in the brain called neurotransmitters, which are involved in brain processes. Patients with Alzheimer's disease have been found to have low levels of one of these neurotransmitters, acetylcholine, compared to controls. This suggests that acetylcholine might have an important function in memory. Drachman and Sahakian (1979) investigated this by administering to a group of participants a drug that blocks the action of acetylcholine in the brain. They then gave the participants various memory tasks that tested either LTM or STM and compared their performance with a control group. They found that the experimental group performed at normal levels on the STM tasks but significantly more poorly in the LTM task. This, again, suggests that STM and LTM work as separate stores involving different neurotransmitters.

Modern brain-scanning techniques such as positron emission tomography (PET) and functional magnetic resonance imaging (fMRI) scans have provided more support for the existence of two separate memory stores. Squire et al. (1993) found that the hippocampus is more active in LTM tasks, whereas areas in the prefrontal cortex are activated for STM tasks.

Although it is generally regarded as good scientific practice to account for all the known facts in the simplest possible way, the multi-store model has been accused of being oversimplified. Human memory is extremely complex, and it is highly unlikely that such a simple model could reflect this complexity. For example, it takes no account of the different types of things we have to remember. While the model places great emphasis on the amount of information we can handle at any one time, it disregards the nature of the information. Everyday experience tells us that some things are easier to remember than others because they are more interesting, more relevant, funnier, etc.

The role of rehearsal in transferring material from STM to LTM is central in the multi-store model. However, not only is there considerable evidence that simple repetition is one of the least effective ways of passing on information, but there is strong evidence that long-term memories can be formed without any apparent rehearsal. For example, Brown and Kulik (1977) have described a special type of remembering called 'flashbulb memory', which is where the insignificant details surrounding highly emotional and shocking events (e.g. the terrorist attack on the World Trade Center in New York) are imprinted directly into LTM without any rehearsal.

Atkinson and Shiffrin believed that information flows through a one-way system and that STM has to process information before it reaches LTM. However, it is clear that information from LTM must sometimes be activated before certain stages of processing in STM can occur. For example, consider Conrad's experiment, described earlier. Participants were shown the letters visually and yet they translated the visual image into an acoustic code. They could only have identified the letter 'B' as the sound 'bee' by getting this stored information from LTM. Further support for the involvement of LTM in STM tasks comes from Ruchkin et al. (1999). They measured brain activity in participants who were required to listen to a set of words and pseudo-words. If people only process information acoustically in STM, there should be no difference in brain activity when processing words and pseudo-words. However, Ruchkin found that there were considerable differences in the recall of the two types of word, which suggests that semantic information stored in LTM was being used in this task.

Much of the supporting evidence for the multi-store model comes from artificial, laboratory studies, which might not reflect how memory works in everyday life. It is sometimes possible to interpret the results of such studies in different ways. It is also sometimes the case that different experimental techniques can yield different results. For example, Brandimonte et al. (1992) showed that, when acoustic encoding is prevented by asking participants to repeat a meaningless chant ('la-la-la') while learning a list of words, STM can use visual encoding instead, which can, according to Brandimonte et al., be more effective than acoustic encoding.

EXAMPLE EXAM QUESTION

Evaluate the multi-store model of memory. Refer to the findings of research in your answer. (6 marks)

Exam hint

There is a great deal of information available to you that would enable you to evaluate the multi-store model. But read the question carefully – it says clearly that you must use the findings of research, so be selective. You could use three findings from studies, linking them clearly to model features and explaining whether or not the findings support the feature.

KEY POINTS

- The multi-store model explains the structure of memory as a flow of information through three storage systems.
- Sensory information from the environment enters its own sensory register, for example, iconic register, echoic register.
- Sensory registers hold large amounts of unprocessed (unencoded) information for a brief period of time before relevant information is selected out for further processing.
- Short-term memory (STM) is a temporary memory store with a limited capacity (five to nine items) and limited duration (up to 30 seconds without rehearsal).
- The dominant code in STM is acoustic.
- Rehearsal of information results in transfer to long-term memory.
- Long-term memory (LTM) is a relatively permanent store of information with potentially unlimited capacity.
- Coding in LTM is mainly semantic.
- The multi-store model is supported by research into the coding, capacity and duration of each store and by research that shows a distinction between STM and LTM.
- However, while the multi-store model describes the structure of memory, it says little about the functions of each of its systems and memory in general.

The working memory model

By the early 1970s it was becoming clear that traditional information processing models, such as that developed by Atkinson and Shiffrin, could not account for some of the findings from memory research, in particular the short-term store. It was also clear that STM was far more complex than existing theories could account for. One feature central to Atkinson and Shiffrin's model was the idea of STM being a single and entirely separate store. Baddeley and Hitch (1974) contested this and pointed out that some of the research findings undermined this idea. They referred to the case of patient KF who, while only having a digit span of two, could transfer new information to his LTM. This suggested to them that though there had been some disruption to STM, other aspects of STM must have continued to function. There must therefore be several components in STM.

To test the idea, Baddeley and Hitch asked participants to perform a reasoning task (a sentence-checking task) while simultaneously reciting aloud a list of six digits. If digit span really is a measure of maximum STM capacity, participants would be expected to show impaired performance on the reasoning task because their STM would be fully occupied by the repetition of the six digits. However, they found that participants made very few errors on either the reasoning or the digit span task (although the speed of verifying the sentences was slightly slower than when the reasoning task was done alone). Baddeley and Hitch concluded that STM must have more than one component and must be involved in processes other than simple storage. They saw STM as a sort of workspace where a variety of operations could be carried out on both old and new memories. Two tasks can be carried out simultaneously in STM provided that they are using different parts of the memory system. They envisaged LTM as a more passive store that maintains previously learned material for use by the STM when needed. They formulated their ideas into the working memory model.

According to Baddeley and Hitch, working memory is a complex and flexible system comprised of several interacting components. Researchers have refined aspects of the working memory model since it was first formulated in the 1970s, most recently in the addition of an episodic buffer.

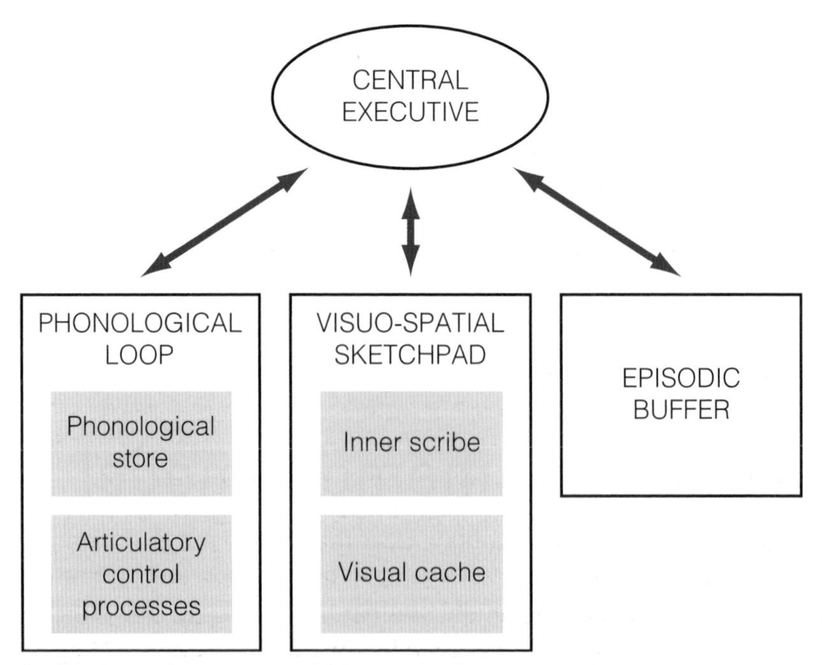

Fig. 2.6 The working memory model developed by Baddeley and Hitch

The central executive

The central executive is a supervisory component, in that it has overall control of working memory. The central executive has limited capacity (as in short-term memory), but can process information from any sensory system, that is, vision, hearing, touch, taste or smell. It has responsibility for a range of important control processes, which includes setting task goals, attention, monitoring and correcting errors, starting the rehearsal process, switching attention between tasks, inhibiting irrelevant information, retrieving information from LTM, and coordinating the activity needed to carry out more than one processing task at a time. This core component is supported by 'slave' systems, the phonological loop, the visuo-spatial sketch pad and the episodic buffer. These can be used as temporary storage systems, freeing up capacity in the central executive to deal with more demanding information processing tasks. The slave systems have separate responsibilities and work independently of one another. This explains how people are able to do a visual and an auditory task at the same time – they are using two separate memory systems. It is much more difficult, if not impossible, to use the same system for multiple tasks, as you will have noticed when you have attempted to listen to the TV and to listen to someone talking at the same time.

The central executive is the most important and most flexible component of working memory. Baddeley himself accepts that this complexity 'makes it considerably harder to investigate' than the slave systems (Baddeley, 1999, page 67). Consequently, there is much less research evidence into the central executive, and such research as there is tends to focus on the different functions of the central executive rather than the system as a whole.

Key terms

The central executive: the part of working memory that coordinates other components.

The phonological loop: the part of working memory that deals with auditory information.

The phonological loop

The phonological loop is sometimes referred to as the 'inner voice'. It is a limited-capacity, temporary storage system for holding verbal information in a speech-based form. The phonological loop consists of a passive storage system called the phonological store, which is linked to an active rehearsal system called the 'articulatory loop' whereby words can be maintained by subvocal repetition (i.e. repeating 'in your head').

In a study into the phonological loop, Baddeley et al. (1975) gave visual presentations of five-word lists for very brief exposures and then asked participants to write them down in the same order. In one condition, the lists consisted of single-syllable English words such as 'harm', 'wit', 'twice'. In a second condition, the words were polysyllabic (having two or more syllables) such as 'organization', 'university', 'association'. It was found that the average correct recall over several trials showed a marked superiority for the short words. Baddeley et al. called this the 'word length effect' and concluded that the capacity of the phonological loop is determined by the length of time it takes to say words rather than by the number of items. They estimated this time to be 1.5 seconds.

Key terms

The visuo-spatial sketchpad: the part of working memory that deals with visual information.

Episodic buffer: a part of working memory which is a temporary store integrating information from the other components.

Fig. 2.7 A Chinese ideograph like the ones used by Klauer and Zhao

The visuo-spatial sketchpad

The visuo-spatial sketchpad is sometimes referred to as the 'inner eye'. It is a limited-capacity, temporary memory system for holding visual and/or spatial information. The sketchpad is thought to consist of a passive visual store called the 'visual cache', which is linked to an active 'inner scribe' that acts as a visual rehearsal mechanism. A number of studies have supported the existence of these two subsystems, for example Klauer and Zhao (2004). They asked participants to carry out one of two tasks, either a visual task (e.g. memory for Chinese ideographs, see Fig. 2.7) or a spatial task (e.g. memory locations of dots on a screen). At the same time as doing one of these tasks, participants were required to do either a spatial interference task, or a visual interference task. There was also a no interference control condition. They found that a spatial memory task was more strongly disrupted by spatial than by visual interference, and a visual memory task was more strongly disrupted by visual than by spatial interference. For Klauer and Zhao, this was evidence for the visuo-spatial sketchpad having distinct visual and spatial components.

Brain imaging studies have also provided evidence for separate spatial and visual systems. For example, there appears to be more activity in the left half of the brain of people carrying out visual working memory tasks, but more in the right half of the brain during spatial tasks (Todd and Marois, 2004).

Episodic buffer

One key function of the **episodic buffer** is to provide a general storage facility, holding and combining information not only from the visuo-spatial sketchpad, phonological loop and central executive, but also from long-term memory. As a relatively new component in the working memory model (the model was devised some 25 years prior to the introduction of the episodic buffer), there is relatively little research directly into the episodic buffer.

The episodic buffer was added by Baddeley (2000) to the working memory model as an explicit component because of research findings that the original model could not explain. One such finding is that immediate memory for prose is generally much greater than that for unrelated words. For example, recall of words is much better when they are presented as a coherent 100 word paragraph of text than when the same 100 words are presented randomly ordered. The working memory model could not explain this phenomenon. Remembering prose requires quite complex information processing, e.g. we must know what words mean, how words relate to other words in sentences, how sentences are structured and combined into more meaningful chunks called paragraphs. This kind of semantic analysis requires information from long-term memory. Baddeley therefore proposed that there must be an additional subsystem – the episodic buffer – that integrated information in working memory with information in long-term memory. Support for this came from studies of individuals who had brain damage resulting in severe memory problems. Baddeley and Wilson (2002) tested the immediate recall of severe amnesiacs. They found that those with intact central executive functions showed unimpaired immediate recall of the prose. After a short delay, however, these individuals had no recall of the prose. For Baddeley and Wilson, the information from this episode (the prose) was temporarily stored (or buffered) by the episodic buffer, making it available for a short period.

EXAMPLE EXAM QUESTION

Outline any two components of the working memory model. [6 marks]

Exam hint

This question is straightforward enough, but look at the number of marks available. You are asked to do two things, so it is a good 'rule of thumb' to think of questions like this as 3 + 3 mark questions. This gives you an idea of how much detail to go into when outlining each component.

Strengths and weaknesses of the working memory model

The working memory model has been extremely influential, and most cognitive psychologists now use the term working memory in preference to the term STM. It is a much more plausible model than the multi-store model because it explains STM in terms of both temporary storage and active processing. It also incorporates verbal rehearsal as just one optional process within the articulatory loop, instead of being the sole modality and means of transferring information to LTM, as suggested by Atkinson and Shiffrin in the multi-store model.

Unlike the multi-store model, which describes the structure of memory, the working memory model attempts to explain how memory functions. Baddeley et al. (1998) have presented evidence that the phonological loop, for example, plays a key role in the development of reading, and that the phonological loop is not functioning properly in some children with dyslexia. While the phonological loop seems to be less crucial for fluent adult readers, it still has an important role in helping to comprehend complex text. It also helps in the learning of new spoken vocabulary.

The working memory model can also account for individual differences in memory processing. Turner and Engle (1989) devised a test to measure the capacity of working memory. They asked participants to hold a list of words in memory while at the same time working out mental arithmetic problems. The number of words correctly recalled in a subsequent test was called the 'working memory span'. This measure of working memory capacity has been shown in a number of studies to be linked to the ability to carry out various cognitive tasks, such as reading comprehension, reasoning, spatial navigation, spelling, note-taking, etc. (Engle et al., 1999). Indeed, because there is such a close relationship between working memory span and performance on various tasks, it has been suggested that working memory capacity might be used as a measure of suitability for certain jobs. For example, there have been investigations into its use as a recruitment tool for the US Air Force (Kyllonen and Christal, 1990).

KEY POINTS

- The working memory model sees short-term memory as an active and dynamic system where information currently in the conscious mind is acted upon.
- The central executive coordinates working memory, for example it decides what information is attended to and directs information from the other components.
- The phonological loop is a 'slave' system that deals with auditory information.
- The visuo-spatial sketchpad is a 'slave' system that deals with visual information.
- The episodic buffer is a general store, integrating information from the other slave systems.
- The working memory model and its components have been supported by a great deal of research.
- It is, however, a model of temporary short-term memory rather than memory as a whole; for example, it has little to say about the workings of long-term memory.

Types of long-term memory

Declarative memory and procedural memory

Research into LTM has shown that it is not a single unitary store, rather it appears to have a number of different components which may be represented by separate brain systems. There appears to be a major distinction between two types of long-term memory. One is the type of conscious memory that we have for events and facts (declarative memory, or 'knowing that' memory, e.g. knowing that the capital of France is Paris). The other type of memory is that which is not open to conscious recollection but that we see in our skilled behaviours and habits (procedural memory, or 'knowing how' memory, e.g. knowing how to tie shoelaces).

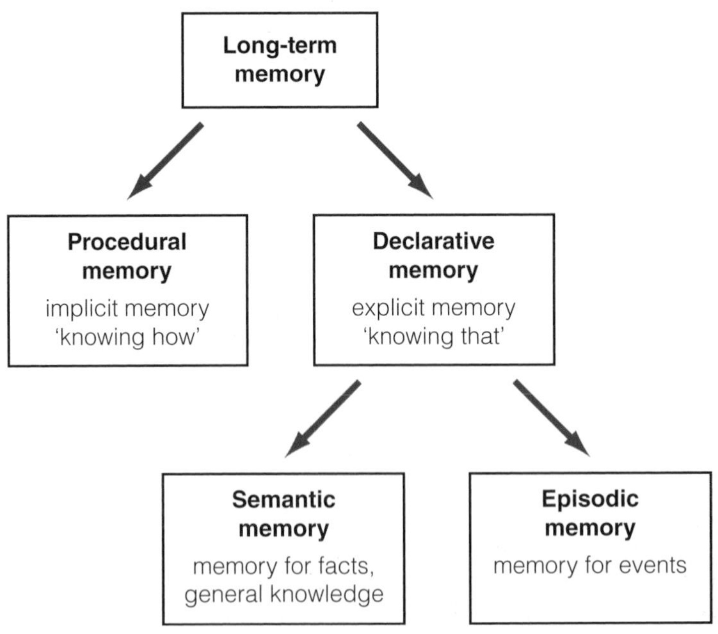

Fig. 2.8 The components of long-term memory

As the psychologist Henry Roediger (1990) pointed out, when people use the term 'remembering' they are generally referring to some kind of process where they consciously recollect things from their past learning. Psychologists call this kind of long-term memory **declarative memory**. It is sometimes referred to as explicit memory because it refers to memories that are consciously recalled. Declarative memory is 'knowing that' something is the case, for example knowing that the local shop closes at 9pm or that a full stop ends a sentence.

This cannot however account for all forms of remembering. Sometimes we demonstrate that we have knowledge by doing something. 'Knowing how' to do something is **procedural memory**. Consider the many skills we have that we cannot recall how to perform. Try describing to someone how to cycle, swim, walk or read – this is difficult to the point of being impossible. It is so difficult to describe that it is, in effect, 'unconscious'. As Roediger points out, it is as though some prior learning actually resists conscious recollection. Because it requires no conscious awareness of previous experience it is sometimes referred to as implicit memory.

One of the earliest pieces of scientific evidence for a distinction between procedural (implicit) and declarative (explicit) memory came from the study of the memory deficits shown by patient HM (see Research methods link box opposite). Milner (1962) discovered that HM was able to learn to trace a shape using its mirror image (a surprisingly tricky thing to do), and retain this skill over a number of days. Curiously, however, he had no conscious recollection of ever having done mirror drawing tasks before and thus acquiring this skill (see Fig. 2.9). It appears that while HM was able to use procedural memory to learn this skill, his operation had damaged his ability to use his declarative memory to consciously recollect this experience.

Fig. 2.9 A mirror drawing task

Key terms

Declarative memory: long-term memory for 'knowing that'.

Procedural memory: long-term memory for 'knowing how'.

Research methods link

HM is an example of a case study. You can read more about this research method on page 28.

EXAMPLE EXAM QUESTION

Research suggests that there are different types of long-term memory.

(a) Identify three types of long-term memory. [3 marks]

(b) Outline research into one type of long-term memory. [4 marks]

Exam hint

For part (a), just name the three types of long-term memory – with three marks available you get one mark for each correctly identified type. Part (b) requires a longer written response, and offers you a choice. You can either consider one piece of research in detail, or more than one in less detail.

Semantic memory and episodic memory

There are at least two distinct types of declarative memory. **Semantic memory** consists of our abstract general knowledge about the world, for example the facts that we learn in school. In addition to all the facts and concepts that make up semantic memory, we also store memories for the things we have thought and the experiences we have had. These personal recollections of episodes of our lives make up **episodic memory**.

Key terms

Semantic memory: a type of long-term memory for information about the world that is not linked to particular events or contexts.

Episodic memory: a type of long-term memory for specific events and experiences in our lives.

While it is possible to define what is meant by semantic and episodic memory, it is not always so easy to distinguish between them. For example, if you can remember your very first swimming lesson does this make it an episodic memory, or does the knowledge of what swimming means make it a semantic memory? This difficulty is due to the relationship between the two. Semantic memories generally originate as episodic memories. Let's say that we learn in infant school that clouds produce rain. This new knowledge is initially linked to a specific event – it is what you learned in school that day. However, as time passes the association between what we have learned and the event during which it was learned diminishes, so that it now becomes something you 'just know'. Everyone knows that clouds produce rain, right? How could there possibly be a time when you didn't know that? This knowledge has become part of semantic memory. It seems, then, that over time a memory can lose its link to a particular event and the episodic memory becomes a semantic memory.

KEY POINTS

- Research has shown that there are different types of long-term memory.
- Psychologists distinguish between declarative ('knowing that') memory and procedural ('knowing how') memory.
- Support for this distinction comes from case studies of brain-damaged individuals who can learn new skills but cannot consciously recall having learned them.
- Declarative memory is further divided into semantic memory (facts and information) and episodic memory (events and experiences).

Explanations for forgetting

One of the most obvious things about human memory is its fallibility. It could be said that one of the key things that makes us consciously aware of the functions of our own memory is the frequency with which it lets us down, and the consequences that this forgetting has for us. There are many reasons for forgetting. As the multi-store model indicates (see page 110), information can be lost (forgotten) in a number of ways and at each stage of processing. The capacity limitations of STM, for example, mean that once full, new information in STM can only be accommodated if existing information is displaced (pushed out). Also, the limited duration of information in STM means that, without rehearsal, information quickly decays (fades), to be irrecoverably lost. On the other hand, forgetting from LTM is often explained by interference theory and failure to find (i.e. retrieve) relevant information.

Proactive and retroactive interference in LTM

According to **interference theory**, forgetting is caused by two memories competing. That is, we are unable to remember something because the memory is either being affected by a memory we already have, or by future learning. The degree of competition between the two memories is thought to increase as they become more similar to one another. For example, interference is likely to be greater when revising French and then Spanish than there would be when revising Maths and then English.

Key term

Interference theory: memory can be disrupted not only by previous learning but also by what is learned in the future.

Research suggests that there are two types of interference. Retroactive interference occurs when new information interferes with old information. As can be seen in Figure 2.10, this can be demonstrated experimentally by giving participants something to learn (A) and then giving them something new to learn (B). When tested for their memory of A, participants do worse than those who did not have to learn B.

A classic study by Waugh and Norman (1965) provides evidence for retroactive interference. They presented participants with a sequence of 16 digits, after which they were shown one of the digits from the list (the 'probe'). Participants had to say which digit in the sequence appeared just prior to this probe. The researchers found that the fewer

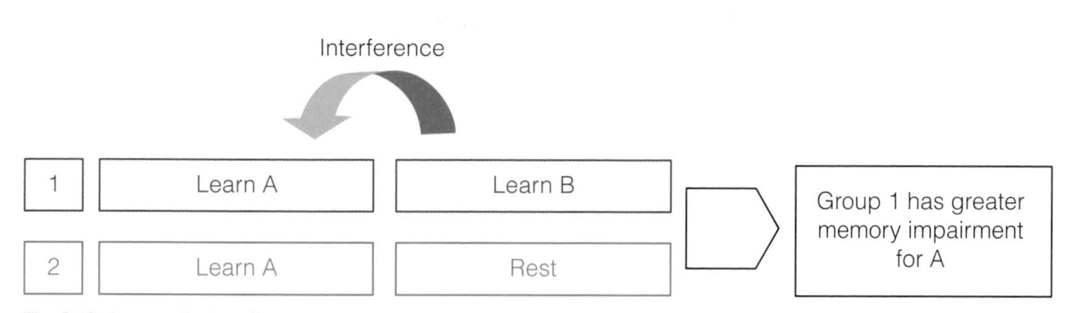

Fig. 2.10 Retroactive interference

items there were following the probe in the original sequence, the more likely participants were to recall the preceding digit correctly. This demonstrates retroactive interference. If the probe occurred early in the sequence then the greater numbers of digits following it increased the chances of interference. Likewise, if the probe occurred towards the end of the sequence then there would be fewer digits to cause interference.

According to Ceraso (1967), there are two possible explanations for retroactive interference. According to the competition of response theory there is no actual loss of information taking place. Rather, poor recall is due to accessing the wrong information in the memory. It is as though the new information has shifted the old and is now where the old information was, but we attempt to retrieve information from the old location (where it no longer is), resulting in errors in memory. Another possible explanation is the unlearning theory. This states that in retroactive interference new learning actually replaces previous learning so that the latter is effectively 'unlearned'.

Proactive interference occurs when old information interferes with new information. Fig. 2.11 shows how this can be demonstrated experimentally. Participants are given something to learn (B), and then something further to learn (A). When tested for their recall of A, participants do worse than those who did not have to learn B.

Proactive interference was demonstrated by Keppel and Underwood (1962). Their experimental procedure was similar to that used by Peterson and Peterson (1959) (see page 116). Participants were required to recall consonant trigrams after varying intervals, during which they counted backwards in threes. As could be predicted from the findings of Peterson and Peterson, while forgetting was found to increase with the interval, Keppel and Underwood noted that there was little or no forgetting of trigrams from the start of the procedure. These results can be explained in terms of proactive interference. The earlier memory for the consonants had entered into long-term memory and was interfering with the memory for later consonants.

Despite there being plenty of evidence for the existence of retroactive and proactive interference effects, one major limitation of the theory is that interference effects are most strongly seen in laboratory-based studies using memory tasks that do not resemble situations that occur in everyday life. It is unclear how much day-to-day forgetting can be attributed to interference, and how important interference is to explaining forgetting in general.

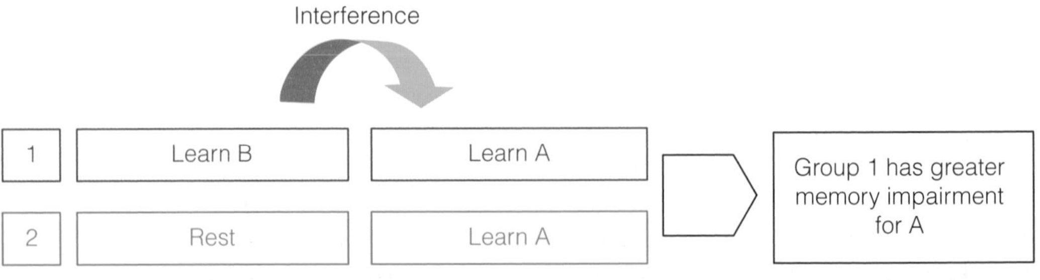

Fig. 2.11 Proactive interference

EXAMPLE EXAM QUESTION

Explain how proactive interference differs from retroactive interference. [3 marks]

Exam hint

Do not simply explain what proactive and retroactive interference are – your answer must clarify what the difference actually is.

Retrieval failure

Key term

Retrieval failure: difficulties in recall are due to the absence of the correct retrieval cues.

Information encoded for storage in long-term memory is useless unless it can be accessed again. The scenario is not dissimilar to storing a file on your computer but not knowing where to find it – it is there somewhere but might as well not be if it cannot be found. Many researchers believe that this failure to retrieve information lies behind most examples of forgetting – we do not literally lose information from memory, rather we just cannot find it because the cues that were encoded with the memory are not available to help us when we attempt to retrieve it.

You have no doubt had the experience of leaving one room and going to another only to wonder what it is you went there for. You might also have been annoyed by finding that on going back to where you came from, you remembered what it was you left the room for! This perplexing phenomenon tells us something important about memory and forgetting – you are more likely to forget something when the context during encoding is different to the context during retrieval. Tulving and Thompson (1973) called this the encoding specificity principle.

The encoding specificity principle can be seen clearly in a study by Marian and Fausey (1986). They found that memory for a story was better if the language in which it was presented and the language that was used to test memory were the same. Participants in their study were residents of Chile who were fluent in their natural language (Spanish) and English. They were required to listen to four academic-type stories (topics about chemistry, biology, history and mythology), two of them spoken in Spanish and two of them in English. Shortly afterwards they were questioned about each story and asked to answer in the same language as the question. Half the questions matched the language of the original story (e.g. English story – English questions) and half did not (e.g. English story – Spanish questions). Marian and Fausey found that participants who heard the story and questions in the same language had greater accuracy of recall than those who had heard the story and questions in different languages. This demonstrated encoding specificity, as memory is better when there is a match between contexts during encoding and retrieval – the language used in the questions provided a retrieval cue for the recall of story details.

The Marian and Fausey study looks at an example of forgetting that occurs because the relevant *environmental cues* during learning were missing during recall. Tulving (1974) referred to this as *context-dependent forgetting*, and distinguished it from *state-dependent forgetting*. This is where relevant psychological or physiological cues present at encoding are later absent. For example, it has been shown that people who are in a happy mood (or state) during learning were better able to recall this material when they were again in a happy mood, as opposed to when they attempted recall in a sad mood (Bower, 1981). Similar findings have been found for physiological states, such as deficits in recall when encoding occurs under the influence of chemical substances. Peters and McGee (1982), for example, gave half their participants a low nicotine content cigarette before learning a list of nouns. Participants who were in the same state the next day (either having smoked or not smoked a cigarette) performed better on a recognition task than those who were in a different state. Peters and McGee concluded that the arousal caused by the cigarette had provided a physiological context, creating a state-dependency effect.

It is worth noting, however, that while state-dependent and context-dependent forgetting are phenomena consistently supported by research, it is not clear how important such effects are in real life. Studies tend to use fairly extreme conditions and use tests of memory that in real life we rarely, if ever, encounter. Also, the changes in recall are not as strong as perhaps the extreme states and contexts used in studies suggest they might be. Despite these issues, it is still worthwhile considering the potential benefits and costs of encoding specificity when marginal differences really matter, such as revising for exams in contexts that resemble the exam conditions. Every little helps!

KEY POINTS

- Forgetting can be caused by interference between competing memories.
- There are two types of interference: proactive interference (where earlier learning interferes with recall of later learning) and retroactive interference (where recent learning interferes with recall of earlier learning).
- There is research support for both types of interference, though it tends to be laboratory-based, so the extent to which it can be applied to everyday memory and forgetting is debatable.
- According to the retrieval failure explanation of forgetting, difficulties in recall are due to the absence of the correct retrieval cues.
- The encoding specificity principle says that forgetting something is more likely when the context during encoding is different to the context during retrieval.
- Context-dependent forgetting is when the environmental cues present at encoding are absent at the time of recall.
- State-dependent forgetting is when the physiological or psychological cues present at encoding are absent at the time of recall.

Factors affecting the accuracy of eyewitness testimony

Memory research can have valuable applications in everyday life. One type of memory that has particular relevance for real life is eyewitness testimony (EWT). Juries appear to place a great deal of reliance on the testimony of eyewitnesses to crime. However, there is a considerable amount of research evidence to suggest that this faith in the accuracy of EWT is misplaced. Fruzzetti et al. (1992) have suggested that thousands of people are probably wrongly convicted every year on the basis of inaccurate EWT. Wells et al. (1998) have reported on 40 cases in the US where individuals convicted on the basis of EWT have since been cleared using DNA evidence. Even more alarming is the fact that five of these wrongly convicted individuals had been sentenced to death and were awaiting execution.

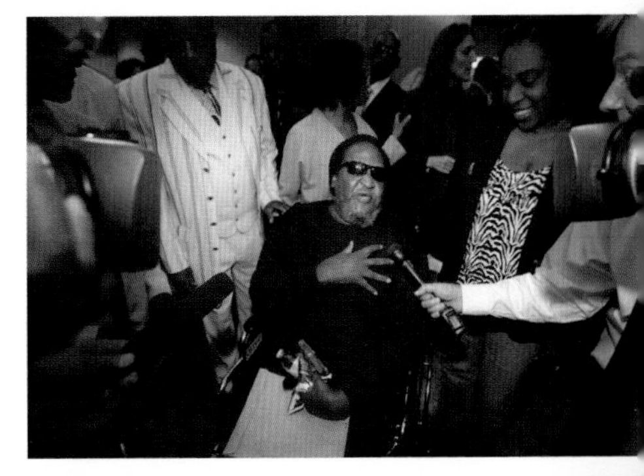

Fig. 2.12 In 1990, Michael Phillips was convicted of rape based on eyewitness testimony, and imprisoned for 12 years. He was recently proved innocent due to DNA testing.

The effects of misleading information on the accuracy of EWT

Research tells us that one of the main factors affecting the accuracy of memory for an event seems to be what happens after the event has taken place. The memories laid down at the time seem to be quite fragile and subject to distortion by post-event information. It appears that misinformation can introduce serious errors into eyewitnesses' recall of the event. Loftus (1992) called this 'misinformation acceptance', where people accept misleading information after an event and absorb it into their memory for the actual event. It seems that as the time since the event increases, the tendency to accept misleading post-event information is greater. This has important implications for the ways in which the police and lawyers question individuals in criminal investigations. Due to the active and dynamic nature of long-term memory, the very wording of this questioning can serve to change the original memory by removing some elements and inserting others.

Leading questions and post-event discussion

Research has consistently shown that witness recall can be influenced by quite minor differences in the wording of a question used to elicit memories of an event. Loftus and Zanni (1975) showed participants brief film clips of a car accident and then asked a series of questions. Half the participants were asked whether they had seen 'a' broken headlight and the other half were asked if they had seen 'the' broken headlight. Although there was no broken headlight in the film, 17 per cent of people asked about 'the' broken headlight reported seeing one as opposed to only 7 per cent of the group asked about 'a' broken headlight. Participants in the 'the' condition also gave fewer uncertain 'I don't know' responses, suggesting that they had greater confidence in memories for events that never occurred. It seems that using 'the' had implanted the idea that there was indeed broken glass, leading some participants to change their recall accordingly. In practical terms, this suggests that the way questions are asked following a crime can lead to inaccuracies in witness recall, and brings into question the reliability of eyewitness testimony. This misinformation effect through the use of **leading questions** has been replicated in many studies.

Key term

Leading question: a question phrased in such a way that it prompts a particular kind of answer.

KEY STUDY: LEADING QUESTIONS AND EYEWITNESS RECALL

Loftus and Palmer (1974) showed 45 participants a film of a car accident. Following this they were asked to describe events as though they were eyewitnesses. They were then asked a series of specific questions about events leading up to the accident. One critical question concerned the speed of the car on impact. One group was asked 'How fast were the cars going when they hit each other?' Other groups of participants were asked the same question, but, in each case, the verb was changed to either 'smashed', 'bumped', 'collided' or 'contacted'.

When the average speed estimate was calculated, it was found that the verb used in the critical question significantly affected speed estimates – 'smashed' produced the highest estimate (40.8 mph) and 'contacted' produced the lowest estimate (31.8 mph).

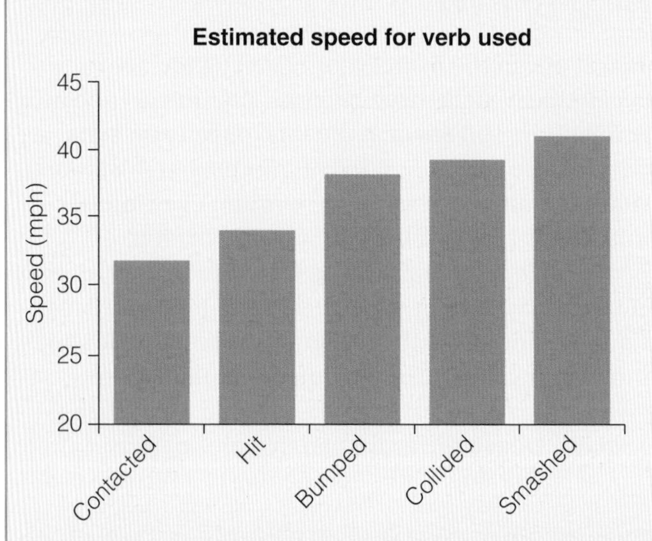

Fig. 2.13 Bar chart showing the results of Loftus and Palmer's experiment

A week later, participants were questioned again about the accident, with a new critical question – 'Did you see any broken glass?' Loftus and Palmer found that participants who had been asked the 'smashed' version of the question were more likely to report having seen broken glass at the scene of the accident, even though there had been none.

It appears that the verb implied further things associated with the speed of the vehicle, for example that fast cars are more likely to 'smash' than slower cars, and that there is likely to be broken glass when cars 'smash', leading to altered perceptions of the event. This led Loftus and Palmer to suggest that post-event information could permanently affect memory.

Research methods link

The Loftus and Palmer study is an example of a laboratory experiment. You can read more about the strengths and limitations of laboratory experiments on page 10.

THINKING SCIENTIFICALLY: THE ARTIFICIALITY OF EXPERIMENTS

Because it was a controlled laboratory experiment, the Loftus and Palmer study has been accused of being artificial, i.e. the conditions of testing do not resemble those in real life so therefore the behaviour of participants is not natural behaviour. A film clip would not have the same emotional impact as witnessing a real-life accident, and because a witness would not be prepared to observe carefully (as they were in the experiment) it could be argued that their recall of a real accident would not be as complete.

EXAMPLE EXAM QUESTION

Outline and evaluate research into the effects of misleading information on eyewitness testimony. (12 marks)

Exam hint

The Loftus and Palmer study is a good example to use in this answer. You can briefly outline what they did (not too much detail!) and what they found. Then you can evaluate it in terms of methodology (limitations due to it being a lab experiment), but more importantly other research that supports it because of similar findings.

See page 147 for a sample student answer to this question, and examiner feedback.

Reasons why memories are affected by misleading information

There are a number of possible reasons why memories are affected by misleading information. One possibility is that, due to the constructive nature of long-term memory, leading questions actually change a witness's perception of the event, resulting in a false memory being stored. Recall therefore reflects the actual memory of the event, though the memory is flawed. On the other hand, Loftus and Palmer (1974) suggested that some people do not have a false memory of an event as such, but rather the retrieval of information from their long-term memory is being influenced by the misleading information.

To investigate this, Loftus (1980) conducted a study where she offered to reward participants with money if they could correctly recall details from a film of an accident. One group saw a film involving a pedestrian being knocked over after a car had stopped at a stop sign. The other group saw the same incident, except that the car had stopped at a yield ('give way') sign. Two days later, participants were given a set of questions about the accident, one of which included some misleading information. In this critical question, participants who had seen the stop sign in the film were misled by a reference to a yield sign, and those who had seen the yield sign were misled by reference to a stop sign. Loftus then asked all the participants to look at pairs of slides and point out, in each case, which one had been part of the original film. Participants were put into one of four groups to do this, varying in the degree of financial reward for giving the most correct answers, from nothing to $25. Loftus found that in spite of the financial incentive, over 70 per cent of the participants made an error on the crucial question, in line with the misleading information that they had received earlier. This suggests that their original memory had been altered as a result of the misleading post-event information.

Misleading information does not have an effect on all witness memory, however. Loftus (1979) gave participants a set of slides that showed a red purse being stolen from a handbag. They were later given an account of the theft that included several errors, including the 'fact' that the purse was brown. In a subsequent recall test, all but two of the participants resisted the misinformation about the colour of the purse, although they were influenced by misinformation about less central elements of the theft. Loftus concluded that memory for information that is particularly striking at the time is less susceptible to the effects of misinformation than memory for more peripheral details. It seems that memory tends to resist being influenced by blatantly incorrect misleading information.

The effect of anxiety on EWT

When psychologists use the term anxiety they are referring to a state of emotional arousal, where there is a feeling or experience of apprehension and uncertainty, brought on by a real or anticipated threat. This mental state can impair physical and psychological functioning. There is sound evidence to suggest that anxiety has a negative effect on memory. Laboratory-based studies have generally shown impaired memory in people who have witnessed particularly unpleasant or anxiety-inducing events. For example, Loftus and Burns (1982) showed some participants a particularly violent version of a crime in which a boy was shot in the face. These participants had significantly impaired recall for events running up to the violent incident. Such findings are supported by Deffenbacher et al. (2004). They did a meta-analysis of experimental studies into the effects of anxiety on eyewitness memory and found that high levels of anxiety had a negative impact, not only on the accuracy of crime-related details, but also on the accuracy of identifying the perpetrator.

Fig. 2.14 Loftus found that eyewitnesses paid particular attention to weapons

Loftus (1979) has also reported on a phenomenon known as the 'weapon effect'. This is where eyewitnesses pay particular attention to the weapon that a perpetrator uses during a crime, resulting in other aspects of the scene going unobserved.

In a study by Loftus (1979), participants were asked to sit outside a laboratory where they thought they were hearing genuine exchanges between people inside the laboratory. In one condition, they heard an amicable discussion about an equipment failure. A man with greasy hands then came out of the laboratory holding a pen. In the other condition, they heard a hostile discussion, followed by the sound of breaking glass and overturned furniture. A man then emerged from the laboratory holding a knife covered in blood. Following these events, participants were given 50 photos and asked to identify the man who had come out of the laboratory. It was found that participants who had witnessed the peaceful scene were more accurate in recognising the man than people who had witnessed the more violent scene (49 per cent correct identification versus 33 per cent correct identification). Loftus believed that the anxiety caused by seeing the blood-stained knife narrowed the focus of attention for the witness (the knife was a source of danger) and took attention away from the face of the man. This appears to fit in with eyewitness reports, which are often rich in detail concerning such things as the type of weapon used, but are much less detailed about other aspects of the scene, such as what the criminal was wearing.

The research by Loftus (1979) was laboratory-based, and this has been the case with most of the research into anxiety and EWT. This raises the possibility that the findings of such studies that use artificial contexts might not reflect what actually happens in real life. A study by Yuille and Cutshall (1986) appears to support this concern. They interviewed 13 witnesses to an actual violent crime some four months after the event. The researchers found that recall was very accurate, despite the inclusion of leading questions in the interview. This suggests that both misleading information and anxiety might not have the same impact on real-life witnesses as it does on participants in laboratory-based studies.

This was supported by Christianson and Hubinette (1993). They carried out a survey among 110 people who had witnessed between them 22 genuine bank robberies. Some of these people had been bystanders in the bank at the time of the hold-ups while others had been directly threatened by the robbers. The victims, that is, the people who had been subjected to the greatest anxiety, showed more detailed and accurate recall than the onlookers. This finding suggests that in real incidents involving high levels of stress, memory can be accurate, detailed and long-lasting.

There are also considerable individual differences influencing the accuracy of eyewitness testimony; one clear finding from research is that not all participants are adversely affected by such things as misleading information and anxiety. Some people appear to be more susceptible to misleading information than others. It is not entirely clear why this should be the case. Tomes and Katz (1997) have suggested that the more susceptible individuals have a number of things in common:

- Their recall of the event is generally poorer, not just those things associated with the misleading information.
- They tend to show higher scores on tests of imagery vividness.
- They tend to be more empathic (i.e. they are good at identifying with the mood of others).

EXAMPLE EXAM QUESTION

Outline one study that has investigated the effect of anxiety on eyewitness testimony. [4 marks]

Exam hint

This question is straightforward enough – select one study that has investigated anxiety and eyewitness testimony. As with all questions, however, you need to look at the number of marks available – make sure you give enough detail to get all the available marks.

KEY POINTS

- Research suggests that eyewitness testimony (EWT) lacks reliability because of the effects of leading questions during post-event interviewing and discussion.
- The effect of leading questions has been supported by numerous studies, for example Loftus and Zanni (1975) and Loftus and Palmer (1974).
- Another factor affecting the accuracy is anxiety – the state of arousal caused by the event can affect its recall.
- Loftus (1979) described the phenomenon of the weapon effect, whereby eyewitnesses pay particular attention to the weapon that a perpetrator uses during a crime, resulting in other aspects of the scene going unobserved.

- Research into EWT has been criticized for lacking ecological validity. This is supported by research of real life eyewitnesses that suggests that their memory can be much better than the results from lab studies indicate it should be.
- Not all eyewitnesses are affected equally by misleading information. There is evidence to suggest considerable individual difference.

Improving the accuracy of eyewitness testimony

Because of the importance of EWT within the legal system and the serious repercussions when it goes wrong, psychologists have tried to develop methods for improving the accuracy of EWT. One suggestion is to improve the ways in which witnesses are questioned by police. For example, research suggests that accuracy should be considerably improved by eliminating leading questions.

That interviewing techniques need improving was shown in a study by Fisher et al. (1987). Over a four-month period they studied real interviews conducted by experienced detectives in Florida and found that witnesses were frequently bombarded with a series of brief, direct and closed questions aimed to elicit facts. However, the sequencing of these questions often seemed to be out of sync with the witnesses' own mental representation of the event. Witnesses were often interrupted and not allowed to talk freely about their experiences. Fisher felt that these interruptions were unhelpful because they broke the concentration of the witnesses and also encouraged shorter, less detailed answers.

Key term

Cognitive interview: an interview technique devised to improve the accuracy of witness recall.

Geiselman et al. (1985) developed a technique to improve the accuracy of eyewitness recall during police investigations which they called the **cognitive interview**. They identified four components of a cognitive interview which they believed would enhance accurate recall:

Component	Instruction to witness
Context reinstatement (CR)	Mentally reinstate the context of the event. Recall the scene, the weather, thoughts and feelings at the time.
Report everything (RE)	Report every detail possible even if it seems trivial or irrelevant.
Recall from a changed perspective (CP)	Try to describe the episode as it would have been seen from different points of view.
Recall in reverse order (RO)	Change the order of recall so that the event is reported in different orders, moving backwards and forwards in time.

Table 2.1

These techniques are all designed to enhance retrieval of the original memory by providing extra cues that might help to jog witnesses' memory for more central details. Subsequent research led to a version of the technique called the 'enhanced cognitive interview'. After looking at current police practice through detailed analysis of taped interviews, Fisher et al. (1987) suggested adding several extra features to a more structured process. For example, they recommended that the interviewer should minimise distractions, actively listen to the witness, ask open-ended questions, pause after each response, avoid interruption, encourage the use of imagery, adapt their language to suit the witness, and to avoid any judgemental comments.

EXAMPLE EXAM QUESTION

Derek was nearing the end of a long and tiring train journey when an argument broke out between two passengers in his carriage. One of passengers was badly injured. As he was a witness, Derek was questioned by the police about the incident using a cognitive interview.

Explain how the police could use a cognitive interview to collect information from Derek about this crime. [6 marks]

Exam hint

You are going to get questions like this – it is very important to engage with the scenario in order to gain more than a couple of marks. In this case, you need to be giving an answer in the context of Derek's experience on the train.

A number of studies support the potential usefulness of the cognitive interview. Geiselman et al. (1985), for example, found that the cognitive interview resulted in more information being drawn from witnesses compared to other interview techniques.

KEY STUDY: THE COGNITIVE INTERVIEW

Geiselman et al. (1985) investigated the effectiveness of the cognitive interview by comparing it to other means used to acquire eyewitness testimony. 89 participants were shown police training films of simulated violent crimes. 48 hours later they were interviewed about the films by an experienced Los Angeles police officer, using either a cognitive interview, a standard police interview, or an interview using hypnosis. The interviews were recorded and eyewitness reports assessed for correct and incorrect responses.

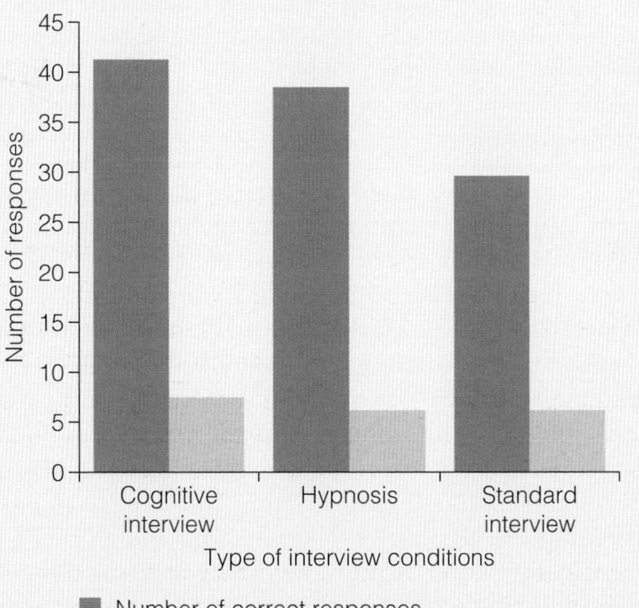

Fig. 2.15 Geiselman et al. (1985) results for statements made by witnesses under three different interview conditions

Geiselman et al. found that the cognitive interview elicited the most accurate recall, followed by hypnosis and then the standard interview. This was especially true for crime film scenarios, which had the highest density of events. There was no significant difference in the numbers of errors made.

The similarity of results for the cognitive interview and hypnosis was thought to be due to the two techniques having similar components, in particular 'report everything' (RE) and 'changed perspective' (CP). The standard interview did worse because of its repeated focus on encouraging recall of key information without aids to memory retrieval.

THINKING SCIENTIFICALLY: EXTERNAL VALIDITY

Experiments are often criticized for their lack of external validity, that is, the extent to which the findings can be generalized beyond the context in which they were discovered. Sometimes this is a fair criticism, but the criticism of a lack of external validity is often over-used or poorly applied. For example, the Geiselman et al. study might be accused of a lack of ecological validity since the participants watched filmed and simulated crimes (even though the interviews were carried out by experienced serving police officers). However, the cost of some ecological validity is more than balanced here by the benefits gained from increased control of extraneous variables. When you also consider that subsequent research in real-life settings has generally supported Geiselman et al., hopefully you will see that poorly applied criticisms like 'lack of ecological validity', just because the study was an experiment, only demonstrate a lack of understanding.

A number of subsequent studies confirmed these findings, although Kohnken et al. (1999) found that witnesses questioned using the cognitive interview also recalled more incorrect information than those questioned using a standard technique. This is possibly because the cognitive interview procedure elicits more information overall than other procedures.

Fisher et al. (1990) have also demonstrated the effectiveness of the cognitive interview technique in real police settings in Miami in the US. They trained detectives to use the enhanced cognitive interview techniques with genuine crime witnesses and found that its use significantly increased the amount of information recalled. Kebbell et al. (1999) carried out a survey of police officers in the UK and found that there was quite widespread use of the cognitive interview. However, while officers generally found it useful, they expressed some concern about the amount of incorrect recall generated and the amount of time it took to complete an enhanced cognitive interview. In practice, it seemed that the officers were using the RE and CR instructions, but rarely used the CP and RO instructions.

Psychologists have tried to test these police perceptions that certain elements of the cognitive interview are more useful than others. Milne and Bull (2002), for example, tested all the cognitive interview procedures either singly or in combination. They found that all four of the procedures used singly produced more recall from witnesses than standard interview techniques. However, the most effective combination appeared to be the use of CR and RE instructions, which is in line with what practising police officers had suspected.

One area where the cognitive interview has not proved particularly successful is in the questioning of young children. Geiselman (1999) reviewed a number of studies and concluded that, while it can be used quite effectively for children aged from about eight years upwards, children under the age of six years actually reported events slightly less accurately in response to cognitive interview techniques. This may be because children find the instructions difficult to understand.

KEY POINTS

- Because of the serious consequences of erroneous EWT, psychologists have devised a method to improve accuracy called the cognitive interview.
- The cognitive interview has four components: context reinstatement (CR), report everything (RE), recall from a changed perspective (CP), and recall in reverse order (RO).
- Research suggests that the cognitive interview is successful in improving the accuracy of EWT.

PRACTICAL ACTIVITY

Loftus and Palmer (1974) found that post-event information could affect memory of the event. In particular, they demonstrated the impact leading questions have on recall. This practical activity aims to replicate the findings of Loftus and Palmer.

First, find an image of a car crash on the Internet. This must be large enough to show some detail, have two cars in it, and no smashed glass on the floor. Think about ethics – make sure that the image could not in any way be distressing to participants.

You will then need to construct two short questionnaires. These should contain non-leading questions about the contents of the image, for example the colour of the vehicles, the number of lamp-posts, etc. One question must ask whether there was broken glass in the image.

The two questionnaires will be identical except for the leading question which will ask participants how fast the cars were travelling when they 'contacted' (in questionnaire 1) or 'smashed' (in questionnaire 2). This is the independent variable. The participant response to this question is the dependent variable.

Now you have to conduct the research. You will need a set of standardized instructions and a debrief (see pages 13 and 38 for information on this), taking into account things like the amount of time participants are allowed to look at the image, the context in which the image is shown, how participants are asked to respond, and ethical issues. You should also consider the experimental design and your sampling method.

Once you have gathered data you will need to analyse it.

- Think of how you could summarize the data and use tables and graphs.
- Do your findings support your hypothesis? If not, why not?
- Think about your findings in terms of the constructive nature of LTM and response bias.
- This is a good study for thinking about validity – is this a valid way of conducting research into eyewitness testimony? What could be done to improve validity?

Exam focus

Read through the following example exam question, example student answer, and examiner comments. Then, have a go at answering the question yourself!

EXAMPLE EXAM QUESTION, TAKEN FROM PAGE 139

Outline and evaluate research into the effects of misleading information on eyewitness testimony. [12 marks]

Petra's answer

Loftus and Palmer carried out one study of eyewitness testimony. Loftus and Palmer used a film of a car crash and they showed it to 45 students. They varied the words used to describe the crash with five different variations: hit, bumped and smashed were three of them. Loftus and Palmer found that using the word 'smashed' led to the fastest speed at about 40mph and using 'contacted' produced the lowest estimate (31.8mph).

Examiner comment: This is an accurate and detailed coverage of one study. It gives more detail than is generally needed for an 'outline'.

One week later Loftus and Palmer asked the students if they had seen any broken glass. The students who had been in the smashed condition were more likely to report seeing glass than those students in the other conditions. This shows how post event information can alter our memory for an event we have seen. Loftus and Palmer's study is a lab experiment, which is good because they can control all the variables (e.g. the same film, the questions, the outside noise and time of day), but it lacks validity because it is in a lab. Because they used an independent groups design, there might have been individual differences between the groups. Students are not representative of real people as they are younger and cleverer.

Examiner comment: These points are stated with little explanation or elaboration. The first point about validity could be developed by explaining exactly what is different in the lab to witnessing a real life car accident – less stress and an expectation in an experiment that something is going to happen.

Examiner comment: Petra has focused her answer on description, selecting and describing a relevant study in plenty of detail. However, the use of only one study limits the amount of analysis and evaluation for Petra. Marks can be picked up quite easily by comparing research studies, or by using a similar study to support the findings. The analysis and evaluation points lack elaboration. This answer would be a Level 2 response, at the top of the band, as the focus is mainly on description, and evaluation is of limited effectiveness. **6/12 marks.**

Part 1: Introductory topics in Psychology

Chapter 3: Attachment

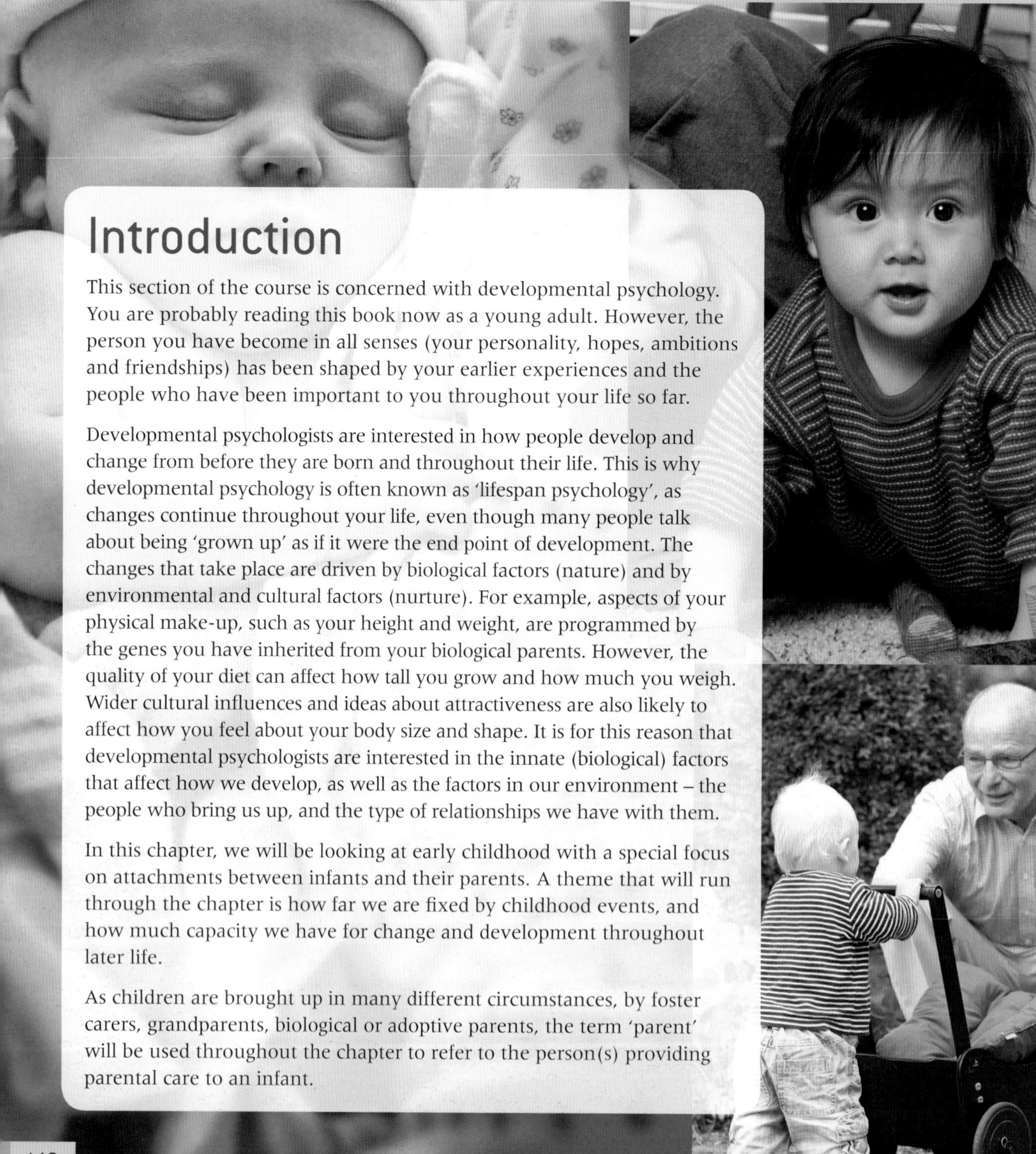

Introduction

This section of the course is concerned with developmental psychology. You are probably reading this book now as a young adult. However, the person you have become in all senses (your personality, hopes, ambitions and friendships) has been shaped by your earlier experiences and the people who have been important to you throughout your life so far.

Developmental psychologists are interested in how people develop and change from before they are born and throughout their life. This is why developmental psychology is often known as 'lifespan psychology', as changes continue throughout your life, even though many people talk about being 'grown up' as if it were the end point of development. The changes that take place are driven by biological factors (nature) and by environmental and cultural factors (nurture). For example, aspects of your physical make-up, such as your height and weight, are programmed by the genes you have inherited from your biological parents. However, the quality of your diet can affect how tall you grow and how much you weigh. Wider cultural influences and ideas about attractiveness are also likely to affect how you feel about your body size and shape. It is for this reason that developmental psychologists are interested in the innate (biological) factors that affect how we develop, as well as the factors in our environment – the people who bring us up, and the type of relationships we have with them.

In this chapter, we will be looking at early childhood with a special focus on attachments between infants and their parents. A theme that will run through the chapter is how far we are fixed by childhood events, and how much capacity we have for change and development throughout later life.

As children are brought up in many different circumstances, by foster carers, grandparents, biological or adoptive parents, the term 'parent' will be used throughout the chapter to refer to the person(s) providing parental care to an infant.

What is covered in Attachment?

Caregiver–infant interactions in humans

What is attachment?

Think about the abilities of a newborn baby. Babies are physically helpless at birth: they cannot feed themselves or escape from danger. They can communicate only in a simple way – by crying. Babies are reliant on other people for their survival for the first years of their lives. Despite their apparent helplessness, babies do survive. They do this because they come into the world with the ability to get other people (generally their biological parents) to care for them, feed and protect them until they are able to do this for themselves. This topic looks at these early relationships and attachments that bind babies and their parents together. First relationships are important to babies as they ensure their survival during a relatively lengthy period of helplessness, but they are also important as the start of the connections that people form with others. Attachments and relationships are, for the majority of people, one of the most important aspects of their lives.

Key term

Attachment: an emotional tie between two people shown in their behaviour.

Although the terms '**attachment**' and 'bond' are often used interchangeably there are differences between them. A bond is a set of feelings that ties one person to another: parents often feel strongly bonded with their newborn babies. An attachment is different to a bond as it involves two people, both parent and baby, experiencing an emotional link which ties them together. Although attachments are formed shortly after birth in many non-human animals, attachments take longer to develop in human babies.

We can see that two people are attached to each other by looking at their behaviour. One indication of attachment is distress on separation. Babies show their distress by crying, but we can also see distress at separation in the emotional farewell of lovers at railway stations. Other signs of attachment include orientation of behaviour towards the attachment figure – effectively attempting to catch and maintain their attention – and in young babies, a fear of strangers which appears at around six months of age.

Early interactions

Although newborn babies cannot feed or protect themselves, a growing body of research has shown how babies are born with primitive reflexes, including sucking and grasping, and with sensory and perceptual abilities that help them to tune into the social world. Because babies have a limited behavioural repertoire, developmental psychologists have devised ingenious methods to work out what very young infants understand about the world. For example, the preferential looking technique involves presenting infants with two visual stimuli and measuring the amount of time the infant spends looking at each. More time spent looking at one stimulus implies that the infant can tell the difference between two images and prefers one to the other. Johnson and Morton (1991) studied babies who were less than one hour old, showing them a schematic face, scrambled face, and control face (See Fig. 3.1), and measured the amount of time spent looking at each. Babies spent more time looking at the schematic than the scrambled or control face, indicating an orientation to face-like stimuli from birth. This interest in faces appears to exist with minimal opportunity for learning, implying that it is innate. Babies can also suck on a pacifier, which can be wired to measure the sucking rate while the baby is exposed to audio stimuli, such as different voices. Mehler et al. (1978) found that one-month-olds would suck faster on a pacifier to listen to their mother's voice than a female stranger's voice, indicating they could tell the difference between them and preferred to listen to their mother. These studies show how babies enter the world already tuned to pay attention to important social signals such as faces and voices.

Fig. 3.1 Johnson and Morton's stimuli; babies prefer the schematic face.

Early communication between parents and newborns is structured around the baby's cry, which is used to signal needs to the parent. The message of a baby's cry is 'something is wrong: sort it out'. Woolf (1969) identified three types of cry: the basic cry is used to signal hunger and consists of half-second rhythmic cries interspersed with short silences of around 0.6 seconds. An angry cry is similar to the basic cry but with shorter periods of silence in between, and a pain cry is qualitatively different: a loud initial cry followed by breath holding. Parents respond to the baby's cries with a range of behaviours designed to nurture, soothe and distract the baby, including feeding, rocking, stroking and singing.

Fig. 3.2 A baby's cry signals needs to the parent

Interactions between very young babies and their parents are 'baby led', with the adult responding to the behaviour of the baby. Kaye (1977) observed mothers and very young babies during feeding. Mothers tended to be quiet and still while the baby was sucking, but when a bout of sucking came to an end, the mothers would interact with the baby, stroking, jiggling them and talking quietly. This instinctive pattern showed mothers taking turns with the infant at being the principal actor, effectively fitting their behaviour around the sucking pattern to create a 'dialogue'. Conversations require two participants to take turns at speaking and listening, each paying attention to the other's contribution and shaping their behaviour to it. Much of this process is non-verbal, with subtle behaviours indicating 'I haven't finished' or 'I'm interested – carry on talking'. Turn-taking in the infant-adult interaction is important for the development of social and language skills (Trevarthen, 1979).

Reciprocity and interactional synchrony

From the age of around three or four weeks, babies begin to communicate with their parents by smiling. Parents generally experience the first smiles as a breakthrough in their relationship with the baby. First smiles are often fleeting and unpredictable, appearing without a clear trigger. However, babies rapidly become communicative

Key terms

Reciprocity: the matching of actions in two people.

Interactional synchrony: the coordination between the speech of a speaker and the movements of a listener during an interaction.

in response to the parent's actions or other environmental stimuli. The message of a smile in contrast to a cry is 'That was good. Do it again'. Smiling is an example of **reciprocity** – when a smile occurs in one person, it triggers a smile in the other. Tronick et al. (1979) asked mothers who had been enjoying a dialogue with their baby to stop moving and maintain a static, unsmiling expression on their faces. Babies would try to tempt the mother into interaction by smiling themselves, and would become puzzled and increasingly distressed when their smile did not provoke the usual response. Thus, babies expect and anticipate concordant responses to their smiles.

From the age of around one month, interactions between babies and parents become increasingly reciprocal, with babies responding to the parent's behaviour and increasingly matching their actions.

Fig. 3.3 Babies as young as 12 days old can imitate facial and manual gestures.

Meltzoff and Moore (1997) carried out experiments using six babies aged 12 to 27 days old and 12 babies aged 16 to 21 days. The babies were shown facial gestures (e.g. sticking tongue out) and manual gestures (waving fingers) in order to investigate their abilities to imitate. The results indicated that babies aged 12 to 21 days old could imitate both facial and manual gestures. Meltzoff and Moore argued that the ability to imitate serves as an important building block for later social and cognitive development.

Condon and Ogston (1971) analysed the movements made by adults when speaking and when listening to a speaker, and found these were finely synchronised. They referred to this as **interactional synchrony**. Remarkably, the same pattern was shown in newborn infants listening to an adult speak. Today, the term interactional synchrony is used more broadly to refer to the finely tuned coordination of behaviours between mother and infant during speaking and listening. Parents and babies develop a shared sense of timing, which develops into a flow of mutual behaviours. Stern (1971) carried out a microanalytic observation of films showing three-month-old babies interacting with their mothers. The films were played in slow motion and the behaviours logged every second. The pattern he found was that the infant would turn their head away for a split second as the mother approached, then turn back towards the mother, resembling the steps of a complex dance such as a waltz – or a flirtation!

Brazelton et al. (1975) observed 12 mother–baby pairs at regular intervals over the first five months of life. They videotaped play sessions lasting around seven minutes and carried out a microanalysis of the videotapes. Babies showed clear cycles of attention and non-attention, with three distinct phases: attention and build-up, turning away, and recovery, with several of these cycles occurring per minute. These interactions represent the first signs of organized infant behaviour.

ACTIVITY 3.1

Watch two people having a conversation for a couple of minutes. Can you see any examples of reciprocal behaviours (i.e. mirroring of postures)? Which non-verbal signals are used to indicate that a listener wants a turn at speaking?

Stages of attachment identified by Schaffer

As we have seen, babies have many skills and abilities and come into the world 'tuned in' to certain kinds of stimuli. Even though the time after birth may be very special for parents to bond with their new baby, the overall process of the formation of attachments takes longer in human infants, and it is around seven or eight months before babies show their first real attachments. The stages of attachment were identified by Rudolph Schaffer and Peggy Emerson (1964) in a longitudinal study of 60 babies drawn from a predominantly working-class area of Glasgow.

KEY STUDY: SCHAFFER AND EMERSON (1964)

Schaffer and Emerson looked at the development of attachment, studying a sample of 60 babies in Glasgow. The babies and their families were visited monthly for the first year of their lives, and again at 18 months. Schaffer and Emerson collected data on attachment by considering two types of behaviour:

- Stranger distress: if the baby showed signs of distress when approached by someone they did not know. Distress at strangers indicates that the baby can recognize familiar people and feels anxious with those who are unfamiliar.
- Separation anxiety: if the baby showed anxiety or distress when the caregiver left them. Separation anxiety indicates that the baby has formed an attachment to the person.

Schaffer and Emerson used a variety of methods to collect their data, including observation of the babies and interviewing their mothers. During each visit, they would approach the baby to see if they cried, whimpered, or showed signs of distress at a strange face. They interviewed the mothers, asking them about the baby's response to various situations; for example, when the baby was left with a babysitter or put in their cot at night. The mothers were asked to rate the baby's behaviour in each of these situations using a four-point scale from 0 ('no protest shown') to 3 ('cries loudly every time').

Schaffer and Emerson found that attachment behaviours developed in stages that were loosely linked to age (see Table 3.1). Most babies started to show separation anxiety from their attachment figure at around 25–32 weeks (six–eight months), indicating that an attachment had been formed. Fear of strangers tended to follow about a month later. In 65 per cent of babies, the first attachment was to the mother. Only 3 per cent of first attachments were to fathers but in around 30 per cent of babies, attachments were formed simultaneously to two people – most often their mother and father. After the first attachment was formed, most babies went on to form multiple attachments with a variety of people they saw regularly, such as grandparents and siblings.

Stage and age	Characteristics
Asocial stage (0 to 6 weeks)	Babies produce similar responses to objects and people and do not prefer specific people to others. They have a bias towards human-like stimuli and prefer to look at faces and eyes. They rapidly learn to discriminate familiar people from unfamiliar by their smell and voice.
Indiscriminate attachments (6 weeks to 6 months)	Babies become more sociable. They can tell people apart and prefer to be in human company. They are relatively easily comforted by anyone and do not prefer specific individuals yet. They do not show fear of strangers.
Specific attachments (7 months onwards)	Two changes take place around seven months. The baby begins to show separation anxiety, protesting when their primary attachment figure leaves them. They also show fear of strangers.
Multiple attachments (10–11 months onwards)	Multiple attachments follow soon after the first attachment is made. The baby shows attachment behaviours towards several different people, such as siblings, grandparents and childminders.

Table 3.1 Stages in the development of attachments; Schaffer and Emerson, 1964

Research methods link

Schaffer and Emerson's research is an example of overt observation. You can read more about observational research on pages 16–17.

THINKING SCIENTIFICALLY: SCHAFFER AND EMERSON

Schaffer and Emerson used a combination of methods of data collection. Babies were observed at home by the researchers, and mothers were asked to rate their baby's response to separation in a wide range of everyday situations. These methods provide data that is very rich in detail, and the use of different measurements make the study high in ecological validity, as the infants' behaviour was seen in the natural environment of the home. The use of different methods to study the same issue is known as 'triangulation'.

However, Schaffer and Emerson's findings reflect the child-rearing practices of the 1960s, when most childcare was carried out by mothers who were less likely to work outside the home. Today, fathers tend to take a much more active role in their children's lives and are more likely to be the first attachment figure than they were in the 1960s.

Exam hint

The question refers to Grace's behaviour at several different ages. Think about the stage of attachments and the characteristics of babies at each stage in constructing your answer to this question.

EXAMPLE EXAM QUESTION

Olivia babysits her baby niece, Grace, every Saturday night. Grace is happy to be left with Olivia and the two enjoy playing games such as peek-a-boo. When Grace is seven months old she starts to scream and protest when her mother leaves her with Olivia. Grandma says that Grace will soon grow out of it. By nine months, Grace is quite happy to be left with Olivia again.

Use your knowledge of the stages of attachment to explain Grace's response to being left with Olivia. (4 marks)

Multiple attachments and the role of the father

Schaffer and Emerson's observational study showed how babies form multiple attachments around the age of 10 to 11 months. In the follow-up at 18 months, only around 1 in 10 babies had a single attachment (13 per cent), and almost one third (31 per cent) had five or more attachments to grandparents, siblings and significant others. Fathers were the first joint attachment figure in about one third of infants in 1964. Fifty years later, many fathers are much more involved with their babies, particularly in western cultures, being present at the birth and taking responsibility for feeding and nappy changing on an equal basis with mothers. Research shows that the relationship between an infant and their father is important in its own right.

Although mothers appear to be quicker at recognising their infants in the first hours after birth (typically because they have spent more time with the baby immediately after birth), fathers interact with their newborn babies in very similar ways to mothers, for example ensuring they are warm (Christensson, 1996). While fathers show similar behaviours to mothers in the first months of the infant's life, their behavioural 'style' appears to be different. They are more consistently involved in play than caretaking behaviours, and their play tends to be more stimulating and unpredictable than mothers, who tend towards soothing their infants. Paquette (2004) found that fathers are more likely to encourage toddlers to take risks and to be brave during physical play than mothers. Fathers commonly structure talk around active play, whereas a mother's talk is primarily emotional, designed to soothe and reassure the infant. However, these differences are not culturally universal (Roopnarine, 1993) and are not shown in middle-class Indian families, for example.

Much research on fathering has focused on the amount of time a father spends with an infant, seeing this as a measure of involvement in parenting (Pleck, 2010), but evidence suggests that 'the amount of time that fathers and children spend together is probably much less important than what they do with that time' (Lamb and Tamis-LeMonda, 2004). One challenge for developmental psychologists involves distinguishing between the quantity and the quality of the involvement of parents, particularly in what fathers give to their children. Lamb et al. (1985) argue that fathers' involvement with their infants can be 'captured' using three dimensions:

- Interaction – how much the father engages with the infant (i.e. quantity)
- Accessibility – how physically and emotionally accessible he is (i.e. quality)
- Responsibility – the extent to which he takes on 'caretaking' tasks.

Fig. 3.4 Research shows the importance of father–infant relationships

Veríssimo et al. (2011) examined the relationship between children's attachment to both of their parents and later popularity in nursery school. They found that the quality of the relationship between fathers and toddlers significantly correlated with the number of friends at preschool, and appeared to be more important than the attachment between a toddler and their mother in subsequent childhood friendships. You can read more about this piece of research on page 171 of this chapter.

KEY POINTS

- Attachments are lasting emotional ties between two people.
- Newborn babies are tuned into social stimuli such as faces and voices and communicate their needs by crying.
- Interactions between parents and babies begin in an asymmetrical manner but become reciprocal over the first few months.
- Interactional synchrony describes the communicative 'dance' that takes place between parents and infants.
- Schaffer and Emerson identified four stages of attachment that unfold over the first year of life.
- Fathers show different behavioural styles to mothers, encouraging physical play and risk-taking in babies and toddlers.

Animal studies of attachment: Lorenz and Harlow

In many animal species, attachments are formed soon after birth. This process was first investigated by Konrad Lorenz, an Austrian ethologist, who studied animal behaviour. In his observations of animals, Lorenz noticed the tendency for newborn animals, such as lambs or chicks, to follow the first large moving object they saw after birth (usually their mother) and to attach themselves to it. In order to investigate this rapid formation of attachment, Lorenz carried out a series of studies with greylag geese in the 1930s, which yielded valuable information about the formation of attachments.

KEY STUDY: LORENZ (1935)

In 1935, Lorenz divided a number of fertile goose eggs randomly into two groups. Half were replaced under their mother and allowed to hatch naturally, and the remaining eggs were kept in an incubator until they were ready to hatch. Lorenz ensured that he was the first object seen by the incubator group when they hatched out of the eggs. The newly hatched goslings followed him closely, as if he were their mother, and appeared to have formed a rapid attachment to him (see Fig. 3.5). A short time after the geese had hatched, Lorenz put both groups of geese into a container to mix them up and then released them. They rapidly separated, the incubator group running to Lorenz and the normally hatched geese towards their real mother.

Lorenz called this formation of rapid attachments 'imprinting'. Imprinting is the tendency to form an attachment to the first large moving object seen after birth. In later studies, Lorenz found that the strongest tendency to imprint takes place between 13 and 16 hours after birds hatch out of the egg. By the time birds reach the age of 32 hours, the tendency to imprint has virtually passed and attachment will not take place. Lorenz argued that imprinting had to take place within the 'window of development', which he called a **critical period**.

Imprinting clearly makes sense in terms of survival for mobile species of animal. As the mother moves around to forage and to escape from predators, the young must remain close to her in order to be protected and survive. Following promotes survival and has evolved via natural selection.

Fig. 3.5 Konrad Lorenz and his 'children'

Key term

Critical period: a window of time in which something (e.g. a behaviour) develops. After the critical period has passed the behaviour will not develop.

Link

Natural selection is explained in the biological approach on page 234.

Harry Harlow was an American psychologist who also made use of animal research. Harlow began his academic career by studying animal intelligence, but became interested in attachment quite by accident. Harlow noticed that baby monkeys, raised in isolation to prevent infection, would cling to the towelling nappies lining their cage, protesting loudly when the soiled cloths were removed. Harlow wondered if the infant monkeys had become attached to the soft cloths in the absence of a real mother.

Harlow decided to test the prevailing idea of the time that babies attached to their mothers because they fed them – the 'cupboard love' theory. He wondered if attachment could be based on other stimuli, such as the contact and comfort mothers provided. As mothers generally provide both milk and comfort to their offspring, Harlow conducted a series of experiments systematically manipulating the different properties of mothers. He used young rhesus macaques, a medium-sized species of monkey found in Asia.

KEY STUDY: HARLOW (1958)

Harlow studied eight newborn macaque monkeys. They were separated from their biological mothers at birth and reared in cages in isolation until they were eight months old. In each cage, Harlow placed two 'surrogate' mothers, one made of wire with a monkey-like face and one made of a wooden block covered in soft towelling fabric. The surrogate mothers had a heating element attached to provide warmth, and both mothers had an attachment which could hold a feeding bottle to supply milk.

Each baby monkey was placed in a cage with both surrogate mothers. Four of the monkeys had the feeding bottle attached to the wire mother and the remaining four had the bottle attached to the cloth mother. Harlow measured the amount of time the baby monkeys spent clinging to each of the surrogate mothers and the amount of time the babies spent crying when either mother was removed from the cage. These two measures were the dependent variables. Harlow found a clear preference for the cloth mother: when the feeding bottle was attached to the wire mother, the infant monkeys would visit for a feed, returning immediately to cling to the cloth mother.

Harlow ran several more experiments with the same monkeys to assess the extent of attachment to both mothers. In one, he separated the babies from their mothers and put them into a wooden box where they could lift a hatch to look at either mother. Harlow found that the monkeys spent almost all of their time looking at the cloth mother and were no more interested in the wire mother than a bare cage used as a control condition.

In another variation, Harlow put the monkeys into a large room filled with toys. When the wire mother was present, the monkeys huddled in a state of frozen terror. When the cloth mother was placed in the room, the baby monkeys would pluck up the courage to explore the toys, returning to cling to the cloth mother if startled or worried by their exploration.

In a final variation of the study, Harlow manipulated the properties of the surrogate mother (Blum, 1994), which he called the 'iron maiden'. The surrogate mother blew cold air out of her body at irregular intervals, throwing the baby monkey against the bars of the cage. Despite the violent and abusive treatment, the baby monkeys would continue to cling to their surrogate mother, demonstrating the strength of their attachment.

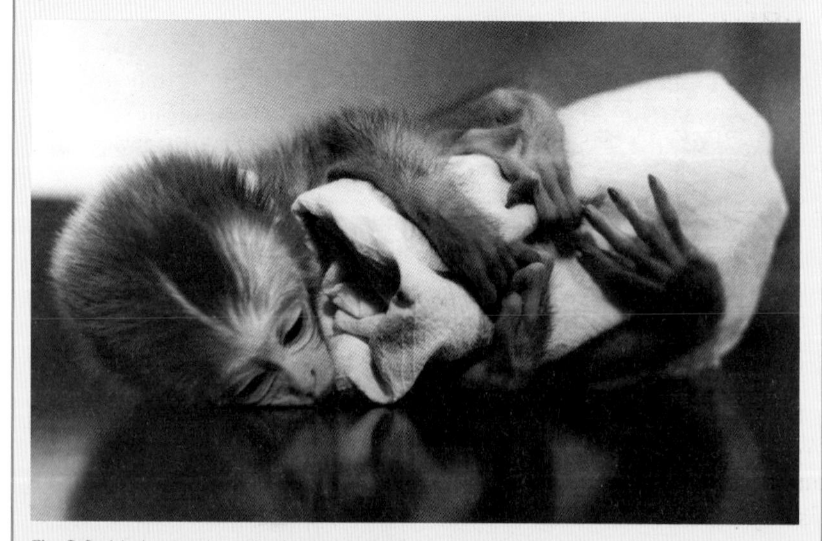

Fig. 3.6 A baby monkey clinging to a towelling nappy in the absence of a mother

THINKING SCIENTIFICALLY: ANIMAL RESEARCH

Harlow chose to use monkeys in this experiment for ethical reasons; even in 1958, this research programme would simply not have been allowed with human infants, and today, research of this nature would not be given ethical approval.

However, there are other advantages to using non-human animals. They provide a simpler model of behaviour, as they are less sophisticated and their behaviours are often easier to interpret. Macaques and humans are also genetically similar, sharing about 94 per cent of their DNA. Nonetheless, a small difference in DNA of this kind can make a huge difference. Despite a 1.2 per cent difference in DNA between humans and chimpanzees, human brains are around three times larger than chimpanzee brains (Toates, 2012). We cannot necessarily assume that human babies would respond in exactly the same way as Harlow's rhesus monkeys.

EXAMPLE EXAM QUESTION

Describe and evaluate two animal studies of attachment. [12 marks]

Exam hint

Two key issues in animal research are generalization and ethics. Discuss these in relation to both studies.

KEY POINTS

- Lorenz showed how rapid attachments are developed in a short critical period after birth in many species of animal.
- This process is referred to as imprinting.
- Harlow's work indicated that contact comfort provides the basis for attachment in infant monkeys rather than feeding.
- Baby monkeys attached to mothers who were abusive, demonstrating the instinctual nature of attachments.

Explanations of attachment: learning theory and Bowlby's monotropic theory

Learning theory

In 1928, the behaviourist John B. Watson wrote the advice below for parents on how to treat their children. Watson's advice is in stark contrast to the current ideas of how to bring up children that emphasize 'attachment parenting', and which stress the utmost importance of the bond between a child and its parents.

> *'Treat them as though they were young adults ... never hug and kiss them; never let them sit on your lap. If you must, kiss them once on the forehead when they say goodnight. Shake hands with them in the morning. Give them a pat on the head if they have made an extraordinarily good job of a difficult task.'* (Watson, 1928)

Watson's advice demonstrates learning theory, with its emphasis on reward and punishment as ways of shaping behaviour. Learning theory argues that attachments are based on the principles of classical and operant conditioning. First attachments are often formed to the person who looks after the infant, who feeds them, changes their nappy and cuddles them when they are afraid. First attachment figures are a powerful source of pleasure, as well as removing physical and emotional discomforts such as hunger, cold and pain.

Link

The mechanism of classical conditioning is explained in detail on page 222.

Classical conditioning refers to learning via association. A newborn baby will cry in response to unpleasant states such as hunger or cold. This response is instinctive (innate) and requires no learning. The parent responds to the cries by breast- or bottle-feeding the newborn baby with milk. In the language of classical conditioning, the parent is a neutral stimulus that does not initially produce a response of pleasure in the baby. However, the association between the parent and milk (an unconditioned stimulus) means that the two are paired together so that, over a short period of time, the parent becomes associated with the provision of milk and comes to produce the response of pleasure. This process is shown in detail in Figure 3.7.

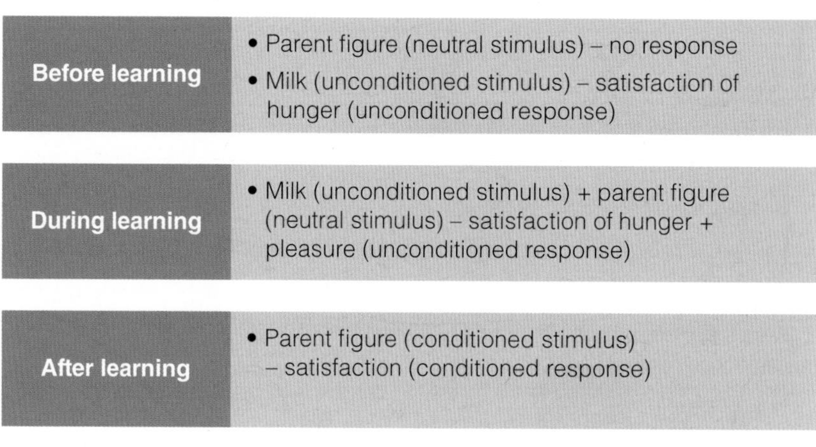

Before learning
• Parent figure (neutral stimulus) – no response
• Milk (unconditioned stimulus) – satisfaction of hunger (unconditioned response)
During learning
• Milk (unconditioned stimulus) + parent figure (neutral stimulus) – satisfaction of hunger + pleasure (unconditioned response)
After learning
• Parent figure (conditioned stimulus) – satisfaction (conditioned response)

Fig. 3.7 Diagram showing the developing association between parent and milk

The second aspect of the learning theory uses the concepts of operant conditioning – learning through reward and punishment. The parent's actions of feeding and cuddling the infant are powerful rewards (or positive reinforcement) for the baby, who will rapidly learn that their cries bring feeds and cuddles. For the parent, the cuddling/feeding behaviour generally switches off the infant's screams of hunger, which acts as negative reinforcement for the parent, so they are likely to repeat the feeding/cuddling the next time the baby cries.

Evaluation

This idea is simple and straightforward, and many people assume that attachment is based on 'cupboard love'/feeding. However, a substantial amount of evidence contradicts learning theory, showing that attachment is not based on association and reward but instead is an instinctive process.

- In Harlow's study, attachment was formed to the soft and cuddly cloth mother even when the wire mother provided milk. This shows how contact comfort is more important than feeding as the basis for attachment, suggesting an evolutionary mechanism. In one of the variations known as the 'iron maiden', infant monkeys continued to demonstrate attachment to highly abusive mothers who blasted the infant monkeys with cold air at irregular intervals.

Attachment occurred in the absence of rewards, showing the instinctive nature of this process.

- In Schaffer and Emerson's observational study, just under half of the babies in the sample (39 per cent) formed first attachments to a person who did not carry out caretaking such as feeds and nappy changes, challenging the claim that attachments are based on the association with feeding. Attachments were more likely to be formed to people who played with the baby. The learning explanation ignores the considerable evidence pointing to the importance of evolutionary (instinctive) aspects of attachment. These aspects are considered by Bowlby's monotropic theory.

Bowlby's monotropic theory

Bowlby's attachment theory arose from his work as a psychiatrist in a child guidance clinic in London in the 1930s and 40s. Based on this work, Bowlby put forward two theories, both of which emphasise the importance of the attachment between a mother figure and baby. The theory of maternal deprivation (which you will read about later in this chapter on page 174) was written in 1951, and the monotropic attachment theory was written in the 1960s. The theories are strongly linked and share many of the same ideas, with attachment theory effectively growing out of Bowlby's work on the importance of mothering.

Bowlby challenged the view put forward by learning theory that attachment was based on learned associations, arguing instead that attachment was an instinctive behaviour pattern. Bowlby drew on a range of theoretical approaches to develop his ideas, including psychoanalysis and ethology, as well as his own clinical practice with troubled children and adolescents.

Attachment as an instinct

In contrast to the learning theory, Bowlby argued that attachment was a mechanism that had evolved through the process of natural selection to ensure the survival of the child. Bowlby noted that babies possess instincts, such as crying (termed 'social releasers'), which encourage caregiving behaviour in parents, and that parents, especially mothers, possess corresponding instincts designed to protect their baby from harm and to nurture them to ensure survival into maturity. Therefore, babies who possessed social releasers would be more likely to survive, reach maturity, and have offspring of their own. Mothers who possessed nurturing instincts would leave behind more offspring who survived to maturity and produced their own offspring.

The internal working model and continuity

Bowlby developed Freud's idea of the mother–child relationship being important for future relationships. He also drew on the work carried out by Harlow with rhesus monkeys, which showed the importance of the mother figure providing comfort and security for the infant, a concept he developed into the idea of a 'safe base'. He argued that the first attachment between the baby and their caregiver provided the child with an internal working model or template for their future

Key terms

Internal working model: a template for future relationships including a model of how you and other people are likely to behave.

Monotropy: the tendency of babies to form a primary attachment to one person.

relationships. In this first attachment, the infant builds up a model of themselves as lovable (or not), a model of the parent figure as trustworthy (or not), and a model of the relationship between the two. This **internal working model**, begun in early childhood, influences the child's later relationships through to adulthood. This is referred to as the continuity hypothesis.

Monotropy

Bowlby did not deny that babies formed lots of attachments, but he believed that for every infant, one relationship was more important than the rest and existed at the top of the hierarchy. He referred to this idea as **monotropy**, and at the time Bowlby was writing, the primary attachment figure was generally the mother, who spent most of her time with the infant. As we will see, this has been one of Bowlby's more controversial claims.

The critical period

Bowlby thought that the process of attachment took place within a critical period, during the first three years of the child's life. He borrowed this concept from the work of Lorenz and other ethologists who had pointed to the rapid formation of attachments in some animal species. From his research with troubled adolescents, he believed that the attachment between caregiver and child should not be disrupted or broken for any reason before the age of three years, or there would be serious consequences.

Evaluation

Acceptance of Bowlby's theory

Much of Bowlby's theory is accepted today. It is widely acknowledged that attachment has an instinctual base and that attachments should take place within the first few years of life. Hence, adoptive agencies will try to place children with families at as young an age as possible in order for an early attachment to develop. Bowlby's ideas have become absorbed into our understanding of the emotional needs of infants, and the importance of 'mothering' in the happiness and adjustment of the child and adult is widely accepted. However, some of Bowlby's claims have led to debate and revision.

Criticism of Bowlby's theory

Many psychologists have criticized Bowlby's ideas regarding monotropy and argued that babies' attachment to the first attachment figure is not necessarily special or unique. Schaffer and Emerson's longitudinal study of 60 Glasgow babies found that multiple attachments seemed to be the norm for babies, rather than the exception. By about seven months of age, just under a third (29 per cent) of babies had multiple attachments and by the age of 10 months, this figure had risen to almost two-thirds (59 per cent). Schaffer and Emerson also found that the strongest bond was not necessarily to the mother as Bowlby had implied. At 18 months, only half of the sample was strongly attached to their mothers and about a third was strongly attached to their fathers. In putting so much emphasis on the biological mother, Bowlby overlooked the importance of fathers, believing them to be of little emotional significance in their children's lives. As we have seen, fathers play an important role in infants and children's lives, often providing a qualitatively different input to mothers.

The concept of a critical period

Bowlby's concept of a critical period has also been challenged. While attachment generally happens in the first years of life, studies with orphaned children who are adopted at the age of three or four have shown that children at that age are still capable of forming strong attachments to their new adoptive parents. You can read about these studies by Rutter, Tizard and Hodges later in this chapter on pages 178 and 175. These studies indicate that while the first years are certainly the optimum time for attachment, close attachments can be formed outside the first three years of life.

Bowlby's concept of the internal working model has generated a more complex debate than any other area of his theory. For that reason we will examine this claim in detail later in the chapter, after we have considered individual differences in attachments.

EXAMPLE EXAM QUESTION

Discuss the learning theory of attachment. [8 marks]

Exam hint

In a mini essay of this nature, you should aim to spend half of your time describing learning theory and the rest of the time on evaluation. A good strategy for evaluation is to provide evidence for and/or against a theory.

ACTIVITY 3.2

Identify and explain three differences between monotropic theory and learning theory of attachment.

KEY POINTS

- Learning theory explains attachment as an association between milk [an unconditioned stimulus] and the parent [neutral stimulus].
- Over time, the neutral stimulus [parent] triggers rewards of satisfaction and pleasure.
- Learning theory is contradicted by evidence from Harlow, and Schaffer and Emerson, demonstrating that attachments are not based on feeding.
- Bowlby's attachment theory conceptualizes attachment as an instinct that promotes survival of the infant.
- Attachment is monotropic, taking place within a critical period and leading to the development of an internal working model.
- The instinctual nature of attachment is widely accepted today.
- Attachment can take place outside Bowlby's proposed critical period.
- There is debate about the monotropic nature of attachments.

Ainsworth's 'Strange Situation' and types of attachment

Research methods link

Controlled observation is described on page 15.

So far we have talked about attachments as if babies and parents all behave in identical ways. Clearly this is not so and there are considerable individual differences in the strength and type of attachments formed between babies and their parents. These differences were explored by Mary Ainsworth, a colleague of Bowlby's at the Tavistock Clinic in London. Ainsworth was interested in exploring the different types of attachment between babies and their caregivers, and she developed a structured observation known as the 'Strange Situation' to do this. In the Strange Situation, babies aged around one year old and their mothers were observed in a range of situations, which allowed the researcher to assess the responses shown by infants to separation from their mother and reunion with her.

KEY STUDY: AINSWORTH (1970): THE STRANGE SITUATION

Infants aged one year to 18 months were observed through video cameras in a purpose-built laboratory playroom with their mothers. The room contained two comfortable chairs and a play area with a set of toys suitable for young children. The procedure in Ainsworth's research consisted of a series of situations, which were standardized for all the babies who took part.

1. Mother and infant enter the room. Mother sits in one of the chairs and reads a magazine. Child is placed on the floor and is free to explore the toys.
2. After about three minutes, a stranger enters, sits on the second chair and talks briefly with the mother.
3. The stranger approaches the infant and attempts to interact and play with them.
4. The mother leaves the room so the infant is alone with the stranger. The stranger comforts the baby if they are upset and offers to play with them.
5. After around three minutes the mother returns and the stranger leaves.
6. Three minutes later the mother departs again, leaving the baby briefly alone in the room.
7. The stranger re-enters and offers to comfort and play with the baby.
8. The mother returns and the stranger leaves.

Using this procedure, Ainsworth was able to monitor the infant's behaviour in a variety of situations, including the departure of the mother to assess separation anxiety, and the introduction of a stranger to measure stranger anxiety. She also examined the baby's behaviour towards the mother in a strange environment to assess whether or not the baby used her as a safe base to explore the room.

Ainsworth identified three broad patterns of behaviour, which she characterized as attachment types. A description of these is shown in Table 3.2.

Type of attachment	Behaviour patterns
Insecure–avoidant attachment (Type A) 15% of babies fell into this category.	• The relationship style of Type A babies involved keeping a distance and avoiding closeness. • Type A babies did not orient their behaviour towards their mother. • They showed some distress at her departure but did not seek comfort from her when she returned. • They rejected the stranger's attempts to comfort them.
Secure infants (Type B attachment) 70% of babies fell into this category.	• Type B babies used their mother as a safe base and were happy to explore the room when she was present. • They showed distress by crying when she left, and welcomed her back on her return, settling back down to play fairly quickly. • They were wary of the stranger and treated them very differently to their mother.
Insecure–ambivalent attachment (Type C) 15% of babies fell into this category.	• Type C babies seemed to expect the relationship to be difficult and they alternated between seeking closeness and wanting distance. • They were very distressed at separation. • They were not easily comforted when the mother returned, appearing angry and rejecting mother's attempts to comfort them. • They kept a close eye on the stranger, especially when she interacted with the mother.

Table 3.2 Attachment types in the Strange Situation (1970)

Key terms

Insecure-avoidant attachment: baby treats mother and stranger similarly, avoiding closeness and contact.

Secure attachment: baby uses mother as safe base, showing distress at separation and joy at reunion.

Insecure-ambivalent attachment: baby alternates between seeking closeness and wanting distance.

THINKING SCIENTIFICALLY: AINSWORTH (1970)

The Strange Situation has been an extremely useful tool, giving a great deal of information in a relatively short space of time about babies' attachments. The methodology is easy to replicate, which led to a substantial amount of research examining variations in attachment, within and between cultures. Some critics argued that the Strange Situation lacked validity because of the unfamiliar nature of the playroom, which was not the child's home. However, the situation is similar to being left with a babysitter or at nursery, suggesting that the method provides a valid measure of a child's response to separation, strangers and reunion.

Ainsworth's approach was categorical, seeking to place babies into one of three mutually exclusive types. Subsequent research indicated that not all babies fit into Ainsworth's original three attachment types, and so a Type D, disorganized attachment, was added by Main and Solomon (1986). The behaviour pattern of these babies did not fit any of the three categories above. For example, the baby responded in different ways in the repeated episodes by crying the first time the mother left, but not the second time. However, disorganized attachment is relatively rare and most babies fit into the three main types identified by Ainsworth. Other approaches to attachment (e.g. Bartholomew, 1990) make use of dimensions rather than categories.

ATTACHMENT

What causes individual differences in attachment types?

Ainsworth's explanation for differences in attachment type rested on the sensitivity of the mother. Ainsworth argued that mothers who were sensitive to their infants' needs, who read their moods and feelings correctly, were likely to produce babies who were securely attached. In contrast, mothers who were less sensitive or responsive to their babies, ignored them, or became impatient with them, were said to be more likely to have insecurely attached infants. These babies would be likely to feel less safe and would be unsure if their needs would be met at any time.

Research methods link

You can refresh your memory about correlation coefficients by looking at page 24.

De Wolff and van Ijzendoorn (1997) carried out a meta-analysis to assess the relationship between parental sensitivity and the security of babies' attachment. They analysed the results of 66 studies on over 4000 families and found a correlation of 0.24 between sensitivity and attachment. This means that there is a weak positive relationship between sensitivity and attachment – generally more sensitive caregivers have more strongly attached babies. While this is not a very strong correlation, it does support the view that the security of the babies' attachment type has some relation to the sensitivity of the caregiver.

Kagan (1987) argued that Ainsworth's explanation places too much emphasis on the role of the mother and ignores the basic temperament of the infant. Temperaments are differences in babies that seem to be inbuilt and visible from birth. There are a number of different aspects to temperament, including:

- activity – how much time the baby spends awake and alert
- emotionality – how much they become upset or aroused by events
- sociability – how much the baby seeks human company.

Thomas and Chess (1989) found three basic temperament types in a study of 138 American babies. Just under a half fell into the category of 'easy' babies – they ate and slept regularly and accepted new experiences easily. About one in ten were classed as 'slow-to-warm-up' babies. These did not actively reject new experiences but took a while to get used to them, whereas 'difficult' babies (15 per cent) ate and slept irregularly and actively rejected new experiences. According to the temperament hypothesis, the attachment type formed by a baby may reflect their own basic temperament rather than how sensitive their caregiver is. If this is true, then the baby should show similar attachments to both parents. Fox (1991) found that children often have the same type of attachment with both parents, implying that attachments may well relate to inbuilt temperaments. Easy babies may go on to be securely attached infants, whereas slow-to-warm-up babies may go on to being avoidant. Difficult babies may turn into ambivalent toddlers. This provides a very different explanation of attachment types to that suggested by Ainsworth.

Belsky and Rovine (1987) argue that individual differences in attachment types may relate to both the inborn temperament of the baby as well as to the sensitivity of the caregiver. They argue that babies with different temperaments present different types of challenges to their caregiver. An extremely reactive or difficult baby may need to be soothed, whereas a slow-to-warm-up infant needs encouragement. This type of baby may go on to develop a secure attachment with a caregiver who is patient, encouraging and responsive. However, with an anxious caregiver, the attachment outcome may be very different.

EXAMPLE EXAM QUESTION

Isla works at a nursery with one-year-old babies. Most babies cry for a short period of time when left by their parents and benefit from a cuddle and distraction with a story. Jack doesn't seem to notice when his mother leaves. Isla tries to encourage Jack to play with toys in the water tray but he doesn't seem interested in her at all.

Use your knowledge of individual differences in attachment types to explain which attachment type Jack shows. (4 marks)

What other information would you need to confirm your answer? (2 marks)

Exam hint

The scenario refers to Jack's behaviour when his mother leaves and his behaviour towards a stranger. You should refer to these in your answer when explaining the type of attachment shown by Jack. In order to answer the second question, think about the other kinds of information included in the Strange Situation to distinguish attachment types.

Cultural variations in attachment, including van Ijzendoorn

Attachments do not just differ between individual babies. They also vary systematically across cultures. This is not surprising, as people bring up their children very differently in different parts of the world and encourage them to develop a variety of abilities and qualities. Fox (1977) studied child-rearing practices in kibbutzim, communal farms in Israel (see Fig. 3.8). Here, babies are placed into communal childcare when they are around four days old and cared for by a nurse who is called a 'metapelet'. The physical aspects of childcare, such as

Fig. 3.8 Children growing up together in Kibbutzim, in Israel

feeding and nappy changing, are carried out by the nurse, and the parents visit the baby to play and cuddle, typically spending about three hours a day with the infant after work. When they are around four months old, babies move to another nursery for older children and continue to be reared as a group cared for by a professional nurse. This approach to child-rearing shows important differences to those that you may be accustomed to. The child is likely to have less adult attention than in a family setting and much more contact with peers of similar ages. Both of these may be important influences on their attachments to parents and on their later relationships.

Because of these variations in child-rearing practices, psychologists have been interested to see how babies vary between cultures in the types of attachment behaviours they show. Many of these studies have used the Strange Situation methodology devised by Ainsworth.

KEY STUDY: VAN IJZENDOORN AND KROONENBERG (1988)

Two Dutch psychologists, van Ijzendoorn and Kroonenberg, performed a meta-analysis of the results of 32 studies carried out in eight different countries, using Ainsworth's 'Strange Situation' to examine cultural variations in attachment types. In total over 2000 babies were studied, making this a substantial piece of research. In each of the 32 studies, babies were classed using Ainsworth's system as Type A, B or C. The results of van Ijzendoorn and Kroonenberg's findings are shown in Table 3.3 below.

Country	Number of studies	Type A Avoidant	Type B Secure	Type C Ambivalent
China	1	25	50	25
United Kingdom	1	22.2	75	22.8
Japan	2	5.2	67.7	27.1
Israel	2	6.8	64.4	28.8
Netherlands	4	26.3	67.3	6.4
Sweden	1	21.6	74.5	3.9
United States	18	21.1	64.8	14.1
West Germany	3	35.3	56.6	8.1

Table 3.3 Comparisons of insecure and secure attachments in eight countries (adapted from Bee, 1995)

Table 3.3 indicates both similarities and differences in attachment patterns which reflect cross-cultural differences in child-rearing in different places:

- Secure attachments (Type B) were the most common form in all the cultures surveyed. The lowest proportion of secure attachments (50 per cent) was found in China and the highest (around three-quarters) in the United Kingdom and Sweden.

- Type A (avoidant attachments) was more common in West Germany than in other Western countries. Avoidant attachments were very rare in Israel and Japan.
- Type C (ambivalent attachments) was most common in Israel, China and Japan. Sweden and the Netherlands had the lowest rate of ambivalent attachments.

As well as differences between cultures, van Ijzendoorn and Kroonenberg also found differences within cultures. In the two Japanese studies, one had no Type A babies, whereas the second had around 20 per cent, which is roughly similar to Ainsworth's original findings. Van Ijzendoorn and Kroonenberg noted overall that the intra-cultural variation (within cultures) was nearly one-and-a-half times the cross-cultural variation. This large variation within cultures demonstrates the common-sense point that it is an oversimplification to assume that all children are brought up in exactly the same way in a particular country or culture.

THINKING SCIENTIFICALLY: CROSS-CULTURAL RESEARCH

This is a substantial meta-analysis considering the attachment behaviours of a very large number of infants. A large sample size is needed in order to generalise findings to the rest of the population. However, over half (18) of the 32 studies were carried out in the US, reflecting the dominance by that country in research in this area. Twenty-seven of the studies were carried out in individualistic cultures, with only five taking place in collectivist cultures. This implies that the sample used may not be truly representative. Ainsworth's Strange Situation method for studying attachment was developed in the US and may be most suited to studying attachment in that country's type of culture. Goldberg (2002) argues that we can only make valid interpretations of the Strange Situation in cross-cultural studies if we understand the attitudes to child-rearing in that culture.

KEY POINTS

- The Strange Situation is a controlled observation consisting of a series of episodes lasting three minutes.
- In the Strange Situation, a baby's response to its mother leaving and returning is measured, along with the baby's response to a stranger.
- In Ainsworth's study, 70 per cent of babies showed a secure attachment pattern, with 30 per cent demonstrating insecure attachment types.
- Differences in attachment type can be explained by the sensitivity of the parent and the baby's temperament.
- Van Ijzendoorn and Kroonenberg carried out a meta-analysis of 32 Strange Situation studies in different cultures.
- Secure attachment types were the most common in all cultures.
- Avoidant attachment types were more common in West Germany and ambivalent attachments were more common in Japan and Israel.
- Variation within cultures was 1.5 times larger than variation between cultures.

The influence of early attachment on childhood and adult relationships including the role of an internal working model

Bowlby argued that the relationship between an infant and their mother figure provided the basis for later adult relationships. According to the attachment theory, the young child develops an internal working model (IWM) from their first relationship, which consists of a view of themselves as loveable or otherwise, a model of other people as basically trustworthy or not, and a model of the relationship between the two. Young children also develop characteristic attachment styles in their early relationships. Ainsworth divided attachment styles into three types using the 'Strange Situation' methodology – insecure avoidant (Type A), secure (Type B) and insecure ambivalent (Type C).

Research has taken place to establish whether these attachment types influence children's friendships, and whether they affect adolescent and adult relationships as Bowlby predicted. We will examine both of these threads of research to assess the extent to which relationships are affected, and limits to continuity.

Influence of early attachment on childhood relationships

According to attachment theory, the child who has a secure attachment style should be more confident in interactions with friends. Considerable evidence has supported this view: a 'secure' attachment in infancy is associated with a range of favourable outcomes in childhood, including closer friendships with peers and greater emotional and social competence in adolescence. Waters, Wippman and Sroufe (1979), Jacobson and Willie (1986), and Lieberman (1977) all found that children classified as 'secure' go on to be more socially skilled in their friendships than both insecurely attached types of children. Hartup et al. (1993) argues that children with a secure attachment type are more popular at nursery and engage more in social interactions with other children.

In contrast, insecurely attached children tend to be more reliant on teachers for interaction and emotional support (Sroufe and Fleeson, 1986). Lyons-Ruth, Alpern and Repacholi (1993) carried out a longitudinal study that suggested that infant attachment type at 18 months was the best predictor of problematic relationships with peers in five-year-olds. Type D (disorganized attachments) seemed to struggle most to make friends with their peers. These studies support the claim that secure attachments enable children to be competent at later friendships.

Veríssimo, Santos, Vaughn, Torres, Monteiro and Santos (2011) studied the impact of attachments with mothers and fathers on the formation and maintenance of friendships in a sample of preschool children aged between 29 and 38 months of age. Thirty-five mother–child and father–child pairs from two-parent families took part in the study. Attachments with both parents were assessed using separate observations in the child's home, which produced an attachment score. At age four, each child was assessed for the number of reciprocal friendships at nursery. The analysis showed a significant positive correlation between attachment security with fathers and the number of reciprocated friends. In fact, a secure attachment between child and father was a clear predictor of friendship regardless of the relationship between a pre-schooler and their mother. These findings imply that the quality of the interaction between child and father is important for later social competence, further emphasizing the importance of fathering.

Evidence also suggests that attachment style may influence adolescent relationships. Moore (1997) carried out a study using 100 adolescents aged 14 to 15 years old. She measured their attachment style using an interview and asked a close friend of each teenager to rate their behaviour for social acceptability. Moore found that secure teens were less likely to engage in risky sexual activities (i.e. unsafe sex) than their insecure counterparts. However, they were more likely to have had sex than those rated as insecure. Moore concluded that secure attachments can help to 'set up' adolescents to handle the transition to adult sexual relationships.

In another study, Feeney and Noller (1992) examined the link between attachments and relationship breakdown in university students. Those with avoidant attachments were (unsurprisingly) more likely to split up. However, they also found evidence for changes in attachment type when relationships changed from casual to committed, showing that attachment type is not completely fixed.

Influence of early attachment on adult relationships

What about the links between childhood attachments and adult relationships? Two methods used to assess the links are correlational studies (Hazan and Shaver, 1987) and longitudinal studies (Waters, Merrick, Treboux, Crowell and Albersheim, 2000).

Hazan and Shaver (1987)

Hazan and Shaver set out to address the question 'Is love in adulthood directly related to the attachment type as a child?' Their research involved a 'love quiz' in their local North American paper, the Rocky Mountain News, which asked people to write into the paper reporting their experiences of their childhood relationship with parents. Respondents were also asked which of these three descriptions applied to their feelings/experiences about romantic relationships:

- I am somewhat uncomfortable being close to others; I find it difficult to trust them completely; difficult to allow myself to depend on them. I am nervous when anyone gets too close, and often others want me to be more intimate than I feel comfortable being.
- I find it relatively easy to get close to others and am comfortable depending on them and having them depend on me. I don't worry about being abandoned or about someone getting too close to me.
- I find that others are reluctant to get as close as I would like. I often worry that my partner doesn't really love me or won't want to stay with me. I want to get very close to my partner and this sometimes scares people away.

Hazan and Shaver selected the first 630 of the responses for analysis. They found a relationship between childhood attachment type and adulthood attachment type. 'Secure' types expressed a belief in lasting love. They found others trustworthy and were confident that they were lovable. 'Anxious avoidant' types were more doubtful about the existence of love, believing that it did not happen in real life. They also felt that they did not need a happy relationship to get lots out of life. 'Anxious ambivalent' types fell in love easily and often but rarely found 'true love'. They felt insecure and experienced self-doubt in love. A replication of this method using 108 undergraduate students provided similar findings.

Research methods link

You can read more about self-report measures on page 18.

However, Hazan and Shaver's study used self-report measures to assess attachment style and relationships with parents. Adults are likely to produce responses that show them in a favourable light; hence such methods are subject to a 'social desirability bias'. This problem is further exacerbated by psychometric measurements, which use single items (such as the love quiz). These may overlap and be insufficient to distinguish between the different behaviours. When asked to recall memories of relationships with parents, these memories are likely to be 'fuzzy' and hard to describe. Although Hazan and Shaver identified a link between childhood and adult attachments, this was simply a correlation rather than a causal link.

In longitudinal studies, participants are tracked from infancy to adulthood and comparisons are made between their attachment styles at the two points. In contrast to Hazan and Shaver's findings, studies using this approach have yielded mixed results. Zimmerman et al. (2000) carried out a longitudinal study of 44 children in Germany. Their attachment type as children was initially assessed between 12 and 18 months of age by seeing how they responded to separation and to strangers, and they were reassessed at the age of 16 years using interviews focusing on their relationship with their parents. Zimmerman et al. found that childhood attachment type was not a good predictor of attachments in adolescence, and that life events often altered secure attachments to an insecure type in adulthood.

Zimmerman et al. (2000) and Waters, Merrick, Treboux, Crowell and Albersheim (2000)

A similar longitudinal study with a longer follow-up period was carried out by Waters, Merrick, Treboux, Crowell and Albersheim (2000), examining stability of attachment from infancy to early adulthood. A sample of 60 white, middle-class infants was assessed in Ainsworth's Strange Situation at 12 months of age. They were contacted 20 years later and 50 of the original 60 agreed to take part in an interview to assess their adult attachment style. Overall, just over 70 per cent of the sample received the same attachment classification in early adulthood, showing strong evidence for stability. Those who had changed attachment style had generally experienced a life event such as the loss of a parent, parental divorce or life-threatening illness of a parent or child. It was found that 44 per cent (8 of 18) of the infants whose mothers reported negative life events changed attachment classifications from infancy to early adulthood. Only 22 per cent (7 of 32) of the infants whose mothers reported no such events changed classification.

Rutter, Quinton and Hill (1999) found that change also occurred in the opposite direction in their study of a group of people who had experienced problematic relationships with their parents, but had gone on to achieve secure, stable and happy adult relationships, which they termed 'earned security'.

ATTACHMENT

Conclusion

Much of the research we have covered supports Bowlby's concept of 'internal working models'. Secure attachments in infancy are associated with positive peer relationships in childhood, greater emotional competence in adolescence, and longer-lasting relationships in adulthood. While there is strong support for continuity of attachment, there is also evidence that positive or negative environmental changes can improve or compromise attachment security respectively (Waters, Merrick, Treboux, Crowell and Albersheim, 2000 and Rutter, Quinton and Hill, 1999). Later relationship behaviour is best predicted by attachment measures that are combined from multiple points in time during childhood.

KEY POINTS

- Secure attachments in infancy are associated with favourable outcomes in childhood. Secure attachments with fathers seem to be most significant for social competence and popularity.
- Correlational studies such as Hazan and Shaver's show a link between childhood attachment type and adult attachment type.
- Longitudinal studies (e.g. Waters et al.) show that attachment types are likely to remain stable when the environment is relatively stable. However, life events such as parental death or divorce can alter attachment types, and earned security can occur when insecure childhood attachments are followed by secure adult relationships.

Bowlby's theory of maternal deprivation

Bowlby's maternal deprivation theory arose from his work as a psychiatrist in a child guidance clinic in London in the 1930s and 40s. During this time, Bowlby provided support and therapeutic help to many troubled children and teenagers. In 1944 he published a piece of research based on case notes from this work called 'Forty-Four Juvenile Thieves: Their Characters and Home Lives' (Bowlby, 1944). Many of the children referred to the child guidance clinic had a history of persistent offending and theft. Bowlby identified a subgroup who appeared to have little guilt, shame or remorse for their actions. He referred to this quality as 'affectionless psychopathy'. Through interviews with the children and their families, Bowlby established that some of this group had experienced early and prolonged separations from their mothers at a young age, often being hospitalised or put in foster care. A summary of Bowlby's data is shown in Table 3.4.

	Separated from mother	Not separated from mother	Total
Affectionless thieves	12	2	14
Other thieves	5	25	30
Total	17	27	44

Table 3.4

Bowlby interpreted the data as showing a link between maternal deprivation (i.e. separation from mother) and the development of affectionless psychopathy later in childhood. He viewed this as a causal link: removal of a young child from their mother caused later emotional difficulties. This was the basis of the maternal deprivation hypothesis, which made three claims:

- Maternal love was as necessary for a child's mental health and emotional development as vitamins were for physical health.
- Loss of the mother figure (i.e. maternal deprivation) during the first few years of life would lead to a child failing to thrive.
- Maternal deprivation would have a lasting effect on the child's emotional adjustment and lead to an inability to form bonds with other people. Today, we would refer to this as an attachment disorder.

Bowlby's ideas were widely accepted and he was commissioned by the World Health Organization (WHO) to write a report on the mental health of homeless children in post-war Europe. The report was translated into 14 languages and was published in 1951 as 'Maternal Care and Mental Health' by the WHO. Penguin Books published a second edition, entitled *Child Care and the Growth of Love,* in 1965.

THINKING SCIENTIFICALLY: DRAWING CONCLUSIONS FROM DATA

Rutter re-examined Bowlby's ideas in his book *Maternal Deprivation Reassessed* (Rutter, 1972). Whilst he accepted the view that early childhood experiences could have serious and lasting effects on children, Rutter noted that Bowlby had made claims about cause and effect that were not warranted given the nature of his data. Rutter pointed out that Bowlby had grouped together a wide variety of experiences under the general heading of 'maternal deprivation' such as hospitalisation, death of mother and family breakdown – all of which could have different effects on children. Rutter argued that an affectionless character was not associated with maternal loss (deprivation) but with lack of love – privation in many of Bowlby's samples. Rutter's own research examining 10- and 11-year-old children on the Isle of Wight indicated that antisocial behaviour was linked with broken homes, but the cause of this was stress and family discord, which often accompanied separation.

The effects of institutionalization

Bowlby's ideas were strongly shaped by the war in Europe. During the 1940s, many children were separated from their parents and the war led to large numbers of children spending some or all of their childhood in institutional care. Conditions in many institutions were poor: physical care was basic and there was little by way of emotional care, warmth or opportunity for attachment. Unsurprisingly, many studies of children raised in such conditions (e.g. Skeels and Dye, 1939 and Skodak and Skeels, 1945/1949) found that institutionally raised children showed permanent emotional and intellectual impairment, scoring lower on intelligence tests. However, subsequent studies of institutionalized children indicated that some of these effects were related to the very poor conditions and lack of stimulation in institutions at that time.

Tizard and Hodges (1984, 1989) examined the progress of a group of 65 children brought up in an institution until the age of four. Good physical care was provided and the environment was stimulating. The only deprivation experienced by the children was the lack of an ongoing secure attachment with an adult caregiver. The prevailing view at the time was that attachments with staff should be discouraged to prevent young children becoming distressed when staff left their jobs. For this reason, staff were discouraged from forming attachments with the children. By the time the children were two years old, they had had on average 24 different carers, and by the age of four, between 50 and 70 carers.

Disinhibited attachments

At the age of two, the institutionalized children showed a range of unusual attachment behaviours. Rather than showing fear of strangers, they would run to any adult who entered the room and demand their attention in an indiscriminate manner. They would also cry when the adult left, despite the fact that they had no attachment with them. These behaviours are characteristic of children raised in institutions and are part of a behaviour pattern known as 'disinhibited attachment'. Rutter (2006) explained this behaviour pattern as an adaptation to the lack of a single caregiver in institutions. When adults are rarely available to children, they become indiscriminately friendly and warm to anyone, unlike normally attached children of the same age.

When the children were around four years old, 25 were returned or 'restored' to their biological parents, who had become able to care for them once again; 33 children were adopted into new 'forever' families; the remaining seven continued in the care system, being fostered for some periods of time and returning to the children's home at others. This constituted a natural experiment, as these events occurred without researcher intervention. Place of rearing after the age of four was the naturally occurring independent variable with three conditions: biological family, adoptive family and institutional care.

Tizard and Hodges visited the children with their families when the children were eight, and at 16 the children took part in interviews with a parent or care worker present. Tizard and Hodges also asked for permission to contact the teenagers' schools and, if this was given, teachers and same-sex peers completed an assessment via a questionnaire to assess their attachment behaviour – the dependent variable.

Family relationships

Tizard and Hodges found that almost all of the adoptees (20 out of 21) and some of the restored children (6 out of 13) formed close attachments to their parents by the age of eight. This situation was similar at age 16, with more adoptees than restored children being close to their parents. This may have been due to the considerable effort made by adoptive families to form strong attachments with their children.

	Close attachment at age 8	Rejecting or hostile	Close attachment at age 16	Rejecting or hostile
Adopted children	20/21	1/21	17/21	4/21
Restored children	6/13	7/13	5/9	4/9

Table 3.5

In terms of relationships with peers and siblings, the restored group had worse relationships with their siblings than adoptees. However, all three groups raised in the institution had difficulties with peer relationships and were less likely to belong to a 'crowd' at school. Teachers rated them as more likely to seek attention from adults, and members of the restored group were more argumentative.

Tizard and Hodges concluded that those who were adopted seemed to develop good family relationships. In contrast, the restored group continued to experience some problems and difficulties in their family relationships, notably with siblings. Both groups showed similar difficulties in relationships with peers. They continued to seem oriented to please adults but less able to form relationships with those outside the family.

Quality of care

The effects of institutionalization depend to a large extent on the quality of emotional care provided in an institution. Dontas et al. (1985) carried out two studies on babies in a Greek orphanage with a very different policy to that studied by Tizard and Hodges. Each baby was allocated a member of staff to care specifically for them and the staff was actively encouraged to form strong emotional bonds with the infants. In the first study, Dontas observed 15 babies aged seven to nine months old in the two-week adjustment period after they had been adopted. Despite having formed an attachment with their favourite nurse in the institution, the babies began to form new attachments with their adoptive parents and adjusted well. A second study focused on peer relationships in institution-raised babies. Sixteen infants aged between five and twelve months were observed playing with familiar and unfamiliar peers of a similar age. Their play showed none of the apparent effects of institutionalization that had previously been noted in Tizard and Hodges's study, leading Dontas to conclude that the negative effects of institutionalization were removed when babies had the opportunity to form close attachments in institutions. Dontas' research shows how important it is for children in institutions to be able to develop attachments to staff between six and eight months of age.

EXAMPLE EXAM QUESTION

Kati was taken into care at 18 months as her mother could not cope with her and often left Kati at home alone. After living in three foster homes, Kati was adopted at the age of five. She has a close attachment to her adoptive parents, but struggles to make friends at school. Kati is sometimes aggressive towards other children.

Discuss Bowlby's maternal deprivation theory. Refer to Kati's experiences as part of your discussion. [12 marks]

Exam hint

You can draw on Bowlby's monotropic theory and the ideas of a critical period in your answer.

Romanian orphan studies

The civil war in Romania led to thousands of children being orphaned, and many of them were raised in institutions in which the conditions were extremely poor. Film coverage indicates that these babies received minimum physical care, often being fed with bottles propped up in their cots. Due to the impoverished nature of the environment and the few staff, there was minimal time for interaction or play and most of the babies spent all day alone in their cots.

Tizard and Hodges's study pointed to an unusual pattern of behaviour in children raised without attachments in institutions. This disinhibited attachment behaviour pattern is examined by Rutter et al. (2007) in their longitudinal study of Romanian orphans adopted by UK families.

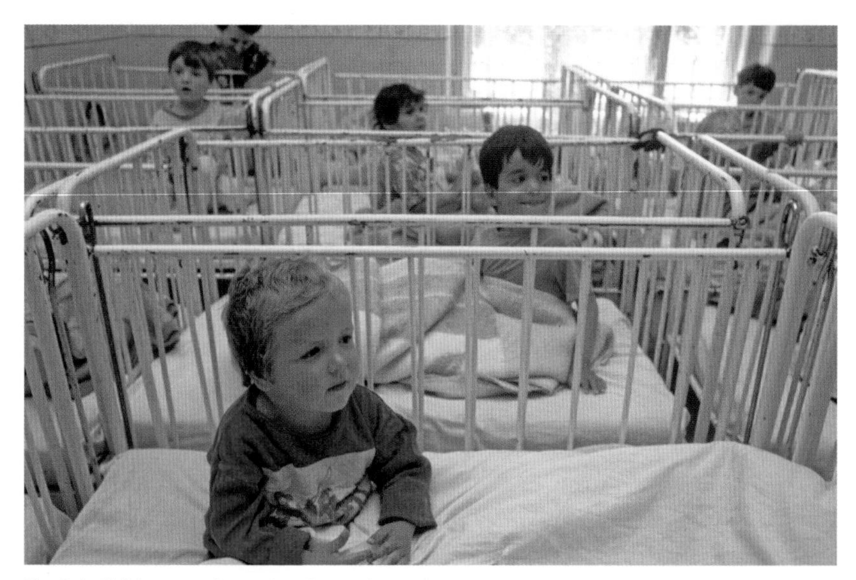

Fig. 3.9 Children growing up in a Romanian orphanage

KEY STUDY: RUTTER ET AL. (2007)

Rutter et al. (2007) are carrying out an ongoing longitudinal study, comparing Romanian orphans who were adopted by UK families with UK-born adoptees who were placed with families before they were six months of age. The Romanian adoptees entered the orphanage as small babies of between one and two weeks old. Conditions in the institutions were very poor. Fifty-eight babies (27 girls and 31 boys) were adopted before they were six months old and 59 (33 girls and 26 boys) were adopted between six and 24 months of age. Forty-eight babies (31 girls and 17 boys) were classed as late-placed adoptees (between two and four years of age). These formed the three conditions of the naturally occurring independent variable. At the time of adoption, over half of the Romanian children showed evidence of severe malnourishment. They were in the bottom third of the population for weight and head size.

Some of these children were followed up at ages four, six and eleven years, using a range of measures including:

- Parental reports at age four to six, focusing on the child's willingness to go off with strangers.
- A home observation at age six measuring the extent to which children made inappropriate contact with the researcher (e.g. trying to sit on knee, cuddle up or hold the researchers hand).
- Assessment of peer relations at age 11 via teacher and parent reports.

Rutter et al. found further evidence of disinhibited attachment at age six, which they defined as 'a pervasive pattern of attention-seeking behaviours with a relative lack of selectivity in social relationships'. As Table 3.6 shows, disinhibited behaviour was most common in the late adopted Romanian group, with over one-quarter (26.1 per cent) showing 'marked' disinhibited attachment behaviours. The behaviour pattern was extremely rare in UK adoptees (3.8 per cent) and early-adopted children (8.9 per cent). This suggests that disinhibited attachments are more likely in children who have experienced longer periods in institutions.

	No disinhibition	Mild disinhibition	Marked disinhibition
UK adoptees	21 (40.4%)	29 (55.8%)	2 (3.8%)
Romanian adopted ≤ 6 months	24 (53.3%)	17 (37.8%)	4 (8.9%)
Romanian – adopted 6–24 months	26 (29.5%)	39 (44.3%)	23 (26.1%)

Table 3.6 Disinhibited attachments in Romanian and UK adoptees aged six years

In 2007, some of these children were followed up at age 11. Rutter found that the disinhibited behaviour pattern had persisted in many adoptees. Of the 83 Romanian children showing mild or marked disinhibited attachment at age six, 45 (54 per cent) of these still showed this five years later. While this indicates a drop in the number of children showing this behaviour pattern at age 11, it is still well over half. Even more worryingly, Rutter found that many of the children showing disinhibited attachments were receiving help from either special educational and/or mental health services.

THINKING SCIENTIFICALLY: DIFFICULTIES IN ESTABLISHING CAUSE AND EFFECT

Rutter's study uses a range of age appropriate measurements to assess the children's behaviour, including semi-structured interviews, observations and teacher/peer reports. The use of different methods provides a rich and detailed picture of the adoptees functioning in different areas of their social world. However, Rutter et al. acknowledge that it has been difficult to obtain information about the quality of care in many of the institutions in Romania, making it difficult to assess the extent of privation in the early environments of the children in the study.

As with Tizard and Hodges's study, participants dropping out is an issue in any longitudinal research. Those who continue to participate in follow-up research may be more likely to feel positive about the adoption process and outcome. Those who drop out may have responded less positively, leading to incomplete data.

EXAMPLE EXAM QUESTION

What does research show about the effects of institutionalization on young children? (6 marks)

Exam hint

This question asks you to focus on findings and conclusions of research into institutionalization. You should only provide enough methodological detail in your answer to put into context the findings of the studies you cover. **See page 181 for a sample answer and examiner feedback.**

ACTIVITY 3.3

Locate and examine some of the footage from news programmes about conditions in Romanian orphanages in the 1990s.

KEY POINTS

- Bowlby's maternal deprivation hypothesis arose from his work in a child guidance clinic.
- Bowlby identified an association between separation from the mother and affectionless psychopathy in his 1944 study of 44 juvenile thieves.
- The maternal deprivation hypothesis predicts that a child who is deprived of their mother during the first three years of life will suffer lasting effects in their emotional development.
- Rutter (1972) argues that the experiences which were classified as maternal deprivation by Bowlby were diverse and often constituted privation (lack of love) rather than loss of the mother.
- The emotional effects seen in Bowlby's sample may have come from trauma surrounding loss of the mother.
- Rutter's Romanian orphan studies are tracking the progress of a group of adoptees who spent their early lives in impoverished institutions.
- Disinhibited attachments are more common in children who spent longer in institutions.

PRACTICAL ACTIVITY

Studying young children poses serious ethical questions for the researcher. For this reason, the activities in this section of the course require you to carry out interviews or questionnaires with adults, rather than to observe young children.

If you have contact with someone who has a preschool child, devise and carry out a short interview asking them about how their child responds to a number of different situations involving short separations, such as being left with a babysitter or at playgroup. You will need to think about what type of interview to use as well as the number and types of questions (open/closed) to use.

You can consider how to analyse the qualitative data produced by interview material. You may also like to think about devising a rating scale similar to that used by Schaffer and Emerson (1964) (see page 153) for parents to rate their child's responses to separation. You can then go on to discuss the relative advantages and disadvantages of quantitative and qualitative data in this type of research.

Reflect on this experience of collecting data and consider the strengths and weaknesses of interviews, the reliability and validity of the data, and the relative advantages and disadvantages of quantitative and qualitative data in this type of research.

You could go on to do a more rigorous investigation of the stages in the development of attachment suggested by Schaffer and Emerson. Devise a short interview schedule as above, but this time ensure the questions will give you data about the child's responses to separation at different ages from 0–12 months.

- Work as a group so that you can collect data about a number of children.
- Sample people whose children are just over one year old so that you would expect the interviewee to be able to recall their baby's response to separation at different ages.
- Pool the data from your group's interviews.
- Consider how to analyse and present the qualitative and quantitative interview material, and whether the interview data supports or challenges Schaffer and Emerson's findings about the age and/or sequence of development of attachment behaviour.

Exam focus

Read through the following example exam question, example student answer, and examiner comments. Then, have a go at answering the question yourself!

EXAMPLE EXAM QUESTION, TAKEN FROM PAGE 179

What does research show about the effects of institutionalization on young children? [6 marks]

Hannah's answer

Institutionalization occurs when young children are raised in an institution such as a children's home or, in some countries, an orphanage. Lots of children were raised in orphanages following the civil war in Romania and Rutter has studied these children to see the effects of institutionalization.

Examiner comment: There is lots of preamble here; this could be shortened, as the focus of the question is on the **effects** of research.

One effect is called disinhibited attachment. Children raised in institutions do not show the normal fear of strangers that other toddlers show. They are indiscriminately friendly (i.e. climbing on people's knees) and sometimes show inappropriate behaviour.

Examiner comment: One effect is identified here, with reference to research; a reasonable explanation of disinhibited attachment.

Tizard carried out another study in a children's home. All the children were in the institution until they were four and then some were restored, some adopted, and others stayed in the home. Children who were adopted did best of all, forming close attachments with their new parents. Children who were restored to their biological families did less well, and only about half had close attachments – perhaps the problems that led to them going into the children's home were still in the family. One notable finding was that all children who had spent time in an institution struggled with friendships and were less likely to have a best friend or belong to a gang.

Examiner comment: There is just enough detail here about method to contextualize the findings.

Examiner comment: It would be good to see some detailed figures in here about how many children formed close attachments.

Examiner comment: Hannah identifies three effects of institutionalization on young children: disinhibited attachments, attachments to parents, and effects on peer relationships. The answer is relevant and focused, but some of the findings could be stated with more precision. This is a Level 3 response which is mostly clear and effective. **5/6 marks**.

ATTACHMENT

Part 1: Introductory topics in Psychology

Chapter 4: Psychopathology

Introduction

When someone's behaviour is considered 'abnormal' it is generally because their behaviour noticeably differs from the behaviour expected by the society in which it occurs. Every society has an idea of what constitutes abnormal behaviour, and this idea of what is considered normal and abnormal is constantly changing. Over time, our understanding about the nature and causes of mental illness and what should be done about it has radically changed. Western culture, for example, has moved away from attributing abnormality to supernatural forces and witchcraft. Nowadays, the predominant thinking is that abnormal behaviour reflects some underlying **psychopathology** (psycho = mind, pathology = sickness). Those with interests in mental health issues might differ considerably in how they view the nature and causes of abnormal behaviour (for example, some may see abnormal behaviour as a disturbance in thinking, while others may see it as a symptom of underlying biological disturbance). However, views are generally confined to a rational medical model of abnormality, i.e. that mental illnesses can be addressed in much the same way as physical illnesses.

There are many different forms of psychopathology, and over many years a great deal of effort has been put into devising ways of describing and categorizing them. This has resulted in two widely accepted systems for categorizing abnormal behaviour: the Diagnostic and Statistical Manual of Mental Disorders (or DSM), and the International Classification of Disorders (or ICD). These systems are regularly updated to take into account changes in the way we think about abnormality and our understanding of the causes of such behaviour. Accurate use of a standard system allows a greater level of agreement (i.e. reliability) in the diagnosis and planning of treatment, enables more accurate record-keeping in the care of sufferers, and helps research into the various psychopathologies.

In this chapter we will be looking at the various ways that behaviour might be defined as abnormal. We will also be looking in some detail at a several psychopathologies in particular. This will include a review of their possible causes and also some of the common therapies available for each psychopathology.

What is covered in Psychopathology?

Definitions of abnormality

There is no one way of defining abnormality. Views alter over time, change in different contexts, and vary considerably across cultures. Ultimately, what constitutes normal and abnormal behaviour is a judgement. There are a number of ways in which this judgement may be made or influenced, and we will consider four of these: deviation from social norms, failure to function adequately, statistical infrequency, and deviation from ideal mental health.

Key term

Deviation from social norms: behaviour that is abnormal violates social rules.

Deviation from social norms

A norm is an expected form of behaviour. All societies have them; they are an important part of the 'glue' that holds societies together. If everyone follows these rules then interactions between people become regulated and easier, and social living feels altogether more safe and predictable. Some of these norms are explicit, written norms. These norms meet the fundamental needs of society, and breaking them is usually punishable by law. For example, respect for human life and the property of others are powerful norms enforced in the UK by a strong legal system.

Many norms, however, are unwritten rules; simple expectations that guide generally accepted behaviour. While there is some flexibility in this type of norm, nonetheless there is a strong expectation that they are observed. For example, in the Western World it is a norm that we eat with a knife and fork. This is a flexible norm, however, since while in company it might be considered polite to use utensils to eat a pizza, in private where there is less pressure to follow this norm we might just use our hands. There are many such norms, most of them so accepted and normalized that they go unquestioned or unnoticed. That is, until they are broken. Consider the example of public transport – you are the only passenger on an otherwise empty bus, but a person gets on and sits right next to you. How would this make you feel? To take another example, that of the great British tradition of queuing: how would you feel if you had been waiting for a while in a queue and someone just strolled along and joined the queue ahead of you? There are no laws against these two behaviours, but nevertheless there is a clear feeling that some rule has been broken.

One way of defining a behaviour as abnormal is to consider how it breaks (or deviates from) these social norms. Although sometimes it is clear when a behaviour is abnormal because it breaks social norms (for example, we should not be hearing and responding to strange voices in our head), at other times it is far from obvious that a behaviour is abnormal. There are clear limitations with this approach.

Limitations of the definition of deviation from social norms

By their very definition, social norms are specific to a particular culture, so that behaviour considered abnormal in one society may not be seen as abnormal in another. For example, in the UK dogs are held in high regard as pets and beloved companions. If someone killed and ate a dog they would probably risk being labelled as abnormal by most people, as this behaviour goes against the norms of British society. However, dogs in China are also seen as food and are widely eaten.

Social norms are not constant, but vary over time. This means that using this approach to defining abnormality is very much era-dependent – behaviours that are considered abnormal now may not be considered abnormal in the future. For example, homosexuality was once considered abnormal behaviour because it broke the social norms of the day. Attitudes have changed considerably now and homosexuality is no longer seen as a psychopathology. (It is interesting to note that attitudes in this regard change slowly – it was not until the 1990s that homosexuality was removed from DSM as a mental disorder.)

Not all behaviours that break social norms are a sign of psychopathology. Many people who do not conform to social norms are not abnormal but are expressing individualism – their attitudes and behaviours single them out as being distinctly different from the society they have difficulty fitting into. These individuals are often labelled 'eccentric' rather than 'abnormal', though the dividing line between abnormal and eccentric is thin and open to interpretation. It is also the case that breaking social norms can be seen as an indication of abnormality. For example, the behaviour of the early suffragettes broke social norms, resulting in social rejection and frequent prison sentences. Ultimately, however, the behaviour of these individuals led to women having the right to vote.

Fig. 4.1 William Archibald Spooner worked at Oxford University for 60 years. People would attend his lectures in the hope of hearing him mix up his word sounds, and his eccentric speech eventually gave the dictionary a new term: spoonerism. A mery eccentric van!

EXAMPLE EXAM QUESTION

Outline the deviation from social norms definition of abnormality. [3 marks]

Exam hint

When you are asked to 'outline' something it means you only have to give a brief account. Even though there are 'only' 3 marks available it is still possible to lose marks due to lack of clarity. Using an example in your answer is often a good way of demonstrating understanding, so don't be afraid to do this.

Failure to function adequately

Key term

Failure to function adequately: abnormality is the failure to cope with the demands of day-to-day life.

Everyday life brings with it collections of demands and mundane requirements. For example, the majority of adults need to earn an income. This requires them to get up in the morning, get dressed, and go to work. Relationships with others have to be managed and their emotional and other needs met. When someone's behaviour suggests that they cannot cope with these everyday demands then they run the risk of being labelled abnormal – they are failing to function adequately. This is often a clear sign of psychopathology, that something is wrong. Someone who is depressed, for example, may fail to get up in the morning, and have difficulties in their relationships with family and friends. Rosenhan and Seligman (1989) have suggested the following features of behaviour that indicate whether or not a person is **failing to function adequately**.

- **Observer discomfort:** another's behaviour causes discomfort and distress to the observer.
- **Unpredictability:** we rely on the behaviour of people around us being predictable, so when behaviour appears unpredictable and uncontrolled it leads us to think that there is something wrong.
- **Irrationality:** we can usually interpret the behaviour of others as being rational, but sometimes behaviours look irrational and hard to understand.
- **Maladaptiveness:** when a behaviour is maladaptive it hinders the ability of a person to adjust to a particular situation. For example, if someone has very extreme shyness, this behaviour might be maladaptive in situations which require them to interact effectively with other people.
- **Personal suffering and distress:** when failure to cope with everyday life causes personal distress/suffering to the individual themselves.

Limitations of definition of failure to function adequately

Sometimes behaviour that looks as though a person is failing to function adequately might make more sense when one considers its context. For example, starving oneself appears on the face of it to tick all the boxes – it is unpredictable, irrational, maladaptive and involves suffering. However, in the context of non-violent political protest it would not be seen as abnormal behaviour.

Another issue with this approach is that abnormality is not always associated with failure to function adequately. People often function adequately with anxiety and depression, and many individuals with other mental health issues can appear to lead perfectly normal lives most of the time. To give an extreme example, Harold Shipman was one of the most prolific serial killers in history, probably responsible for about 250 deaths and possibly many more. However, many people who knew him, including his former patients, described him as a good and caring family doctor.

Patterns of behaviour vary from culture to culture, therefore what 'failing to function adequately' actually is can look very different. What might be seen as a failure to function in one culture could be viewed as functioning adequately in another. For example, a woman who always covers up her face when she goes out into a public place might seem to fit several of Rosenhan and Seligman's criteria for abnormality, but when a cultural context is added the behaviour can be seen as reflecting aspects of what many people consider normal religious and cultural practice.

The failure to function adequately approach does not provide an objective indication of abnormality. What Rosenhan and Seligman propose is not a scale or measuring tool, it is a set of criteria for recognizing features of abnormality. Judging the extent to which a feature indicates abnormality is largely subjective, based on the opinion and understanding of the observer. For example, personal suffering and distress is something normally associated with the grief of bereavement, but it is much less clear when this suffering and distress becomes an abnormal bereavement reaction.

Statistical infrequency

This approach defines abnormality as behaviour that deviates from the norm, or average. The idea behind this approach is that the less frequently a behaviour occurs in people, the more likely it is to be abnormal. The difference between normal and abnormal then is one of quantity rather than quality – the majority of people are normal with a minority abnormal. The judgement of whether a behaviour is statistically frequent or infrequent is based on the mathematical principle of the normal distribution.

It so happens that, when measured and plotted on a graph, most human characteristics fall within a normal distribution.

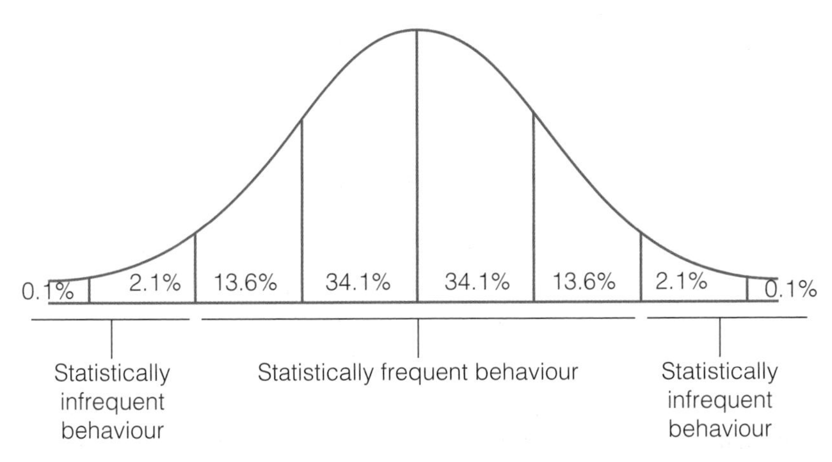

Fig. 4.2 A normal distribution curve showing that any behaviour occurring in less than about four per cent of the population is statistically rare and therefore abnormal

The majority of characteristics would cluster around the middle of this graph. Any characteristic in this region would be considered statistically common. A minority of characteristics would be out at the edges, or tails, making them statistically rare and therefore a **deviation from statistical norms**.

Key term

Deviation from statistical norms: behaviour that deviates from the majority or statistical average is abnormal.

Exam hint

It is important to read all of the question before you begin your answer. It would be unwise to explain a definition in (a) which you then struggle to evaluate in (b).

EXAMPLE EXAM QUESTION

One definition of abnormality is deviation from statistical norms.

(a) Identify and explain one other definition of abnormality. [3 marks]
(b) Evaluate the definition of abnormality that you identified in your answer to (a). [4 marks]

Limitations of the definition of statistical infrequency

This definition is positive in that it offers the prospect of clear guidelines for identifying behaviours as normal or abnormal. This introduces an element of objectivity into the process so that different mental health care workers can all view the same kind of behaviour in the same kind of way.

However, one significant limitation of this definition lies in the general assumption that anyone who differs significantly from the average is technically 'abnormal'. It does not take into account the desirability of behaviour. For example, highly intelligent people are statistically rare and are thus, according to this definition, abnormal.

Behaviours that were statistically rare years ago may not be statistically rare now, and vice versa. What this suggests is that statistical definitions run a risk of being era-dependant by adopting a statistical norm that could be outdated.

There are issues of cultural relativity with this definition in that cultures differ in terms of what they consider normal behaviour. For example, it would be very unusual in British culture for someone to take an extended rest period during the working day. In other cultures, however, this is very common.

The statistical approach requires a decision about the point at which a behaviour becomes statistically abnormal. For example, it is not at all clear at which point energetic and excitable behaviour from a child becomes a 'problem' behaviour requiring specialist intervention. This leaves the definition open to criticism, for instance for its apparent arbitrariness or potential for interference from political and social interests.

Deviation from ideal mental health

This approach is different to the preceding ones in that it does not try directly to define abnormality. Instead, it attempts to define an **ideal state of mental health**, so that abnormality is defined by the absence of features characterizing ideal mental health. One of the first attempts to identify the features of ideal mental health came from Jahoda in 1958, who listed the following characteristics:

- **Positive attitude towards self:** an individual should be in touch with their own identity and feelings.

Key term

Ideal mental health: abnormality is the failure to meet the criteria for psychological well-being.

- **Self-actualization:** individuals should be focused on the future and their own personal growth and development.
- **Resistance to stress:** individuals should be able to resist the effects of stress by having effective coping strategies.
- **Autonomy:** individuals should be independent and self-reliant.
- **Accurate perception of reality:** individuals should have an accurate and realistic view of the world.
- **Environmental mastery:** individuals should be flexible and adaptable in order to meet the demands of everyday life.

EXAMPLE EXAM QUESTION

The deviation from ideal mental health definition of abnormality suggests that failing to meet certain criteria indicates abnormality.

(a) Give two other criteria for ideal mental health. [2 marks]

(b) Outline two limitations of the deviation from ideal mental health definition of abnormality. [4 marks]

Exam hint

Look at the marks available and adjust what you write accordingly. Part (a) is clearly going to give one mark for each criteria, so there is no need to go into any kind of description. Given that part (b) is only offering four marks for two things, you are not expected to write a great deal here either.

Limitations of the definition of ideal mental health

The definition has value in its positive approach to defining normality. Rather than looking for things that are wrong about an individual, it provides a set of standards for normality that can be used for self-improvement.

Jahoda's ideas about ideal mental health are rooted in a Western view of the value of personal growth and development. Many of the concepts, such as autonomy and self-actualization, would not be recognized as aspects of ideal mental health in many cultures.

It is very difficult for most people to meet all the criteria set down by Jahoda for ideal mental health. As a result, under this definition the majority of us are abnormal. This is clearly not the case, suggesting that these conditions for ideal mental health are a little too stringent. It might be more useful to consider these characteristics as things we should be striving for rather than things that we must have achieved.

KEY POINTS

- 'Abnormal behaviour' is a term used to describe behaviour that is in some way psychopathological. There are a number of ways of deciding whether behaviour is abnormal, though no one approach by itself could be accurately used to define behaviour as abnormal.
- The deviation from social norms definition of abnormality says that behaviour is abnormal when it breaks accepted social rules. There are problems with this definition however, as social norms change over time and across contexts.
- The failure to function adequately definition of abnormality says that behaviour is abnormal when it has one or more features that make it look as though a person is struggling with the demands of everyday life. There are problems with this definition however, for instance abnormality is not always characterized by a failure to function.

- The statistical infrequency definition says that behaviour is abnormal when it is statistically rare. There are problems with this however, for instance not all statistically rare behaviours are abnormal or undesirable.
- The deviation from ideal mental health definition says that anyone not meeting the criteria for healthy mental functioning is abnormal. There are problems with this definition however, for instance it is difficult for most people to meet the full criteria, meaning that the majority of people could be labelled abnormal.

Phobias

Characteristics of phobias

Key term

Phobia: an irrational fearful anxiety response to a specific object or situation.

A **phobia** is a disorder in which a fearful anxiety occurs in response to specific objects or situations. Although it may be acceptable, and sometimes even sensible, to show a fear reaction in a threatening situation, the phobic person shows a marked and persistent fear out of all proportion to the actual danger posed by the situation. The sufferer recognizes that this reaction is beyond voluntary control and is unreasonable and excessive, and can only be endured with extreme anxiety or stress. Psychologically, symptoms may include feelings of restlessness and dread, difficulty with concentration, and irritability. Physical symptoms include shortness of breath, nausea, shaking/trembling, headaches and palpitations, and muscle tension. These symptoms are so unpleasant that sufferers attempt to avoid the object/situation. These avoidance behaviours can significantly interfere with normal routines. Indeed, much of their behaviour involves dealing with the unpleasant feelings caused by anticipating these symptoms, further affecting normal daily life.

Approximately five to ten per cent of people in the UK have some form of phobia, probably making it the single most common mental disorder. The rates are likely to be much higher than this, however, since many people cope with their problem and do not report it. There are three types of phobia: specific phobia, social phobia, and agoraphobia (see Table 4.1).

Exam hint

There is a lot you could say here and the temptation will be to write a longer answer than is required. Remember, you don't want to be wasting time in the exam, but investing it wisely. With just four marks available, select the key features that best demonstrate your understanding. Likewise, you won't get four marks for simply saying that phobia is a fear!

EXAMPLE EXAM QUESTION

Briefly outline what is meant by phobia. [4 marks]

Type of phobia	Description
Specific phobia	Sufferers are anxious in the presence of a particular object or specific situation. There are animal types (e.g. rats and spiders), natural environment types (e.g. heights, water), blood-injection types (e.g. blood, syringes), situational types (e.g. planes, lifts), and 'other types' (those that do not fit into the other types, such as choking, clowns). This is the most common category of phobia.
Social phobia	Sufferers experience inappropriate anxiety in social situations (e.g. restaurants, meetings) and even thinking about them causes anxiety. This results in avoidance of these situations, which can have a detrimental effect on their quality of life. Estimated to occur in three to seven per cent of the population, they usually begin in adolescence and often have no obvious triggering reason.
Agoraphobia	Sufferers are anxious when they are in a situation that they cannot easily leave, such as when they are in open spaces or in a crowd. They therefore avoid these situations and feel very anxious when anticipating them. Most cases begin in the early or mid-twenties and the first episode typically occurs without warning in a public place (e.g. a supermarket queue, on a bus, etc.). The individual experiences extreme anxiety, feels faint and has palpitations, which rapidly recede when they return home. The sequence of anxiety and avoidance leads to an increasing habit of avoidance of public places, resulting in a significant deterioration in quality of life. This is the least common category of phobia.

Table 4.1 Types of phobia

Some examples of phobias

Fur – doraphobia
Flowers – anthophobia
Germs – spermophobia
Horses – hippophobia
Spiders – arachnophobia
Snow – chionophobia
Insect stings – cnidophobia
Crowds – ochlophobia
Beards – pogonophobia
Dolls – pediophobia

Behavioural explanations of phobias

The behavioural approach to explaining phobias proposes that phobias are acquired through classical conditioning and maintained through operant conditioning. This is sometimes referred to as the **two-process model**.

Phobias are acquired by associating a neutral stimulus with a fear response. The first attempt to explain this process in terms of classical conditioning was by Watson and Rayner in 1920 when they conditioned Little Albert, a young baby, to fear a white rat.

Little Albert was shown a white rat which was a neutral stimulus – it produced no fear response in him. The researchers then paired showing Albert the rat with a loud noise (which naturally brings about a fear response). After several pairings of the noise and rat, when shown the rat without the noise Albert showed a fear response. Then, whenever Albert was shown the rat, he showed a fear response that he had not shown prior to conditioning – he had, in effect, learned to be afraid of rats.

Key term

The two-process model: the theory that phobias are acquired through classical conditioning and maintained through operant conditioning.

Link

You can read more about the behaviourist approach in the *Approaches to Psychology* chapter on page 221. This includes more detail about classical and operant conditioning theories.

Link

You can read more about Little Albert in the *Approaches to Psychology* chapter on page 223.

Figure 4.3 shows the acquisition of Little Albert's phobia of rats through classical conditioning. Something that does not bring about a fear response (a neutral stimulus, such as a rat) is paired with something that does bring about a fear response (such as a loud noise). This association causes the neutral stimulus to become a conditioned stimulus, bringing about the fear response (the rat now becomes a source of fear).

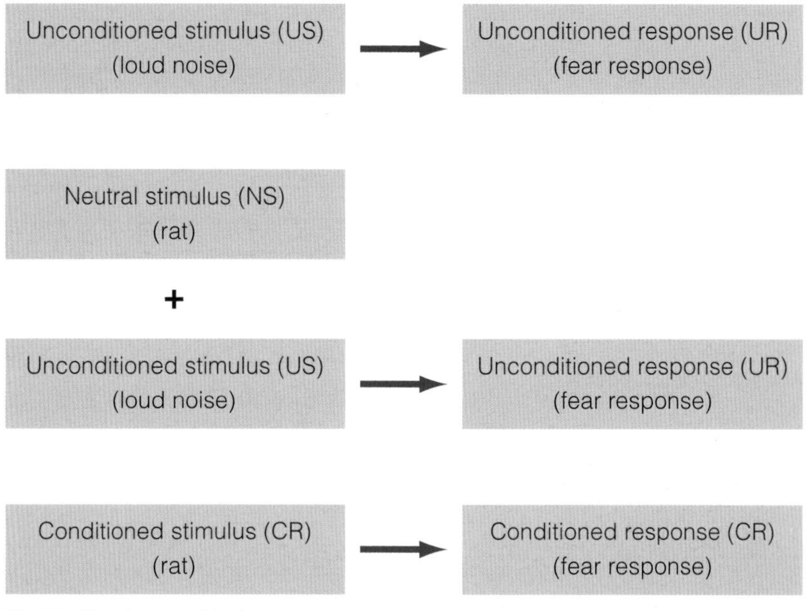

Fig. 4.3 Classical conditioning

Operant conditioning serves to maintain the phobia once it has developed. The phobic response is an unpleasant one, and escape from the object or situation causing the fear reduces these unpleasant feelings. This reduction in anxiety due to escape is rewarding, which means that anxiety reduction acts like a negative reinforcement. One result of this is that the likelihood of avoiding the object/situation in future is increased, because avoiding fear-inducing objects or situations has been rewarded by a reduction in anxiety, so now avoiding those situations also becomes rewarding.

It appears that we more readily acquire phobias to some objects/situations than to others. According to Seligman, it would have been beneficial to the survival of our ancestors to have a fear of potentially dangerous things in our environment, such as snakes and spiders. He suggested therefore that we are now biologically 'prepared' to react anxiously to things that were threatening to our prehistoric ancestors and, due to conditioning processes, are more likely to develop phobias to these kinds of stimuli. This seems to be borne out in the observation that the vast majority of phobias appear to be related to things that might once have threatened our survival, for example snakes, spiders, heights, dead things, and the dark. Seligman's preparedness theory also helps explain why there is often no clear conditioning event which has led to a phobia – we don't need much of an 'event' to develop a phobia of something that we are biologically prepared to be anxious of.

KEY STUDY: CONDITIONING A PHOBIA

Ohman et al. (1975) presented participants with various stimuli, classified as either fear relevant (e.g. images of spiders and snakes) or fear irrelevant (e.g. images of flowers and mushrooms), paired with a brief uncomfortable electric shock. Later, they measured anxiety levels in participants when they were again shown the images without the electric shock.

They found that fewer electric shocks were needed to condition an anxiety response to fear relevant than fear irrelevant stimuli. They also found that while learned responses to the fear irrelevant stimuli extinguished (disappeared), they persisted with the fear relevant stimuli. The results suggest that people are more likely to learn fear responses to some stimuli than others, much as predicted by Seligman's preparedness theory. Ohman et al. also suggest that because we have a built-in propensity to fear some things, phobias of such things are likely to be more resistant to treatment resulting in permanent cure.

THINKING SCIENTIFICALLY: ETHICAL ISSUES

The Ohman et al. study raises interesting ethical issues. Although the shocks were not dangerous and were individualized for discomfort rather than pain, participants were still subjected to a stressful experience. Also, none of the participants had phobic reactions before the study but it is possible that the conditioning experience might have triggered an anxiety response to stimuli lasting beyond the study. Even though the participants were all volunteers, some psychologists argue that, even with full informed consent, the costs of such procedures outweigh any possible benefits from the findings.

Evaluation of behavioural explanations of phobia

The study on Little Albert by Watson and Rayner (1920) provides support for the theory that fears are learned by association through classical conditioning. Many other studies have also demonstrated that a fear response can be conditioned. For example, Bandura and Rosenthal (1966) had participants observe a confederate receive an electric shock every time a buzzer sounded. In response to the buzzer, the confederate pretended to show a fear response by reacting to pain, twitching and yelling. Having observed this several times, the participants now too began to show a fear reaction in response to the buzzer. This is an example of what Bandura and Rosenthal called 'vicarious classical conditioning', which is where a conditioned emotional response can be acquired by observing other people's fearful reactions. There is plenty of anecdotal evidence to support the idea that we readily learn phobias through observing other people's phobic reactions. For example, many phobic sufferers point to particular instances in childhood where they experienced a parent reacting fearfully to the object/situation that they now have a fear of.

Research methods link

For more about ethics and research, see pages 35–38.

The theory predicts that phobic individuals would have experienced a triggering event at some point in their past – a moment in which a fear response was associated with the now phobic object/situation. This is supported by DiNardo et al. (1988), who found that over 60 per cent of people with a fear of dogs (cynophobia) could relate their fear to a particular frightening experience. Also, Munjack (1984) found that half of people with a driving phobia could relate their phobia to a frightening or traumatic experience in a car, such as an accident.

While it is possible to see that some people do indeed develop a phobia after an identifiable fearful incident, not all people do. In the DiNardo et al. (1988) study, for example, in a control group of participants without a phobia of dogs, a similar proportion of participants had experienced a fearful incident with a dog but had not developed a phobia. Similarly, in the Munjack (1984) study, half of the people in a control group did not have phobia despite having had a frightening or traumatic experience in a car. It seems that although classical conditioning can explain the acquisition of a phobia in some people, an association between two events is not enough to induce a phobia in all people. There are clearly individual differences in the development of phobias and these have yet to be adequately explained by behavioural theory.

The behavioural approach to treating phobias

Not only does behavioural theory appear to explain some cases of phobic disorder, it has also given rise to several widely used therapies for treating phobias. The aim of all behavioural therapies is to remove or extinguish the conditioned association between the fear and the situation/object. Two of the most commonly used behavioural therapies for phobias are systematic desensitization and flooding therapy.

Systematic desensitization

Key term

Systematic desensitization: a behavioural therapy used to treat phobia by working through an anxiety hierarchy in a relaxed state.

Systematic desensitization was developed by Joseph Wolpe (1958). This therapy is based on the principle that one cannot simultaneously be in a state of relaxation and fear. Wolpe called this reciprocal inhibition. The first step in this therapy therefore is to teach the phobia sufferer relaxation techniques. Once they are in a state of deep relaxation, the therapist works with the phobic individual to develop a so-called 'hierarchy of fear'. They think about their feared object/situation and create a list of situations involving the phobic object in ascending order of fear. For example, someone with a fear of spiders might put 'hearing the word "spider"' at the bottom of the list as the least fear-inducing situation and 'having a real spider on me' at the top. With the aid of the therapist, and in a state of relaxation, they start to think about the situations on their list, beginning at the bottom. They may be presented with the fear situation for real (called *in vivo* desensitization) or it is imagined (called covert desensitization). Over a period of several sessions, the client is gradually taken through the hierarchy, all the time associating items on the list with deep relaxation. The ultimate goal of the therapy is to reach the top item on the hierarchy while remaining in a state of relaxation.

EXAMPLE EXAM QUESTION

Ever since Paul was stung by a wasp he has had a fear of them. His fear of wasps is so bad that he now tends to avoid going outside to play with his friends.

(a) Suggest how the behavioural approach might be used to explain Paul's phobia of wasps. [4 marks]
(b) Describe how a therapist might use systematic desensitization to help Paul overcome his phobia of wasps. [6 marks]

Exam hint

This question requires quite a bit of thought. It is testing your knowledge on a number of levels. You have to apply your knowledge and understanding to the context of Paul – failure to do this will mean a loss of marks. You also have to demonstrate your understanding of the behavioural approach to explaining and treating phobia.

See page 211 for an example student answer to this question, and examiner comments.

Flooding

Although with systematic desensitization the learned association between the stimulus and response is extinguished in a gradual fashion, **flooding** involves putting the phobic individual in a situation where they would be forced to face their phobia. This inescapable exposure to the feared object or situation lasts until the fear response disappears. For example, someone who has a fear of enclosed spaces (claustrophobia) might be shut in a small room until their initial levels of anxiety reduce. As there is a limit to how long the body can sustain a fear response, there is an assumption with this procedure that as the physical response to fear reduces, so too will the high levels of anxiety associated with facing the phobic object/situation. It is important therefore that the session does not end before a reduction in anxiety, otherwise the experience may have the opposite to the desired effect and reinforce the phobia.

Key term

Flooding: a behavioural therapy where a person is inescapably exposed to the object of their phobia.

Flooding typically involves presenting the feared object/situation itself (called *in vivo* exposure). For practical reasons it is sometimes necessary to use in imaginary (*in vitro*) exposure, in which case the therapy is referred to as implosion therapy. For example, a person with a fear of spiders might be exposed to a continuous barrage of detailed descriptions of spiders until their reactions had subsided. This can take several hours, though the process can be speeded up by the therapist focusing on descriptions that create the most intense reactions.

Effectiveness and appropriateness of behavioural therapies for phobias

Behavioural therapies are most effective when it is possible to identify a particular object or situation as the source of the phobia. For example, it would be possible to treat arachnophobia (fear of spiders) quite quickly and effectively with either systematic desensitization or flooding therapy, but not a social phobia where the particular source of the phobia cannot be identified. From a review of treatment studies, Choy et al. (2007) concluded that a range of therapies is effective for the treatment of phobia. For example, people with claustrophobia respond best to cognitive therapy, and exposure to the phobic situation is particularly effective with social phobia and agoraphobia. Behavioural therapies such as systematic desensitization and flooding appear to be most effective with particular subtypes of specific phobias.

One major drawback with the systematic desensitization and flooding therapies is that they require exposure to the phobic object/situation. Even the prospect of this can cause extreme anxiety for someone with a phobia, therefore individuals have to be highly motivated to take part. It is unsurprising then that the drop-out rate is high, and many sufferers choose to live life coping with their phobia.

Clearly systematic desensitization, and especially flooding, are highly threatening and stressful procedures, and because of this many experts believe they should only be carried out by trained therapists and with medical supervision. Shipley and Boudewyns (1980) carried out a survey of therapists using flooding to investigate the common view that flooding may produce 'serious negative side effects'. They found that 0.2 per cent of 3493 clients undergoing therapy experienced side effects, most of these being brief panic reactions. They concluded that flooding produced the same or fewer side effects compared to other forms of therapy, making it a safe, effective and appropriate treatment for the majority of clients.

Willis and Edwards (1969) compared the effectiveness of systematic desensitization compared to implosion therapy. Their sample consisted of fifty female undergraduate students, all with a fear of mice. One group of participants underwent systematic desensitization, another group received implosion therapy, and a third group were in a control condition and received no therapy for their aversion to mice. Willis and Edwards assessed the degree of aversion to mice in participants seven to eight weeks after treatment and found that those who had received systematic desensitization showed the best outcome in terms of behaviour related to the avoidance of mice, with implosion therapy being no more effective in this regard than having no treatment at all.

KEY POINTS

- A phobia is a disorder in which an irrational fearful anxiety occurs in response to specific objects or situations.
- Symptoms affect the sufferer both physically and mentally, and include feelings of restlessness and dread, difficulty with concentration and irritability, shortness of breath, nausea, shaking/trembling, headaches and palpitations, and muscle tension.
- There are three types of phobia: specific phobia, social phobia and agoraphobia.
- The behavioural approach to explaining phobias proposes that phobias are acquired through classical conditioning and maintained through operant conditioning. This is sometime referred to as the two-process theory.
- The aim of behavioural therapy is to remove or extinguish the conditioned association between the fear and the situation/object.
- Systematic desensitization is a behavioural therapy that works through an anxiety hierarchy in a relaxed state.
- Flooding therapy is where a person is inescapably exposed to the object of their phobia.

Obsessive–compulsive disorder (OCD)

We all have occasional irritating intrusive or repetitive thoughts and behaviours from time to time, such as checking for the third time that you really did switch the downstairs light off, or walking in ways to avoid stepping on the cracks in the pavement. Sometimes, however, these thoughts and behaviours can become so extreme that they interfere with daily life, in which case they have become an **obsessive–compulsive disorder (OCD)**.

Key term

Obsessive–compulsive disorder (OCD): a condition whereby a person has obsessive thoughts and compulsive behaviours, causing them anxiety.

Characteristics of OCD

In OCD, obsessions are recurrent, intrusive thoughts, ideas, images or impulses that an individual has great difficulty resisting or eliminating. These are unreasonable and disproportionate, rather than excessive worries about real-life problems. Individuals find the experience distressing and, sometimes, even abhorrent or morally repugnant. Because the experiences are unpleasant and seemingly impossible to control, the person feels increased anxiety. This anxiety is an out-of-proportion fearful emotional reaction that causes them difficulty in doing everyday things and leading a normal life. Whilst most people with OCD have both obsessions and compulsions, not everyone does. For instance, Wilner et al. (1976) estimated that whilst 69% of OCD patients have obsessions and compulsions, 6% have compulsions only and 25% have obsessions only.

Compulsions are irresistible, repetitive physical or mental actions that people feel compelled to carry out. Apparently meaningless, they are often performed in a similar way according to a rigid set of rules. Individuals usually recognise that these actions are unreasonable and excessive, but they cannot stop themselves. Individuals believe that by carrying out this behaviour they can prevent some dreadful consequence and can reduce their distress, and while performance of the behaviour is never directly pleasurable, there is satisfaction in that it relieves some tension and anxiety. Being unable to perform the compulsive behaviour produces even greater anxiety.

Compulsions can be seen as behaviours that in some way contain or abolish obsessions, and as such most people with OCD have both obsessions and compulsions. Although some people experience just one of these, they still have OCD.

There are many different compulsions, but they usually fall into one of two categories. They can be annoying and preoccupying *checking behaviours*, such as repeatedly checking that the lights are switched off or the doors are locked. The other type of compulsion is the *cleaning ritual*, such as hand washing or surface cleaning (see Fig. 4.4). This kind of compulsion can cause injury, for example the hands can be rubbed raw by constant scrubbing.

Fig. 4.4 Checking behaviour and cleaning ritual

Exam hint

Make sure you do more than just describe compulsions and obsessions in your answer, make the difference between them clear.

EXAMPLE EXAM QUESTION

Distinguish between obsessions and compulsions. [3 marks]

Biological explanations for OCD

Biological explanations of OCD have focused on whether individuals inherit a genetic predisposition to develop OCD, and on whether the disorder is due to some underlying biochemical imbalance in the brain or to neuroanatomical abnormalities.

Genetic explanations

Family studies have shown that relatives of OCD sufferers have a greater tendency to suffer from OCD and anxiety-related problems themselves. That the disorder seems to be transmitted through families indicates a possible genetic contribution to OCD. Nestadt et al. (2000) found that first-degree relatives (i.e. parents, siblings, children) of OCD sufferers had an 11.7 per cent chance of developing the disorder, compared to a 2.7 per cent risk in first-degree relatives of control patients without OCD.

Twins have also been used to investigate the role of genes in OCD, since in terms of family genetic resemblance there is no-one more similar than a pair of identical (monozygotic) twins. Since monozygotic twins are genetically identical and share very similar environments, if OCD was genetic, when one twin develops it so should the other. According to Miguel et al. (2005), if one identical twin has OCD, then there is a 53 to 87 per cent chance that the other twin will also develop it. Identical twins share the same genes, unlike non-identical fraternal (or dizygotic) twins, who share only half their genes and show a 22 to 47 per cent chance of both suffering. It is argued that the difference in upbringing between a pair of identical and a pair of fraternal twins is fairly minimal, so different environments cannot be used as an explanation for the difference in incidence of OCD. This difference therefore must be due to the greater genetic similarity in monozygotic over dizygotic twins. While research seems clearly to indicate a genetic contribution to OCD, environment is also implicated. Fraternal twins are no more genetically similar than any other brother or sister, but their risk of OCD is significantly greater. The key difference between dizygotic twins and siblings is that the environments of the former are much more similar, having been born at the same time and reared together.

Research indeed suggests that as family resemblance increases so does the likelihood of co-suffering with OCD. Exactly how genetic factors contribute to the disorder is unknown, but it is thought that they might operate by influencing brain structure and neurochemistry.

Neural explanations

Various areas of the brain have been implicated in OCD. One suggestion is that there is some abnormality in a part of the brain called the basal ganglia. According to Wise and Rapoport (1989), OCD is often found in cases of Huntington's chorea, Parkinson's disease and Tourette's syndrome, which are all disorders that involve the basal ganglia. Further indications of the role of the basal ganglia come from the aftereffects of head trauma and brain surgery. Max et al. (1994) suggested that surgery that disconnects the basal ganglia from the frontal cortex can reduce symptoms in cases of severe OCD, and that head injuries that result in damage to the basal ganglia can give rise to OCD-like symptoms.

Another part of the brain implicated in OCD is the orbitofrontal cortex. The orbitofrontal cortex is part of a brain circuit that includes the caudate nucleus, thalamus, and amygdala (see Figure 4.5). This circuit has many complex functions, one of which appears to be turning sensory information into thoughts and actions. Primitive impulses, for example to check and clean, arise from the orbitofrontal cortex in response to sensory inputs.

The orbitofrontal cortex may be somehow involved in controlling these behaviours. It is suggested by Ursu and Carter (2009) that the orbitofrontal cortex contributes to flexible behaviour regulation by

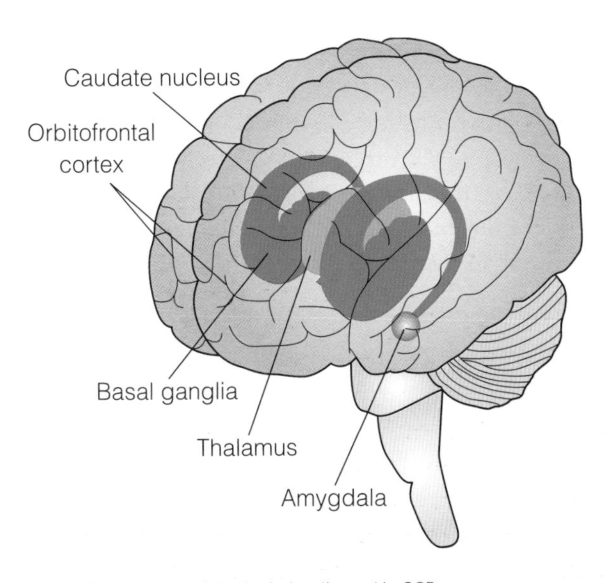

Fig. 4.5 The parts of the brain implicated in OCD

PSYCHOPATHOLOGY

'representing the anticipated affective value of future events', that is, by having an emotional awareness of what the possible outcome of a future behaviour is likely to be. If functioning in this area is impaired then a consequence may be some of the compulsive behaviours seen in OCD. Ursu and Carter monitored the brain activity of fifteen OCD patients using fMRI and found hyperactivity in the orbitofrontal cortex. This could perhaps explain the tendency of OCD sufferers to compulsively focus on potential future negative events, for example 'What if I didn't really lock that door?'

Neurotransmitters have also been implicated in the cause of OCD. Serotonin appears to be the principal neurotransmitter associated with OCD, although dopamine may also play a role. Serotonin has a wide-ranging effect on brain cells and has been implicated in many behaviours, such as sleep, memory, emotions, appetite, and social and sexual behaviour. Although its contribution to OCD is not yet fully understood, it is thought that serotonin has a role in preventing repetition of tasks. A lack of serotonin therefore results in the loss of a mechanism that inhibits task repetition. You can read more about neurotransmitters in the chapter *Biopsychology*, pages 251–253.

Evaluation of genetic and neural explanations of OCD

While evidence strongly suggests a genetic component to OCD, the figures suggest that the disorder is not entirely genetic in origin. As monozygotic twins are 100 per cent genetically the same, if OCD was entirely genetic then it would be the case that if one twin gets OCD then so should the other. This is clearly not so, indicating that although genetic factors play a role in the expression of OCD, environmental factors are vital in its development. All the available evidence suggests that OCD is a complex interaction of nature and nurture.

The relationship between OCD and the functions of the basal ganglia is not straightforward. Neuro-imaging studies have so far failed to identify basal ganglia impairments in all OCD sufferers, and some people with brain impairments involving the basal ganglia show no signs of OCD (Ring and Serra-Mestres, 2002).

Support for the role of serotonin in OCD comes from Thoren et al. (1980). They found increased levels of 5-HIAA in the cerebrospinal fluid of people with OCD. 5-HIAA is the main metabolite of serotonin. After the body has used serotonin it is broken down, including into 5-HIAA, and eventually passed in urine. Levels of this substance are measured to determine serotonin levels in the body. Following successful treatment, levels of 5-HIAA were discovered to decrease.

Other evidence for the involvement of serotonin in OCD comes from the effects of drugs known as serotonin reuptake inhibitors (SRIs) (see the discussion of SRIs below). SRIs have the effect of increasing levels of serotonin and are beneficial for some OCD sufferers. Further support comes from observations of the effects of the recreational drug m-CPP (meta-Chlorophenylpiperazine). This drug can induce OCD-like symptoms in users and worsens symptoms in people who already have OCD (Hollander et al., 1992). It has been found that the effects of mCPP reduce following treatment with an SRI.

EXAMPLE EXAM QUESTION

Outline and evaluate two biological explanations for obsessive–compulsive disorder. Refer to research evidence in your answer. [12 marks]

Exam hint

The specification requires you to know about genetic and neural explanations, so this is the logical approach to take with your answer. The question now effectively becomes two 6 mark answers – much less daunting! The challenge is to outline and evaluate for just six marks. The question tells you to refer to research in your answer – if you fail to do this you can be sure that you will be penalized.

Biological treatments for OCD

The growing body of research suggesting that OCD has mainly biological origins has had implications for its treatment, the logic being that a problem with a biological origin is best addressed with treatments that address this biology, i.e. medication. Research has shown that the only medications consistently effective in treating symptoms of OCD are those that affect the action of the neurotransmitter serotonin. Because of the effect they have on serotonin in the brain, these drugs are known as serotonin reuptake inhibitors, or SRIs. These drugs were developed to treat depression, but were also found to have beneficial effects on the symptoms of OCD in those who were co-morbid, i.e. suffered both depression and OCD (about 40 per cent of OCD sufferers also have major depression requiring medication). Although there are a number of SRI-based drugs, since the 1970s the most widely used drug for treating OCD has been an SRI called clomipramine. More recently, other drugs have been developed called selective serotonin reuptake inhibitors (or SSRIs). They are called 'selective' because they have a more specific effect on serotonin neurotransmitters in the brain. The most common SSRIs used in treatment of OCD are fluoxetine (more commonly known by its brand name Prozac) and citalopram.

Effectiveness and appropriateness of drug therapy for OCD

One disadvantage of SRIs is that, like many other drugs, there are potentially unpleasant side effects, which makes their use more appropriate for some more than others. For example, high doses of clomipramine have associated risks of impotence, tiredness, weight gain and heart seizures. The more recently developed SSRIs avoid some of the worse side-effects of SRIs like clomipramine.

Although SRIs have a fairly rapid effect on serotonin activity in the brain, it can take several months for them to have an effect on the symptoms of OCD. Further continuous treatment is needed for up to a year before medication is gradually reduced and withdrawn. Nor are SRIs successful for all OCD sufferers. This suggests that the causes of OCD may not originate solely with levels of serotonin, and there are probably significant behavioural components to the disorder.

Even in those sufferers that do respond to treatment, many report symptom improvement rather than cessation. For example, they may report being less occupied by their obsessions and compulsions, though they are still there 'in the background'. However, this symptom reduction may be sufficient to allow sufferers to resume a more-or-less normal life, which for many will be experienced as a very successful outcome of drug therapy.

The relapse rate following discontinuation of medication is quite high. According to Simpson et al. (2004), up to 45 per cent of patients treated with clomipramine relapsed back into the disorder within 12 weeks of completing medication. This is poor, and especially so in comparison to only a 12 per cent relapse rate in the same period for those who had received a psychological therapy. This also suggests that although drugs are widely used in the treatment of OCD, other treatments are equal to, if not superior to, drug therapy. This is supported by Foa et al. (2005) who found that while drug therapy was better than no therapy at all, it was less effective than cognitive behavioural therapy by itself or combined with drugs.

KEY STUDY: A COMPARISON OF TREATMENTS FOR OCD

Foa et al. (2005) compared the effectiveness of a monotherapy using clomipramine to other forms of therapy, namely cognitive-behaviour therapy (CBT) and combined CBT/clomipramine. The outcomes of these three therapies were compared to the outcomes for a control group of participants who received an inactive pill placebo.

They found that after 12 weeks, all three kinds of treatment were superior to the placebo in their effectiveness. There was no difference in outcomes between the CBT and drug/CBT combination, and both of these treatments were superior to drug monotherapy (just one therapy, i.e. clomipramine alone). These findings suggest that there are a range of treatments that might help sufferers of OCD, but treatment by an SRI alone is not the most effective of them.

THINKING SCIENTIFICALLY: RANDOMIZED CONTROL TRIALS

The Foa et al. study is an example of a randomized control trial (RCT). This is an important type of experiment used in medical research, where individuals are randomly assigned to different treatments (these are known as 'conditions' in non-medical experiments). Random allocation of participants to different treatments ensures that allocation bias is minimized. It is not always possible to know all the factors that will influence the effectiveness of a medical treatment, for example something about the biology or past experience may make one person more or less responsive to treatment. Randomly allocating participants therefore ensures there is no clear bias towards one group or the other, and in all likelihood chance will have averaged out any effects of individual difference.

KEY POINTS

- In obsessive–compulsive disorder (OCD), obsessions are recurrent, intrusive thoughts, ideas, images or impulses that an individual has great difficulty resisting or eliminating, and compulsions are irresistible, repetitive physical or mental actions that people feel compelled to carry out.
- Research shows that relatives of OCD sufferers have a greater tendency to suffer from OCD themselves, indicating some genetic contribution to OCD.
- Various areas of the brain have been implicated in OCD, for example there may be an abnormality in the parts of the brain called the basal ganglia and orbitofrontal cortex.
- The principal neurotransmitter associated with OCD is serotonin, although other neurotransmitters, such as dopamine, have been implicated.
- Research has shown that the only drug therapy consistently effective in treating symptoms of OCD are those that affect the action of the neurotransmitter serotonin.

Depression

Characteristics of depression

The term **depression** is used in everyday speech, usually to convey a temporary mood state. These states are commonly normal reactions to events and are transient experiences, part of the ups and downs of day-to-day life. A true 'clinical depression', on the other hand, is a collection of physical, mental, emotional and behavioural experiences that are more prolonged, severe and damaging. Depression is the most common psychiatric condition in the UK, with up to one in ten people having it at any one time, and one in five suffering it at some point in their lives. It is estimated to be the third most common reason for visits to the GP. There are a number of different types of depressive disorder, the most common being that which is often referred to as clinical depression, also as unipolar depression and major depression. In the most recent Diagnostic and Statistical Manual of Mental Disorders (DSM) it is referred to as major depressive disorder (MDD). MDD is a complex disorder, affecting a person mentally, emotionally and physically. It can be extremely debilitating, with many symptoms going beyond the sadness typically associated with depression, making the sufferer unable to function normally and robbing them of pleasure. Behavioural symptoms include reduced activity and productivity, speaking and moving less, staying longer in bed, and disturbances in appetite and sleep. Cognitive symptoms include negative views of self and feelings of helplessness.

Key term

Depression: a complex disorder affecting a person mentally, emotionally and physically, characterized by low mood, making the sufferer unable to function normally.

Cognitive explanations of depression

According to Beck (1967), depression is a disorder of thought rather than mood. It is a result of how an individual thinks about themselves, their world and their future. Beck called this the negative triad.

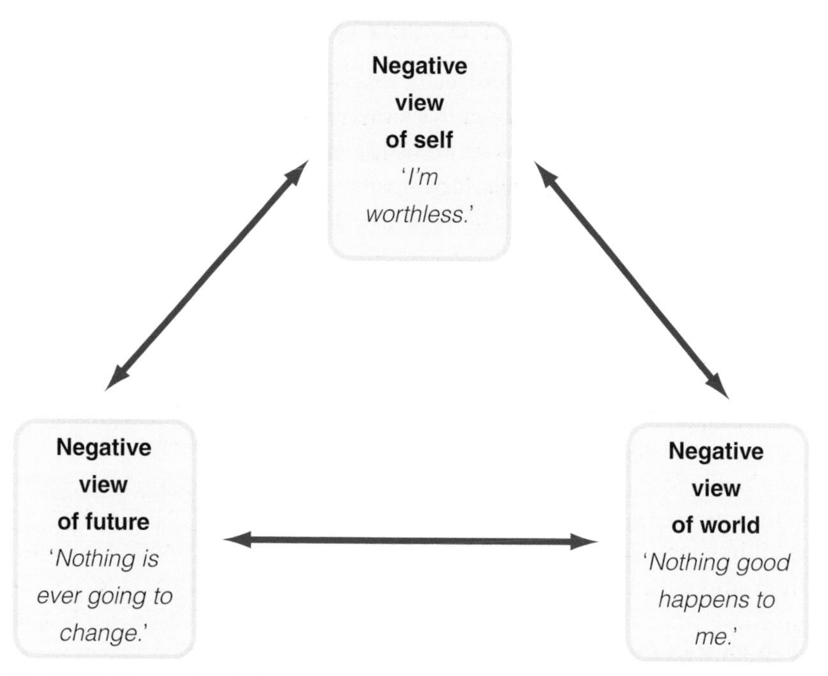

Fig. 4.6 Beck's negative triad

The model proposes that the foundations for thinking in this way are often laid in childhood. As a result of unhappy experiences individuals develop negative schemas (patterns of thought and behaviour) that lead to automatic negative thoughts. Events in everyday life can trigger memories in an individual of the circumstances that first led them to acquire negative schemas. For example, a child who was frequently criticized and corrected for making mistakes might develop a schema about being incompetent. If in later life the individual's performance at work is criticized, this schema is reactivated – they are reminded of past failures and now expect only failure in the future too.

Life is inevitably full of stresses and challenges, and in these situations negative self-critical ways of thinking lead to faulty logic and flawed interpretations of events. Beck called these errors of logic cognitive distortions or biases (see Table 4.2).

Cognitive distortion/bias	Examples
Overgeneralization	A tendency to make general conclusions based on single events, e.g. 'This always happens to me'.
Personalization	The negative feelings of others are attributed to something about you, e.g. 'He didn't say hello when he passed; he must not like me'.
Minimization	Underplaying positive events and outcomes, e.g. 'That Grade A was just a fluke'.
Magnification	Exaggerating the significance of events, e.g. 'I couldn't do that, I'm just hopeless at everything'.
Selective abstraction	A tendency to focus on some (usually negative) aspects and ignore other things that could lead to a positive conclusion, e.g. despite everything else going well at an interview, you dwell on the one thing you feel did not go so well.

Table 4.2

According to Shahar et al. (2008), three types of negative self schema are typically seen in individuals vulnerable to depression.

- Sociotropic schemas relate to close interpersonal relationships and attachments, and individuals with this negative schema type see themselves as failing at relationships.
- Autonomous schemas relate to personal achievement and social rank, and individuals with this negative schema type see themselves as failing to achieve goals in life and work.
- Self-critical schemas relate to a person's perceptions of their shortcomings.

Another cognitive explanation for depression was developed by Ellis (1987). According to Ellis, emotional problems and associated maladaptive behaviour is the result of irrational thinking. It is not a life event that causes difficulty but the way we think about them. For Ellis, we all have the goal of happiness in life, happiness with ourselves, with others and with life choices and situations. However, normal life is such that these goals are frequently blocked. Our reaction to these blocks can be rational or irrational, and it is the irrational reaction that can give rise to feelings of depression. So it is not the events in our lives that give rise to depression but the beliefs we have that govern our reaction to these events. Ellis described this as a simple ABC process (see Fig. 4.7).

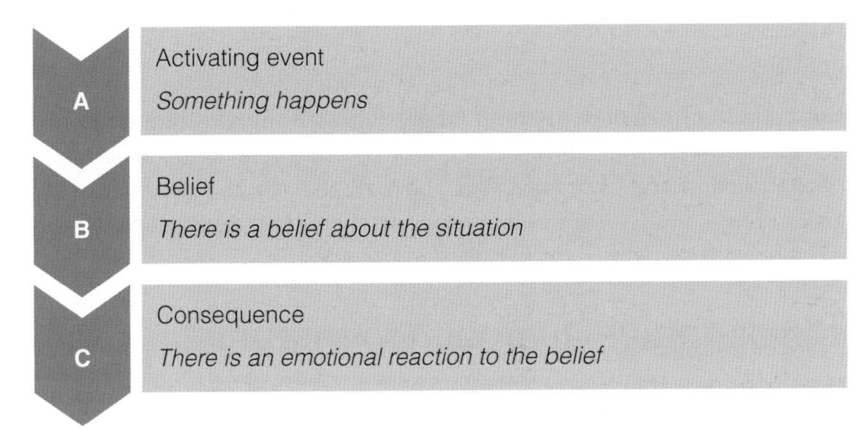

Fig. 4.7 Ellis' ABC process

The key thing to note about this process is that it is not the activating event that causes the consequence; the consequence is caused by beliefs about the activating event. Having irrational beliefs leads to unhealthy negative reactions, which can in turn result in depression.

EXAMPLE EXAM QUESTION

Outline the cognitive approach to explaining depression. [4 marks]

Exam hint

With only four marks available you need to be selective in what key features you use in your answer. You need to communicate the essence of the cognitive approach in relatively few words – much trickier than it appears, and it is something well worth practicing with all the approaches to psychopathology you need to know about.

Evaluation of the cognitive explanation of depression

In a study by Lloyd and Lishman (1975), participants with depression were presented with stimulus words in response to which they were required to recall pleasant or unpleasant experiences from their past. They found that those with low-level depression responded faster when recalling pleasant memories than those participants with deeper depression, with response times increasing with the severity of depression. This supports the idea that depressed people have automatic negative thinking.

Hammen and Krantz (1976) investigated the errors in logic that depressed people are prone to, according to cognitive theory. They gave their female participants paragraphs about women in difficult situations to read and interpret. Hammen and Krantz found that those diagnosed with depression made more errors in logic in their interpretations than the non-depressed participants.

It is difficult to determine the extent to which distorted and irrational thinking patterns cause depression. Whilst numerous studies have shown that depressed people do indeed show more negative thinking than non-depressed people, there is no convincing evidence that negative thinking precedes depression. It may be that negative thinking is a consequence of depression rather than a cause of it. Research into the neurochemistry of depression suggests that depression may be caused by an insufficiency in certain neurotransmitters. Drug treatments, for example those that increase serotonin levels in the brain, are a successful treatment of depression for many sufferers. This suggests that negative thinking could, at least in some people, be a symptom rather than cause of depression.

Cognitive theories of depression have been extremely influential and have stimulated huge amounts of research that have contributed to our understanding of the disorder and how to treat it. They have given rise to a range of therapies and, on the whole, these seem to have been very helpful for people with depression.

The cognitive approach to treating depression

A number of psychological treatments to help people with depression have been derived from cognitive theory. The most widely used is some form of cognitive behaviour therapy (CBT). This therapy was developed by Beck and is based on his theory of depression. Beck's CBT was intended to be relatively brief, consisting of about 20 sessions over 16 weeks (although more recent cognitive behaviour therapies aim to be even briefer than this). It is an active, directive therapy that focuses on the here and now, although, in the initial session, the therapist often asks for background information about the past to throw some light on current circumstances.

The therapy aims to identify and alter negative beliefs and expectations (the cognitive element) and to alter dysfunctional behaviours that are contributing to or maintaining the depression (the behavioural element). In doing this, the therapist employs a range of strategies, some of which are outlined in Table 4.3.

Behavioural activation	Encourages the client to identify pleasurable activities that they no longer participate in and to identify and overcome cognitive obstacles in carrying them out.
Graded homework assignments	Given to allow the client to try out new ways of thinking and to engage in progressively more rewarding activities.
Thought-catching	The client is encouraged to record their automatic negative thoughts and thoughts of how they might challenge these.
Cognitive restructuring	Restructuring negative thought processes to overcome cognitive distortions and biases.
Problem solving	The client is taught ways of thinking more constructively about problems and solutions, e.g. by using a systematic method to get at the root cause of the problem rather than making assumptions and flawed conclusion. One method is the 5-step Kepner-Tregoe technique where the problem is defined, the problem is described, and possible causes are established. Probable causes are tested, and root causes are verified.

Table 4.3 Some cognitive behaviour strategies

Based on his ABC model, Ellis developed a therapy called rational emotive behaviour therapy (REBT). The main goal of REBT is to change irrational beliefs into rational ones so that individuals react to events in healthy ways. However, Ellis points out that this is not necessarily easily achieved, as people cling on to irrational beliefs using 'musturbatory thinking'. This refers to the underlying assumptions an individual holds, which Ellis referred to as the 'three musts'. These are:

- I must do well and win approval of others or I am no good.
- Other people must treat me kindly and in the way I expect to be treated.
- Life must be easy and without inconvenience.

Therapy requires an individual to tackle these 'musturbatory' irrational beliefs, so that they accept themselves faults and all, they accept others for what they say and that other people will not necessarily be fair or kind, and accept that life has its ups and downs. The client is helped to challenge their irrational beliefs and replace them with rational alternatives. In effect, they are being moved from an unhealthy reaction (C) by changing their beliefs (B) about the activating event (A).

PSYCHOPATHOLOGY

Effectiveness and appropriateness of cognitive behavioural therapy for depression

A number of studies have attempted to compare the effectiveness of CBT with other forms of therapy, including antidepressants and other types of psychological therapy. In a review of 57 studies into the effectiveness of treatments for depression, Robinson et al. (1990) found that psychological therapies were comparable in their effectiveness and appropriateness to drug therapy, and better than no treatment at all. However, they could find no significant evidence that CBT was more effective than other forms of psychological therapy. Interestingly, while CBT was better than no treatment, Robinson et al. found that CBT was no more effective in reducing depressive symptoms than a placebo treatment (a dummy treatment). It seems that, for at least some sufferers, thinking that they are in treatment has a similar effect to actually having the treatment. This fits in with a criticism of psychological therapies in general – that it is a relationship with a therapist that is important rather than any particular therapeutic technique.

CBT appears to be as effective as medication in reducing symptoms of depression in the acute phase (i.e. when depression is at its worst), and some research has shown that CBT is superior to drug therapy in treating the residual symptoms, that is, the symptoms that remain after a course of medication (Fava et al., 1994). CBT is often used effectively in conjunction with antidepressant medication. For example, in a large comparison study, Keller et al. (2000) found that the recovery rates were 55 per cent using the drugs alone, 52 per cent using CBT alone, but 85 per cent when the two therapies were used in combination.

Research suggests that at least some of the variations in CBT outcomes are due to the competence of the therapist. Kuyken and Tsivrikos (2009) looked at the progress made by 69 clients with depression who were seeing one of 18 cognitive behavioural therapists. As expected, they found that the outcome of therapy varied with the complexity of the case, for instance whether there was co-morbidity (the condition occurring with another). However, they also found that the therapists who were assessed as most competent had better patient outcomes regardless of the complexity. It appears that, to some extent at least, the effectiveness of CBT depends on the skills of the therapist.

Like other psychological treatments, CBT is more appropriate for treatment with some people more than others. For example, Simon et al. (1995) found that CBT is not effective for people who have very rigid attitudes and are resistant to change, or for people who have high stress levels in response to genuinely difficult life circumstances that therapy cannot resolve.

A strength of CBT can be seen in how its techniques are appropriate for use in a wide variety of situations and modes of delivery. It has been used successfully with individuals of all ages with degrees of depression from mild to severe. The flexibility of this treatment and strength of some of its techniques can be seen in its success when used remotely (e.g. by telephone or online video chat). Recently, interactive software programmes have been approved for use by NICE (The National Institute for Health and Care Excellence, who provide national guidance and advice on healthcare in the UK) and two programmes are currently supported by the NHS.

Exam hint

The question uses the terms 'appropriateness' and 'effectiveness', so make sure you use these terms in your answer too. Whilst the question is specifically about CBT, the generic evaluation of cognitive therapy in the chapter applies to both Beck's and Ellis's approaches to therapy.

EXAMPLE EXAM QUESTION

Evaluate cognitive behaviour therapy (CBT) as a treatment for depression in terms of its appropriateness and effectiveness. [8 marks]

KEY STUDY: CBT ON THE INTERNET

Christensen et al. (2004) looked at the effectiveness and appropriateness of an internet-based form of CBT called MoodGYM for individuals with MDD. MoodGYM is an interactive web program which has an interactive game, anxiety and depression assessments, downloadable relaxation audio, a workbook, and feedback assessment. Participants were randomly assigned to either access MoodGYM, to access Blue Pages (a depression information website), or to a control condition (a placebo 'attention' group). The outcome of these conditions was measured by a clinical depression scale and a dysfunctional thoughts questionnaire.

They found that MoodGYM was comparable in its effectiveness to both face-to-face CBT and drug therapy, therefore making it appropriate for use with depressed individuals. It was also noted that MoodGYM was the most cost-effective treatment. Whereas there is a constant ongoing cost with face-to-face CBT and drug therapy, with MoodGYM the main cost lies in its initial development, and offers further value for money when the numbers of sufferers it is able to help is factored in.

THINKING SCIENTIFICALLY: THE IMPORTANCE OF CONTROL GROUPS

In the experimental method, participants in the experimental groups (in medical research these are often referred to as the treatment groups) receive the independent variable, whilst participants in the control group do not. Outcomes from the control group participants are then used as a standard of comparison. Any difference in outcomes between the conditions is likely to be due to what differs between the groups (the independent variable).

It is important to control extraneous variables as much as possible to give greater confidence that the result is only due to the independent variable. One control employed by Christensen et al. is common in medical research – a placebo. To ensure that the improvement in therapy was not just due to the attention clients receive rather than the therapy itself, participants in the control group received attention which was equivalent to the other participants but was not therapeutic.

KEY POINTS

- When someone has depression they have prolonged, severe and damaging feelings of hopelessness and sadness affecting all aspects of their life.
- There are a number of different types of depressive disorder, the most common being major depressive disorder (MDD).
- According to Beck's cognitive theory, depression is a disorder of thought resulting from the negative triad: how an individual thinks about themselves, their world and their future.
- According to Ellis, depression is not caused by life events but rather our irrational thinking in relation to events.
- Beck's cognitive behaviour therapy aims to identify and alter negative beliefs and expectations and to alter dysfunctional behaviours that are contributing to or maintaining the depression.
- Ellis developed a therapy called Rational Emotive Behaviour Therapy (REBT), the main goal of which is to change irrational beliefs into rational ones so that individuals react to events in psychologically healthy ways.

PRACTICAL ACTIVITY

Are we prepared to fear some animals more than others?

Bennett-Levy and Marteau (1984) suggested that we are more likely to fear something we perceive as ugly, and that this is linked to an evolutionary adaptation to avoid potentially dangerous things.

You can investigate this yourself. The first thing you will need is about 12 similar-sized images of various animals. The animals Bennett-Levy and Marteau used are listed in the table below. Select a range of animals from very ugly to not so ugly (the correct way to do this would be to get several people not involved in the study to select the six most and six least ugly pictures and use their views to guide your selection).

Rat	Cockroach	Jellyfish	Spaniel (dog)
Spider	Slug	Grass snake	Lamb
Beetle	Lizard	Worm	Rabbit
Frog	Moth	Crow Ant	Cat
Mouse	Squirrel	Grasshopper	Ladybird
Caterpillar	Baby seal	Blackbird	Robin
Hamster	Baby Chimpanzee	Butterfly	Tortoise

You will now need to devise a way for participants to rate each animal for how much they fear each one, and how ugly they find each one. Bennett-Levy and Marteau used 3-point scales – for fear, 1 = not afraid, 2 = quite afraid, 3 = very afraid, and for ugly, 1 = not, 2 = quite, and 3 = very. Once your volunteer samples have rated each animal for fear and ugliness you will need to record their scores in a table, which might look something like this:

Fear score	Ugly score

Now you need to analyse this data to see if you have found a relationship between 'fear' scores and 'ugly' scores – check the section on correlation in *Research Methods*, on page 22.
You could do a scattergraph, calculate a coefficient, or do both.

This is a good activity for demonstrating the importance of thinking carefully about ethics. You should get full informed consent from each participant and, as part of this process, participants who claim to have a phobia of any animal must be excluded. Also, the right to withdraw should be explained, confidentiality assured, and debriefing should occur.

Exam focus

Read through the following example exam question, example student answer, and examiner comments. Then, have a go at answering the question yourself!

EXAMPLE EXAM QUESTION, TAKEN FROM PAGE 195

Ever since Paul was stung by a wasp he has had a fear of them. His fear of wasps is so bad that he now tends to avoid going outside to play with his friends.

(a) Suggest how the behavioural approach might be used to explain Paul's phobia of wasps. [4 marks]
(b) Describe how a therapist might use systematic desensitization to help Paul overcome his phobia of wasps. [6 marks]

Karl's answer

The behavioural approach would suggest that Paul has learned his phobia of wasps through classical and operant conditioning. The dual process model combines both these approaches. Before Paul was stung by the wasp, insects would be a neutral stimuli which did not produce a response. But the pairing of the wasp with pain would lead the wasp to become a conditioned stimuli which produced the conditioned response of fear. Once Paul has developed a fear of wasps he starts to avoid these and refuses to go outside to play. Avoiding wasps reduces his anxiety, but means that he now has a phobia.

Examiner comment: Good engagement with the scenario here, and an accurate explanation.

Paul may also become afraid of other similar stinging insects, such as bees. Little Albert became afraid of a pet rat when it was paired with a loud noise, but then generalized his fear to other white furry things. This could happen to Paul too.

Examiner comment: This last paragraph of Karl's answer to (a) loses focus and doesn't add that much by way of value to the answer. It could be omitted. Level 2 response, **3/4 marks**.

In order to desensitize Paul from his fear of wasps, a therapist would use the following approach. He would start by teaching Paul to relax, as the relaxation response is not compatible with the fear response. Paul and the therapist would then draw up a hierarchy of situations involving wasps – from a simple photo of a wasp on a tree, to being shut in a room with a wasp's nest. They would start with the least fearful items, and Paul would imagine each one and try to replace his fear with relaxation. They would work through the hierarchy together until Paul is able cope with even the most fearful item on the hierarchy. He would then go out and confront real wasps (in vivo desensitization). The therapy is based on the idea of counter conditioning – i.e. replacement of one response with another incompatible one.

Examiner comment: Clear engagement with the scenario is demonstrated in this example.

Examiner comment: The second part of Karl's answer is well focused and there is systematic application to the scenario. All the stages of SD are explained. **6/6 marks**.

Part 2: Psychology in context

Chapter 5: Approaches in Psychology

Introduction

This section of your Psychology course focuses on approaches within psychology. Approaches (sometimes called 'perspectives') can be seen as different ways of understanding and explaining psychological phenomena, such as attachment, aggression or depression. You will meet three of these approaches in your first year of study (or AS): the learning, cognitive and biological approaches feature in the chapter on psychopathology (see page 182) and in other areas of the course. If you are taking the full A Level, you will meet two more approaches – psychodynamic and humanistic – which also make important contributions to psychology.

Each approach draws on a set of assumptions about what needs to be explained. If we take the example of a low mood, a biological psychologist would be interested in physiological processes which occur inside the body, such as levels of hormones and neurotransmitters, and they would collect data about these. In contrast, a behavioural psychologist would focus on the environment and the existence of rewards. Finally, a cognitive psychologist would be interested in the mental processes accompanying the mood such as internal dialogue or self-talk. Each of these approaches would take a different level of analysis (e.g. within the body, or the outside environment), would use different methods, and would seek different kinds of evidence for their claims.

Psychology is a relatively young science, which is still in development. As you read this chapter you will see how psychology has developed over the last hundred years or so to have a number of different approaches or threads. Each of these yields useful data and you should avoid thinking about which approach is right, or indeed wrong. Today, approaches coexist and psychologists acknowledge that different methods are appropriate for different kinds of questions. Humans are complex organisms and therefore it makes sense to have a range of approaches with differing assumptions and methods in order to investigate the range of behaviours and experiences which constitute 'being human'.

What is covered in Approaches in Psychology?

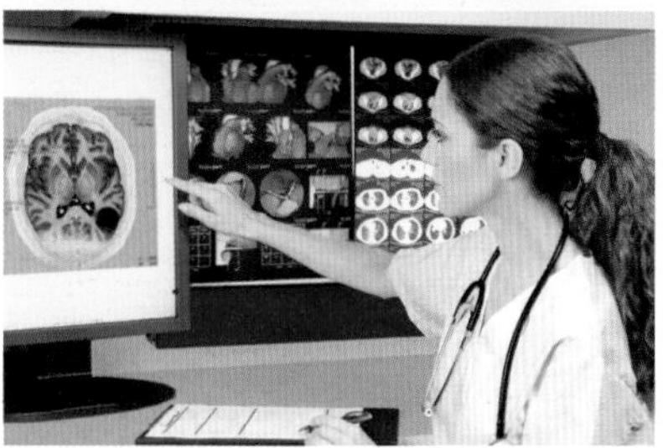

Fig. 5.1 (top) Wundt in his laboratory, compared with a modern laboratory (bottom)

A short history of psychology: Wundt's introspectionism to scientific psychology

Even before psychology was first established as a distinct discipline, philosophers, biologists and medical scientists had considered human behaviour. For example, Charles Darwin carried out what is believed to be the first documented scientific observations using his baby son in 1839. Darwin kept a detailed log of the infant's behaviour for nearly five years as he attempted to infer the mental processes that might be taking place in the child's mind (Phoenix and Thomas, 2007).

The birth of psychology is generally identified as being in 1879, when Wilhelm Wundt established the first psychological laboratory in Leipzig, Germany. Granville Stanley-Hall established the first American psychological laboratory in 1883, and the American Psychological Association was founded in 1892. The first laboratory to exist in the UK was established in 1891, and the British Psychological Society was founded in 1901. Although these were called 'laboratories', they were very different to the labs used by psychologists today.

Wundt favoured a variety of methods to collect data in his psychological laboratory, the most well-known of which is **introspectionism**. This method involved asking participants to 'observe' their inner mental processes (such as emotions) and to report on these in terms of their intensity, quality or duration. Wundt trained his participants in the skills of observing their mental processes, and also presented them with controlled stimuli (such as a picture) and asked them to describe what they experienced.

Key terms

Introspectionism: a method of collecting data, which involves observing and describing inner mental states.

Behaviourism: An approach which studies observable behaviour in tightly controlled conditions (see page 221).

The psychodynamic approach

At the same time Wundt was working in Germany, Sigmund Freud, an Austrian doctor, was developing his ideas about the unconscious mind. Drawing on clinical evidence from his work with patients, Freud became convinced that some areas of the human mind were inaccessible and could only be reached with the help of an analyst. This formed the basis of the **psychodynamic approach** (see page 216).

The behaviourist approach

Wundt and Freud both defined the focus of psychology as 'the mind' and put forward methods to study inner mental states. The American John B. Watson strongly rejected the focus on inner mental states and the methodological approach of introspectionism. Watson was impressed by the developments in other natural sciences, such as physics and chemistry, and argued that psychology should also adopt a scientific approach. For Watson, the key issue was the collection of objective data using scientific methods such as experimentation. Hence, for behaviourists, the study of psychology should focus on observable behaviour rather than what goes on in the head. In 1913, Watson published 'Psychology as the Behaviourist Views It' in the *Psychological Review*, setting out the elements of a new science – **behaviourism**.

Link

You can read more about each of these approaches later in the chapter.

Behaviourism dominated psychology until the 1940s, but it became apparent that it was limited in scope. Tolman (1932) showed how rats running mazes could find food even when their usual route was blocked, indicating they had developed an internal map to show where food was located. This demonstrated the importance of studying what goes on 'inside the head', as well as observable behaviour.

The cognitive approach

As the limitations of behaviourism became clear, the **cognitive approach** emerged in the 1940s (see page 158). Donald Broadbent was an influential British cognitive psychologist. Broadbent served in the RAF and became interested in incidents and errors made by pilots. After the war, Broadbent studied psychology at Cambridge, focusing his work on how we select some information for processing and discard other information. The 1950s and 60s also saw the development of the first computers, and the focus for cognitive psychologists was on information processing – how we select, perceive and memorize information from the outside world. Once again, the concern for psychology was what goes on inside the head, but this time the approach was scientific and based on experimental methods and computer models.

The humanistic approach

A very different approach, the **humanistic approach**, emerged in the 1960s (see page 174). While cognitive psychologists concerned themselves with processes, humanistic psychologists concerned themselves with people. This approach developed as a reaction against the negative depictions of human psychology, put forward by the psychodynamic approach and the behaviourist approach. Humanistic psychologists focused on the capacity for individuals to have meaningful lives using independent decision-making to achieve personal growth.

The biological approach

Throughout the 19th, 20th and 21st centuries, the **biological approach** has been quietly going about its business of studying the biological bases of behaviour (see page 166). Paul Broca's early discovery (1861–1865) that a specific area of the brain in the left frontal lobe was responsible for speech production marked the first milestone for biological psychology. Broca's findings had further implications – notably that certain aspects of behaviour were clearly localized within the brain, so that brain damage could have very specific effects on behaviour. All of our behaviour, from playing tennis, through to chatting with friends and worrying the night before exams, emerges from our biology, in particular that of the brain. So everything we do has a biological basis that can be explored. Techniques have developed and the focus of biological psychology has switched, to some extent, from case studies and research with non-human animals to brain scanning. The combination of cognitive and biological approaches has resulted in the development of cognitive neuroscience.

And what of introspectionism? In recent years there has been a resurgence of interest in the study of consciousness. Although cognitive neuroscientists still pursue objective data as the best form of evidence, there is acknowledgement that the only way to study subjective, conscious experience is to make use of subjective and personal reports – those advocated by Wundt at the dawn of psychology.

Exam hint

The specification requires you to know about the history and development of psychology as a scientific discipline. Each approach can be seen as a reaction against some elements of the approach that preceded it – for example, behaviourists measured only behaviour, ignoring what goes on in the head, whereas cognitive psychologists focus on what goes on inside the head. Use the timeline on page 180 to see how the approaches developed chronologically. You can use this information if you are asked to evaluate an approach in a question.

The psychodynamic approach

History and context

The psychodynamic approach originated in the work of Sigmund Freud (1856–1939), although it has been substantially revised and broadened since. Freud was born in Vienna, where he studied medicine and became a doctor. At the age of 29, Freud worked in Paris with a French psychiatrist, Jean-Martin Charcot. Some of Charcot's patients showed symptoms, such as paralysis of limbs, with no apparent physical cause, and Charcot experimented with hypnosis to treat them. He found success with hypnosis, as some patients recalled events and feelings that they had little awareness of in their daily lives, and their symptoms improved. Freud also worked with Joseph Breuer, who was treating a female patient, Bertha Pappenheim (referred to in case studies as 'Anna O'). Bertha suffered from a phobia of drinking water. Under hypnosis she recalled an event where her governess had allowed a dog to drink from her glass, which had disgusted Bertha. Once the event was recalled, the irrational fear of drinking water was removed (Stevens, 2007).

Freud wondered if some part of the mind could possibly be inaccessible under normal conditions – a concept he went on to define as the 'dynamic unconscious'. Freud published his first work, *The Interpretation of Dreams,* in 1900, setting out his early ideas on the unconscious mind and the repression of material into the unconscious. Freud spent the next thirty years developing his ideas. In 1910 he founded the International Psychoanalytic Association.

Freud refined and amended his ideas over many years, making the psychodynamic approach one of the most complex psychological approaches, with many interrelated concepts. It was substantially developed by neo-Freudians including Alfred Adler, Melanie Klein and Carl Jung, some of whom developed their own schools of analytical psychology. Freud moved to London to escape Nazi persecution, where he died in 1939. You can visit his treatment rooms in Hampstead, London, where the Freud Museum is now based.

The structure of personality

Freud conceptualized the personality (or psyche) as having three components: the **id**, the **ego** and the **superego**. The id (German for 'it') is present from birth. The id is the instinctual basis of personality, which drives us to satisfy basic biological needs. Gratification of the id results in pleasure and frustration of the id leads to tension – an unpleasant state. The id continues to demand throughout life and operates on the pleasure principle.

The ego appears from the age of around two years as the young child develops an element of reasoning ability, and learns that they cannot always have exactly what they want, when they want it. The ego is the planning part of personality, which operates on the reality principle.

Key terms

Id: the instinctual basis of personality present from birth, which drives us to satisfy biological needs such as eating.

Ego: the rational planning part of personality, which arbitrates between the demands of the id and superego.

Superego: the moral aspect of personality, which develops around age 4 to 5.

The superego develops from the age of around four or five years as the child internalizes moral rules about right and wrong. The superego produces feelings of guilt for wrongdoing and also includes an ego ideal – a guide of how we should behave. The superego works on the morality principle.

Freud saw the three components of personality in an ongoing, dynamic relationship – hence 'psycho + dynamic'. Freud believed that a healthy adult would have a strong ego, which was able to mediate between the instinctual demands of the id and the moral rules of the superego in an appropriate way. However, the id or the superego could also dominate the personality. If the id was in charge, behaviour would be hedonistic and pleasure-seeking, with little concern for moral rules. If the superego were dominant, the person would be ruled by feelings of guilt towards even socially-acceptable pleasures.

Fig. 5.2 From left to right: the superego, ego, and id

The role of the unconscious

Freud became convinced that a large area of the mind was inaccessible except under specific circumstances. He hypothesized that the mind was structured into 'zones', a model that is sometimes likened to an iceberg (see Fig. 5.3).

Freud believed that the unconscious mind was a repository for material that was distressing, painful, or embarrassing, and which would damage the psyche if recalled. Hence, it was safer in Freud's view to keep it locked away in the unconscious where it could do little damage. However, material could 'leak' from the unconscious during dreams, which Freud described as the 'royal road to the unconscious'. Freud believed that dreams contained hidden desires and wishes, which were often sexual or aggressive in nature.

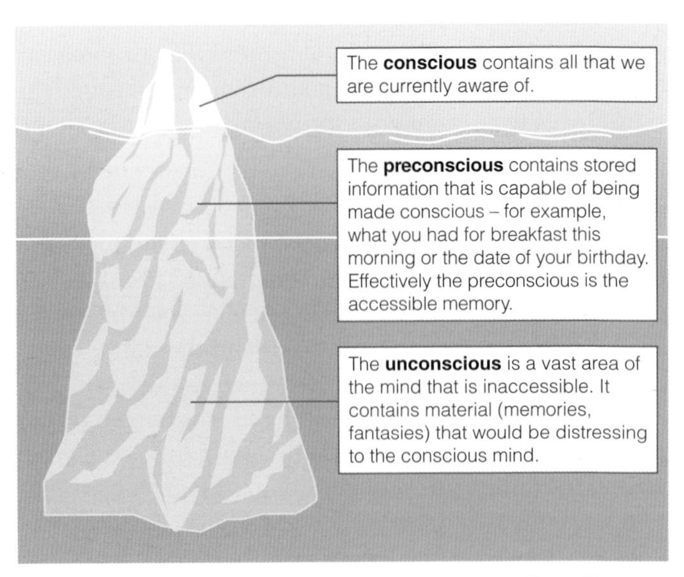

The **conscious** contains all that we are currently aware of.
The **preconscious** contains stored information that is capable of being made conscious – for example, what you had for breakfast this morning or the date of your birthday. Effectively the preconscious is the accessible memory.
The **unconscious** is a vast area of the mind that is inaccessible. It contains material (memories, fantasies) that would be distressing to the conscious mind.

Fig. 5.3 The conscious, preconscious and unconscious zones, according to Freud

A process called 'dream work' ensured that the unconscious desires were disguised through symbols, so the dream would have to be analysed carefully to identify the underlying content (or hidden meaning) from the actual events in the dream (the manifest content).

Freud also believed that the unconscious could be accessed through a process of free association. He made extensive use of this method during therapy, where he asked patients to say the first thing that came into their mind in response to words or images. When they stumbled or hesitated to do this, Freud believed that this showed a link to unconscious material, which led to further probing. Freudian slips – saying something in error that reveals subconscious feelings – could also reveal the unconscious.

Defence mechanisms: repression, denial and displacement

Freud believed that **defence mechanisms** are used to reduce anxiety and to neutralize threatening material that could potentially damage the ego. The most fundamental defence mechanism is **repression** – pushing material out of the conscious into the unconscious mind in the way that Anna O had forgotten the event that led to her fear of drinking water. For Freud, forgetting was largely motivated – we forget for a reason. Other important defence mechanisms include **denial** and **displacement**. Denial is a simple mechanism in which unpleasant or worrying information is ignored. Following a sudden bereavement, there is often a period of denial in which it is impossible to believe a loved one has died. Denial can also be seen as a response to diagnosis of serious illness in some people.

Displacement is a more complex mechanism in which feelings are redirected onto a less threatening target than where they originated. An example of displacement would be taking your frustration out on your family because a classmate had given you a hard time at college. Effectively the feelings are directed elsewhere. The concept of displacement has been influential in the explanation of racial prejudices (Adorno et al., 1950), where unpleasant attributes are displaced onto members of minority groups.

Key terms

Defense mechanisms: unconscious methods of protecting the ego from unpleasant or potentially disturbing feelings.

Repression: unpleasant material is pushed into the unconscious mind.

Denial: unpleasant material is ignored.

Displacement: feelings caused by one person or event are pushed onto another unrelated person or event.

The psychosexual stages

In his therapeutic practice, Freud noticed that many patients recalled sexual events from childhood. Initially he believed that this implied a widespread sexual abuse of young children, but over time he refined this view to suggest that the unconscious contained not just actual events, but also unacceptable fantasies and desires often relating to parents. In 1905, Freud published 'Three essays on the theory of sexuality', and it is this element of his work that has generated more debate than any other. You may find some of Freud's ideas very strange indeed.

Freud used the term 'sexual' in a very broad sense to refer to any kind of bodily stimulation that produces sensations of pleasure (Stevens, 2007). He suggested that infants go through a series of stages in which different parts of the body are the source of physical pleasure.

- The first stage lasting from birth to around 18 months is the oral stage. In this stage, pleasure is obtained through feeding, sucking, and biting, and babies around the age of 6 months put most objects into their mouth.
- Between 18 months and three years the anal stage occurs, when the focus for the child becomes the retention or expulsion of faeces. During this stage, toilet training is achieved as the young child develops control over their behaviour.
- In the third stage, Freud believed that the focus moved to the genitals (phallic stage), with both boys and girls experiencing pleasure in self-exploration and masturbation. An important element of this stage for boys was the Oedipus complex. Freud believed that young boys pursue their mother as a love object, and experience feelings of hostility and aggression towards their father, who they see as a rival. As these feelings are uncomfortable, they are repressed into the unconscious mind and the young boy identifies with his father, copying him and developing a masculine gender role. In girls, the parallel Electra complex is triggered with the realization that the girl and her mother lack a penis. According to Freud this leads to a sense of loss called 'penis envy', so the girl turns to her father as a love object. Motherhood and giving birth to a male child resolve the Electra complex.

Freud believed that parents played an important role in a child's development during progression through the psychosexual stages. If the child was allowed to experience too much or too little gratification at any of the stages, a process called fixation could occur in which the adult personality could show permanent signs reflecting the stage at which fixation occurred. For example, the child who was fed on demand could become orally fixated, which could take the form of chewing sweets or smoking in adult life. A child who received too little gratification in the anal stage from very strict toilet training could show obsessive orderliness and cleanliness in adult life.

Contribution of the psychodynamic approach

The psychodynamic approach was an important influence on psychology for the first half of the twentieth century. Freud's ideas about the importance of unconscious motives and feelings were absorbed into popular culture, including films and novels, and are largely taken for granted today. Freud's claims about the importance of early childhood were accepted and developed by researchers such as Bowlby (1951) in his influential attachment theory. Theorists such as Erikson also built on Freud's ideas about development taking place in stages. Freudian concepts have been used to explain behaviours, including aggression, prejudice, and some psychological difficulties, such as eating disorders.

Freud made extensive use of the case study method. His therapeutic work with patients suffering from 'neuroses' and other problems associated with anxiety and depression gave him a gloomy interpretation of human nature. Later approaches such as the humanistic school reacted against this, producing a much more positive approach to psychology. Today Freud's methods are largely seen as prescientific, with little emphasis on rigorous collection and interpretation of data. The behaviourist approach, with its methodological emphasis on rigorous control and experimentation, was a direct reaction against this kind of unscientific psychology.

Freud's views were also strongly shaped by the time and culture in which he lived, with its emphasis on repression of feelings and lack of sexual openness. These are likely to have contributed substantially to Freud's ideas.

Exam hint

This is an application question, so you should look for 'hooks' in the scenario to develop your answer. Think about the different elements of personality shown by Gina and Clare.

EXAMPLE EXAM QUESTION

The psychodynamic approach

Clare and Gina are out shopping. They both like a pair of expensive earrings, which neither can afford to buy. Gina says she will steal two pairs of the earrings while Clare distracts the shop assistant by asking if she can try on other jewellery. Gina is proud of her earrings and wears them all weekend. But Clare feels guilty and she posts her pair of earrings back to the shop anonymously.

How would the psychodynamic approach explain the differences between Clare and Gina? Refer to the structure of personality in your answer. (4 marks)

KEY POINTS

- The psychodynamic approach originated from the work of Freud in the late 19th century.
- Freud emphasized the importance of unconscious processes and early childhood experiences on later development.
- Personality was conceptualized as three interrelated structures – id, ego and superego – which were in conflict with each other.
- Development took place in three psychosexual stages.
- The psychodynamic approach has been criticized for overemphasizing the importance of childhood sexuality.
- The psychodynamic approach has contributed to Bowlby's attachment theory and to therapeutic approaches for some psychological problems.

The learning approach

History and context

The **learning approach** is an umbrella term for a group of theories which emphasize the importance of learning. These include behaviourism and social learning theory. Behaviourism arose from dissatisfaction with the psychodynamic approach to psychology. At the start of the twentieth century, sciences such as chemistry and physics were making dramatic discoveries based on rigorous experimentation. The psychodynamic approach, with its emphasis on the invisible and untestable unconscious, was lacking this same scientific rigor.

Watson was convinced that the methods used by psychodynamic psychologists like Freud and Wundt were inappropriate and unscientific in the extreme. He wished to make psychology into a science comparable with other natural sciences, and was convinced that a scientific method was the way to achieve this. In 1913, Watson published his work 'Psychology as the Behaviourist Views It', setting out his ideas of a science based on behaviour and learning.

Watson argued that psychology should focus on observation and measurement, concerning itself only with that which could be seen – in effect, behaviour. Watson believed that mental states (such as moods and emotions) were not appropriate for psychological investigation, as they could not be seen. Watson was also critical of the importance attached to instincts in the Freudian school (Littleton, Toates and Braisby, 2007). Though he did not deny that instincts existed, he believed that they had been given too much emphasis. Instead, Watson focused on the importance of environment and of learning.

Key terms

Learning approach: focuses on mechanisms of learning including conditioning and social learning.

Classical conditioning: association between a neutral stimulus and an unconditioned stimulus to produce a response.

The behaviourist approach: Classical conditioning

Classical conditioning originated in a series of experiments carried out in America and Russia in the early part of the twentieth century. Ivan Pavlov was a Russian physiologist who was studying dogs to establish how digestive juices (for example, saliva) were secreted in response to different kinds of food. He became interested in learning this when he noticed that the dogs in his laboratory would start to salivate at the appearance of the research assistants who fed them. Pavlov referred to this kind of salivation as 'psychic secretion' and he was initially irritated by the disruption of his research. However, Pavlov became intrigued as to how the process occurred and he carried out a series of experiments, which established the basis of classical conditioning.

Pavlov was awarded the Nobel prize for medicine in 1904 and you can read translations of his lectures online.

KEY STUDY: PAVLOV (1927)

Pavlov carried out tightly-controlled laboratory experiments using dogs to explore the process by which salivation came to occur at the presence of the research assistants. Pavlov observed that the presentation of food to a hungry dog led to salivation. This was a reflex response that required no learning. He described this link as an unconditioned stimulus (food) leading to an unconditioned (i.e. instinctive) response – salivation.

In a series of trials, Pavlov presented a neutral stimulus (the sound of a bell or buzzer) just before food was given to the dog. At the start of the experiment, the sound of the bell produced no response from the dog – it was a genuinely neutral stimulus. The pairing of the bell and food was called a contingency.

After the bell and food were presented together several times, Pavlov found that the sound of the bell on its own was sufficient to lead to salivation. In simple terms, the dog had learned that the bell would be followed by food. In the language of classical conditioning, the neutral stimulus (bell) had become a conditioned (learned) stimulus, which produced the conditioned response of salivation.

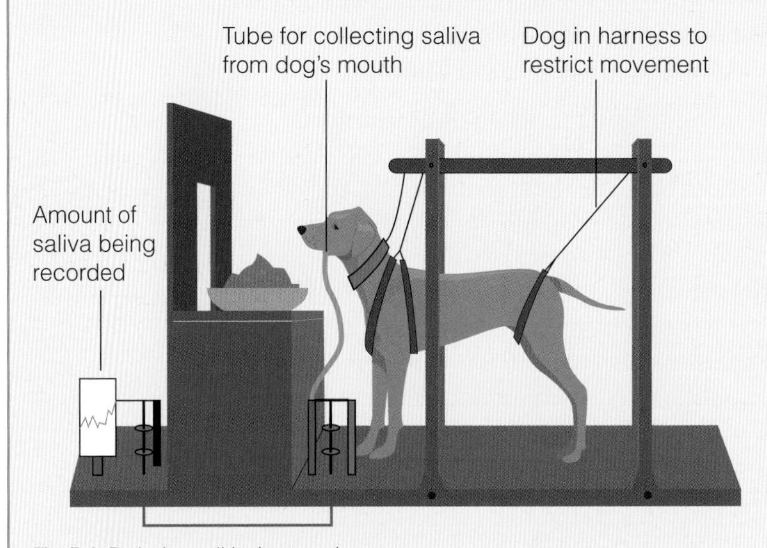

Fig. 5.4 Pavlov's conditioning experiment

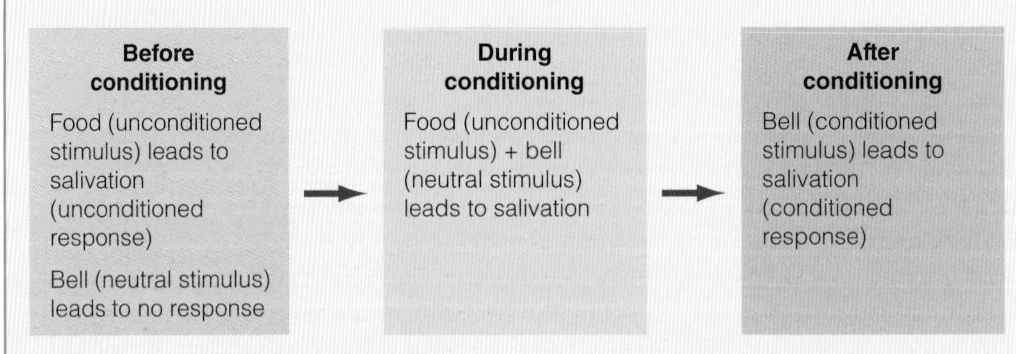

Fig. 5.5 The conditioning process of Pavlov's dogs

THINKING SCIENTIFICALLY: PAVLOV (1927)

Pavlov's experiment is an excellent example of the behavioural approach to psychology, with its emphasis on observable and measureable behaviours. The dependent variable measured by Pavlov was the amount of saliva secreted by the dog in response to the bell. Pavlov's experiment was also characteristic of the behavioural approach in its use of non-human animals. Behaviourists emphasized common features of learning amongst humans and non-human species. As we will see, Skinner also preferred to use non-human animals such as cats, rats and pigeons in his work. The behaviourist approach is also referred to as the comparative approach as it compares different species.

Another notable element of the behavioural approach is the tight amount of control in the experimental method. In Pavlov's experiment, every element of the environment was controlled so the only thing that altered was the independent variable. We will examine this in more detail after Skinner's experiments.

At around the same time as Pavlov was establishing the principles of classical conditioning in Russia, Watson was exploring the same principle of learning in the US. Rather than using animals, Watson and his colleague Rayner carried out a now infamous experiment using an infant, 'Little Albert'. At the start of the process, ten-month-old Albert showed little fear and was a bold child. The only stimulus that appeared to frighten Albert was loud noises, which made him cry. Albert had a pet rat, of which he was very fond. In a series of trials, Watson conditioned Albert to be afraid of the rat by pairing it with a loud noise. Each time Albert reached out to touch his pet, Watson struck an iron bar with a hammer. In a very short length of time, Albert showed extreme fear towards his pet rat and would cry whenever he saw it.

Research methods link

Refresh your memory about the British Psychological Society's ethical principles on pages 35–36. Which principles does Watson and Rayner's study violate?

ACTIVITY 5.1

See if you can identify the neutral stimulus and the unconditioned stimulus in Watson's experiment, along with the unconditioned and conditioned responses. Draw a diagram similar to the one in Figure 5.4 to illustrate the process of classical conditioning using the Little Albert example.

Operant conditioning and types of reinforcement

Pavlov and Watson had both been interested in how reflexes are shaped by the environment. In contrast, B.F. Skinner was interested in behaviours that are freely made rather than responses that are made reflexively. Skinner referred to these freely made behaviours as 'operands' (the animal operates on the environment), and identified a second type of conditioning that emphasized the importance of consequences on behaviour, which he called **operant conditioning**.

Key term

Operant conditioning: learning through consequences such as reward and punishment.

KEY STUDY: SKINNER (1953)

Initially, Skinner placed hungry rats in mazes and timed how long it took them to find food. This method was time-consuming, so Skinner devised a piece of apparatus, which is known as a Skinner box (see Figure 5.3). The Skinner box consists of a controlled environment in which a hungry animal (such as a rat or pigeon) can be placed. The exact make-up of the box depends upon the type of animal it is designed for. A Skinner box for a rat would contain a lever, which could be pressed to deliver a food pellet from an outside hopper. The box for a pigeon would contain a shape that could be pecked for the same delivery of food. Outside of the Skinner box would be a device, to record the frequency of lever pressing or pecking.

Skinner placed the hungry rat in the box and watched it explore the environment. At some point, the animal would accidentally press the lever and receive a pellet of food. As the rat learned the connection between an action (lever pressing) and reward (food), the frequency of lever pressing would increase. Skinner referred to the process of providing a reward as **positive reinforcement**. Skinner also experimented with unpleasant environmental stimuli such as loud noises, which could be switched off by pressing the lever. This was referred to as a **negative reinforcement** – the removal of unpleasant stimuli through a behaviour. Both positive and negative reinforcement led to an increase in the lever-pressing behaviour in the rat. Finally, Skinner experimented with the use of **punishment** by delivering an electric shock following each lever press. This (unsurprisingly) led to a decrease in lever-pressing by the rat. Skinner also demonstrated that learning could be extinguished. If reinforcement ceased to be provided for lever-pressing, the rat would effectively unlearn the connection between the two and lever pressing would cease.

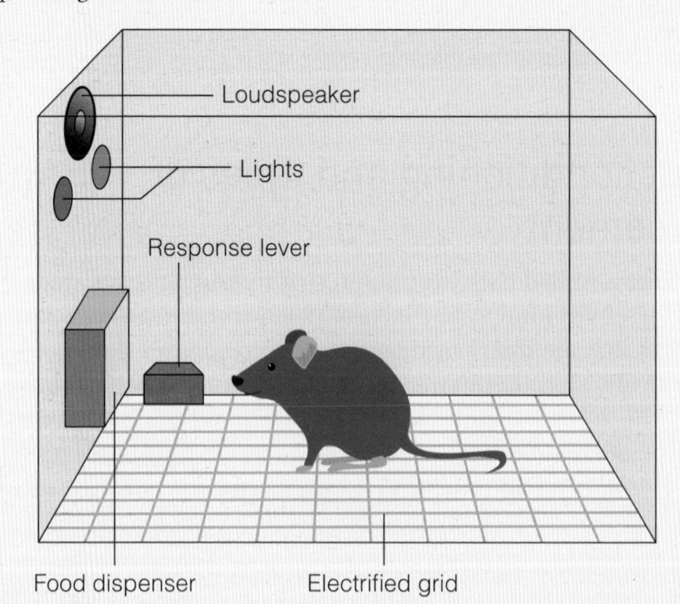

Fig. 5.6 An example of a Skinner box for a rat

Key terms

Positive reinforcement: occurs when behaviour leads to the provision of a reward (such as a food pellet). Positive reinforcement increases the likelihood of the behaviour being repeated.

Negative reinforcement: occurs when behaviour switches off an unpleasant stimulus such as a loud noise. Negative reinforcement increases the likelihood of the behaviour being repeated.

Punishment: occurs when behaviour leads to an unpleasant outcome such as an electric shock. Punishment reduces the likelihood of the behaviour being repeated.

THINKING SCIENTIFICALLY: SKINNER (1953)

The Skinner box provides an excellent example of a highly controlled environment. Every element of the environment can be controlled and there are no distractions from the outside world. This ensures that any changes in the animal's behaviour can be attributed to the specific changes in the environment made by Skinner.

The Skinner box also enabled Skinner to vary how often reinforcement was provided. Providing a food pellet for every lever press/peck was referred to as continuous reinforcement, and providing food for every third (or tenth) lever press was referred to as partial reinforcement. Skinner found that partial reinforcement led to behaviour that was very difficult to extinguish. An animal would continue lever-pressing for a much longer period if they expected a reward every fifth or tenth action. This is the principle that makes fruit machines, and other kinds of betting such as lottery scratch cards, so addictive.

EXAMPLE EXAM QUESTION

Discuss the contribution of behaviourist psychologists such as Pavlov and Skinner to our understanding of human behaviour. [16 marks]

Exam hint

There are 6 A01 marks and 10 A03 marks available for this question. The question asks about the *contribution* of the two psychologists to our understanding of human behaviour, so do not fall into the trap of describing Pavlov and Skinner's work in detail. Level four marks are awarded to answers which are clear, coherent, and focused on contributions to understanding human behaviour. **See page 245 for a sample answer to this question, and examiner comments.**

Social learning theory

In 1961, Albert Bandura identified a third kind of learning after classical conditioning and operant conditioning. Bandura's focus was learning from others through **imitation** and **modelling**, and from this he developed his **social learning theory**. Bandura and colleagues set up series of laboratory experiments known as the 'Bobo doll' studies, which involved examining the effects of a violent model on children's behaviour. Unsurprisingly, these experiments have received considerable criticism for the possible negative impact on the children involved.

Key terms

Imitation: copying the behaviour of a role model.

Modelling: learning that involves observation of actions, extracting information about those actions, and making a decision about whether or not to perform them. Learning can take place through modelling but the learner chooses not to perform the actions at that time.

Social learning theory: an explanation put forward by Bandura to explain learning through observation and modelling.

KEY STUDY: BANDURA, ROSS, AND ROSS (1961/1963)

In 1961, Bandura, Ross and Ross studied a sample of 72 children aged around 4 years old drawn from the nursery at Stanford University, San Francisco. The children were placed into one of three conditions (groups) each consisting of 24 children, 12 boys and 12 girls.

In condition 1, each child was taken into a room by a female experimenter and seated at a table with crayons and paper to play with. A few minutes later, a second experimenter entered the room and used a mallet to attack a five-foot tall inflatable doll. The doll was kicked and punched and the attacker used several statements, including 'Punch him on the nose' and 'He sure is a tough fellow'. Bandura used two aggressive models so that he could examine the effects of a male or female model on the children. Overall, the attack lasted around ten minutes. In condition 2, the same procedure was adopted but the adult assembled a construction toy and did not show aggression towards the doll. Condition 3 served as a control condition and did not include an adult model.

After the first stage of the experiment, each child was taken to a second room filled with attractive toys. When they started to play with them, the researcher told them that the toys were 'for other children' and they were taken to a third room, which contained ordinary toys and a bobo doll. The child was filmed for twenty minutes through hidden cameras as they played in the third room.

Bandura, Ross, and Ross analysed the films, paying particular attention to imitative aggression (direct copying of the adult model's actions), partial imitation (for example, using the mallet to hit another toy), non-imitative aggression (i.e. novel acts), and aggressive gunplay. They found that the children who had witnessed the aggressive model showed higher levels of aggressive behaviour to the doll than those in either of the other two conditions.

In the 1963 experiment, Bandura adopted the same basic procedure but examined the effects of different types of aggressive model on 96 children:

- Condition 1: a live adult model abused the bobo doll
- Condition 2: a film of the aggressive adult model was shown on a television (filmed model)
- Condition 3: a film was shown in which the aggressive model was dressed in a black catsuit (fantasy model)
- Condition 4: the children did not witness aggressive behaviour. This was the control condition.

The children in conditions 1–3 (i.e. all of those who had seen an aggressive model of any kind) showed higher levels of aggression than those in condition 4. It made little difference what type of model was used – all three led to increased aggression in the children. Boys showed more aggression than girls in all conditions, implying that factors other than observational learning were taking place.

Fig. 5.7 A series of images showing an experimenter and two children interacting with the bobo doll

THINKING SCIENTIFICALLY: BANDURA, ROSS, AND ROSS (1961/1963)

Bandura's work demonstrates the key principles of the learning approach. The experiment took place in a controlled environment, similar to Skinner and Pavlov's work. The experimenter manipulated the IV (exposure to violent model in experiment 1 and type of model in experiment 2) and measured the DV (amount of aggression).

However, Bandura's work has been criticized for several reasons. The setting was strange to the children and they were exposed to unusual behaviour from both the adult model and the female researcher who ignored the aggressive behaviour of the model while in the same room. This would have been puzzling to the children, who would normally expect aggressive behaviour to be commented on and stopped. It may have given the children the view that such treatment of the bobo doll was acceptable – or even expected in this situation (Oates, 2012).

Observation took place for a very short period after exposure to violence and it is not known what longer terms effects, if any, there may have been on the children. Finally, it is worth noting that the behaviours measured were not the same as genuine aggression, which would be directed towards another person or their property. We cannot assume that the children in this experiment would act aggressively towards another child from their actions towards the bobo doll.

Social learning theory: imitation, identification, modelling, and vicarious reinforcement

Bandura used the findings of both the 1961 and 1963 studies to develop social learning theory. He argued that we do not simply learn through personal experience of reward and punishment, but also through observation and imitation of role models, called modelling. Models are more likely to be imitated if the child or adult **identifies** with them in some way. This is most likely if the model is similar, for example in age and sex (Bandura, 1973), or if they are powerful or influential in some way, such as famous footballers or celebrities. Behaviour that brings reward/reinforcement to a role model is most likely to be imitated. This is referred to as **vicarious reinforcement**.

In order for imitation to take place, four factors are required. Firstly, the learner must pay attention to the model, and secondly, they must remember what they have seen (retention). Thirdly, they must be physically capable of performing the behaviour, and lastly, they must be motivated to do so.

Key terms

Identification: a connection between a child and a role model, often based on perceived similarity (e.g. in age and sex).

Vicarious reinforcement: learning takes place through observing the consequences of a model's actions in terms of reward and punishment.

Systematic desensitization: a behavioural therapy used to treat phobia by working through an anxiety hierarchy in a relaxed state.

Contribution of the learning approach

The behavioural approach has made an important contribution to psychology. Classical conditioning provides a powerful explanation for the development of some anxiety disorders, such as phobias, as you have seen in the chapter on psychopathology (see page 190). It also provides an extremely useful therapeutic approach, called **systematic desensitization**, to treat phobias based on counter-conditioning. In systematic desensitization, the phobic object or situation is paired with a relaxation response. Flooding is a much faster approach to treatment for phobia – although this approach is highly stressful and raises serious ethical issues. Classical conditioning also helps to explain a range of human behaviours. For example, drug addicts are more likely to die of an overdose when taking the substance in an unfamiliar environment (Siegel, 1984). Under normal conditions, the body responds via classical conditioning to signals, which are associated with drug taking, and prepares for the onslaught of the drug. When it is taken in a different environment, this preparation does not occur – hence an ordinary dose becomes an overdose without preparation.

Social learning theory has also made a valuable contribution to psychology. As well as playing a part in aggressive behaviour, there is strong evidence that a range of behaviours also involve an element of social learning. These include food preferences and eating disorders (such as anorexia nervosa), addictions such as smoking, and the development of masculine and feminine behaviours (gender roles). Social learning theory can also be used as a treatment for phobias, where it is referred to as 'modelling'.

Exam hint

This scenario refers to the mechanism of social learning, so you should draw on this approach to construct your answer to this question. Remember to use the language of social learning theory (vicarious reinforcement, etc.) in your answer.

EXAMPLE EXAM QUESTION

Three-year-old Kia likes to play with the sand and water toys at playgroup, so her mother dresses her in jeans when she goes there for the morning. Kia's friend Abby wears pretty dresses to playgroup. The play workers often compliment Abby on her pretty dresses. Kia asks her mother if she can wear a dress to playgroup.

How would the learning approach explain Kia's request to wear a dress to playgroup? [5 marks]

KEY POINTS

- Behaviourism emerged due to a dissatisfaction with studying unobservable concepts, such as mind.
- Watson suggested that psychology should use scientific methods and focus on observable behaviour.
- Pavlov, in his experiments with dogs, demonstrated classical conditioning. Watson and Rayner showed how this also applied in the case study of Little Albert.
- Skinner, who emphasized the importance of consequences and reinforcement in shaping behaviour, demonstrated operant conditioning.
- Bandura, in the bobo doll studies, showed how children learn behaviours from observation and imitation of role models.
- Social learning takes place when models are observed and a child is both motivated and capable of repeating their behaviour. It also takes place when a child identifies with the model and the model receives reinforcement of their actions.
- The learning approach has made an important contribution to understanding and treating phobias.

The cognitive approach

History and context

Behaviourism was the main approach during the first thirty years of the 20th century, advancing our understanding of the impact of the environment on behaviour and learning. The 1930s were marked by a growing realization of the limitations of stimulus–response psychology, with an increasing acceptance that psychologists needed to look inside the 'black box' placed between stimulus and response in behaviourist psychology. Tolman showed how rats prevented from using their usual route to food in a maze appeared to develop a cognitive map of the maze, and were able to use a different combination of turns in order to find their way to a reward. This and other studies pointed to the limitations of behaviourism as an all-encompassing explanation of human behaviours, and led to an interest in the importance of cognitive processes in the 1940s and 50s.

World events and advances in technology also played a part in the development of the cognitive approach in the 1940s and 50s. One of those world events was the Second World War. In 1943, seventeen-year-old Donald Broadbent joined the RAF. During flight training, Broadbent noted many 'near miss' incidents, which resulted from poor instrument panel design. Broadbent became fascinated by how pilots, and people in general, pay attention to multiple sources of information and discard irrelevant information to focus their attention on a task requiring concentration. On leaving the RAF, Broadbent studied psychology at the University of Cambridge and his filter model of attention provided the basis for experimental cognitive psychology (Edgar and Edgar, 2012).

The 1950s marked a rapid development in computer technology, with the use of the term 'artificial intelligence' originating from this period. Cognitive psychologists drew on advances in computer science, adopting the computer model of information processing and assuming that people operate in a similar way to computers. In 1956, George Miller presented his ideas about the capacity of short-term memory (Miller's magic number 7, better known as 7+ or −2, see page 114) and Noam Chomsky presented a paper on his theory of language at the Massachusetts Institute of Technology. These events marked the birth of the new science of cognitive psychology (Eysenck and Keane, 1996).

The study of internal mental processes and the use of computer models to infer 'what goes on in the head'

Cognitive psychologists are interested in mental processes. These processes are often referred to using the general term 'thinking'. Thinking includes perception and attention, memory, language, and problem-solving. Like other psychological phenomena such as emotions, cognitive processes cannot be seen, although we may be able to guess from someone's behaviour that they are remembering

Key term

Information processing model: a hypothetical model showing how sensory information is processed in the brain.

or trying to solve a problem. For this reason, cognitive psychologists have developed models of how internal mental processes might operate. **Information processing models** provide a useful way of conceptualizing things that cannot be seen and provide a unified approach to understanding different cognitive processes (Eysenck and Keane, 1996).

In the 1950s and 60s, cognitive psychologists adopted the computer as a metaphor for human information processing. In simple terms, a computer accepts inputs, carries out processes of various kinds on inputs, and produces outputs. We can explore this analogy using the multi-store model (MSM) of memory (Atkinson and Shiffrin, 1968, see page 110). Sensory information from the environment (for example, a new name and/or face) is the input. This enters a sensory registration store where it is held for a very short length of time. If attention is paid to the input, it is transferred to the short-term memory store where the name is held in an acoustic (sound) format for a few seconds. Rehearsal (e.g. repeating the name over and over again) can keep the information in STM and can transfer it for more permanent storage in the long-term memory. When we meet the person again, we retrieve the information (i.e. remember the name), which is the output.

The MSM illustrates the key components of the information processing approach to cognition:

- The model makes use of computer terminology such as input and output processes.
- Information is processed through a sequence of stages.
- Key processes include attention and rehearsal.
- Storage systems include the sensory registration store, STM and LTM.
- The model makes use of flow diagrams with arrows.

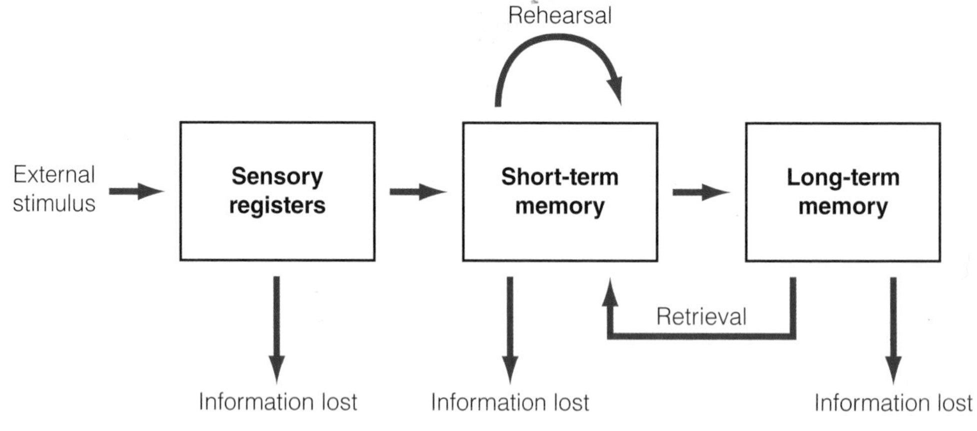

Fig. 5.8 The multi-store model of memory

Today, models based on this analogy are the accepted way to describe cognitive processes such as memory and attention (Edgar and Edgar, 2012). Models generate predictions, which can be tested using tightly-controlled experiments – the preferred tool of cognitive psychologists.

The MSM focuses on how we process incoming information from the senses. This is referred to as bottom-up processing. However, much of the time, we use our existing knowledge derived from experience to deal with and interpret sensory input.

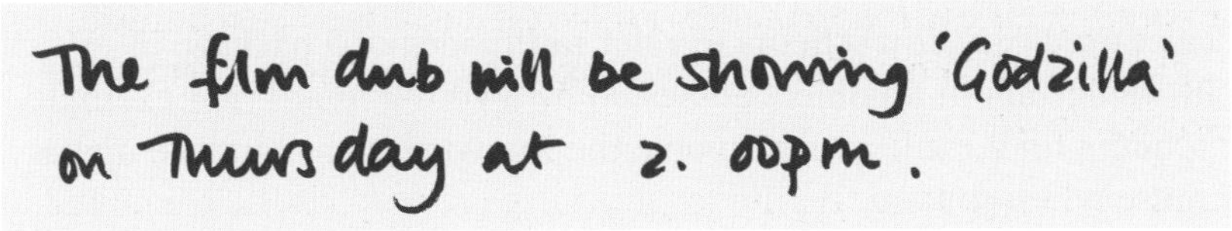

The film club will be showing 'Godzilla' on Thursday at 2.00pm.

Fig. 5.9

In Figure 5.9, knowledge of context and meaning enable us to interpret the incomplete and ambiguous stimuli in the writing. This incorporation and use of existing knowledge is referred to as top-down processing. In practice, most cognitive processes involve the integration of bottom-up (sensory-driven) and top-down (knowledge-driven) information.

While cognitive psychologists use experiments to test theories about human cognition, cognitive scientists construct computer models of cognitive processes such as language processing. These models are also referred to as connectionist models or neural networks. Marr (1982) constructed computer programs designed to replicate the processing of visual information in humans. An accessible example of a computational model is McClelland and Rumelhart's interactive-activation model (1981), which focuses on the processing of written words – reading. The model identifies three levels of feature detection, which operate in word recognition. Imagine you are shown, as a stimulus, the capital letter T:

- The feature level: this involves matching elements of a stimulus against a set of 14 stored features. For letters, these features would be the curves and slanting lines that make up the shapes of different letters.
- The letter level: once features have been detected, the overall letter is identified as a T on the basis of its distinctive pattern of features – the horizontal top bar and the vertical middle bar.
- The word level: once each letter has been identified in this way the overall word is recognized.

Today computers can carry out a range of impressive tasks. Robots can assemble cars and the computer 'Deep Blue' beat chess grandmaster Gary Kasparov in 1997. But are these machines really intelligent? The Turing test, devised by English mathematician Alan Turing in 1950, refers to whether a computer can carry out a cognitive task (e.g. problem solving) as well as a person could, such that it is impossible to distinguish between them. A computer that passes this test would be said to possess intelligence.

ACTIVITY 5.2: SPOT THE DIFFERENCE

Many cinemas use voice recognition software to respond to phone calls for booking films. How can you tell you are talking to a computer when booking cinema tickets and how is this different to making a booking on the phone answered by a real person? Compare your answers with a classmate.

Schemas

> **Key term**
>
> **Schema**: a mental structure which contains knowledge about an object based on experience.

The term **schema** was first used by the philosopher Immanuel Kant and was adopted by Jean Piaget, a Swiss developmental psychologist. Piaget used the term schema to refer to the idea of a package of knowledge about an object possessed by a young infant. For example, a schema for a rattle could involve the knowledge that a rattle makes a noise when shaken.

> **Link**
>
> If you are interested in the concept of schemas you can find out more in the topic 'Cognition and development' in Book 2.

The idea of the schema was taken up by Frederic Bartlett, who was interested in memory. Bartlett argued that existing knowledge in the form of schemas plays an important role in memorizing information. Bartlett (1932) carried out an influential piece of research in which he asked participants to listen to and then recall a Native American folk tale called the 'War of the Ghosts'. Bartlett found that participants left out elements of the story that were culturally unfamiliar to them (e.g. references to spirits and ghosts), added material to the story to make it more coherent in line with their schema, and changed some elements (e.g. canoes became boats). Bartlett showed how people use their schemas and existing knowledge to make sense of new incoming information – a process he referred to as 'effort after meaning'.

Bartlett's work has important implications for the accuracy of eyewitness testimonies, as it shows how memories of events are likely to be comprised of real memories and 'filling in the gaps' using schema-driven knowledge.

Since Bartlett's work on memory, the study of schemas has also become important in relation to social information processing. As well as object schemas, we also have schemas relating to people (also known as stereotypes), social roles (e.g. police officer), and situations (known as scripts). For example, a simple interview schema could involve wearing appropriate clothing and being asked questions by a panel of people. Schemas are important as they help us to simplify a complex social world, to take shortcuts, and to predict what might happen on the basis of past experience.

The emergence of cognitive neuroscience

> **Key term**
>
> **Cognitive neuroscience**: the use of scanning techniques and the study of 'neurotypical' individuals to locate the physical basis of cognitive processes in the brain.

A recent development in cognitive psychology is the specialized field of **cognitive neuroscience**. This approach brings together the brain-scanning technologies used by biological psychologists with the study of cognitive processes such as memory and attention. Cognitive neuroscientists study neurotypical individuals, and patients who have experienced damage to the brain from trauma (e.g. car accident, stroke), disease or surgery. The brain injuries can be mapped using technologies such as positron emission tomography (PET) and functional magnetic resonance imaging (fMRI) (see page 281 for more on these technologies). Patients are asked to undergo cognitive tests (e.g. a memory test) while scanning is taking place, so the brain can be seen 'in action'. The patterns of activity shown in the scan are compared with activity from a normal, intact brain. These are used to make inferences about how cognitive processes normally function.

Double dissociation: an example of the cognitive neuroscientific approach

One of the most useful neuroscientific discoveries is the existence of a 'double dissociation'. This occurs when two patients show a 'mirror image' of impairment; for example, person 1 can do task A but not B, and person 2 can do task B but not A. This was demonstrated in a patient known as 'KF', reported by Warrington and Shallice (1969). KF had a very poor short-term memory with a digit span of 2 (the normal digit span is around 7 items), but a fully functioning long-term memory. KF had sustained damage to the left parietal occipital lobe of his brain during a motorcycle accident. The opposite case of 'HM' was reported by Scoville and Milner (1957). HM had undergone surgery for epilepsy, in which his hippocampus was removed. HM was unable to put any information into his long-term memory after the surgery and was sentenced to living in the present. His short-term memory was completely normal. These two cases represent evidence of double dissociation, and the reasonable conclusion is that short-term and long-term memory are located in different areas of the brain.

However, studies of this nature should be viewed with some caution: damage to the brain sustained during trauma is rarely neat and the brain shows a remarkable ability for plasticity, when new brain areas take over or compensate for the damage to the original structure. This is most evident in children.

Link

You can read more about plasticity on page 276 of *Biopsychology*.

Contribution of the cognitive approach

The concern with thinking led to 'a tidal wave of research in cognitive psychology and the emergence of cognitive science as a unified programme for studying the mind' (Eysenck and Keane, 1996). Today cognitive psychology is at the forefront of many university departments, and research increasingly links cognitive processes with brain areas in the specialized study of neuroscience.

The cognitive approach has also made a substantial contribution to our understanding of the causes of psychological problems, such as depression and phobias, where specific patterns of thinking are closely linked to emotional experiences. As Beck has identified, depression is characterized by negative thoughts about the self, the world and the future. Cognitive psychology makes an important contribution to cognitive behavioural therapies. Cognitive behavioural therapy (CBT) is the most commonly prescribed therapy in the UK today, used to treat anxiety problems and affective disorders such as depression. CBT has an excellent track record in providing quick and effective treatment for many people (see page 206).

EXAMPLE EXAM QUESTION

Explain what is meant by the term 'schema'. Use an example to illustrate your answer. [3 marks]

Exam hint

This is a straightforward AO1 question. You can choose your example from your studies of memory and eyewitness testimony.

KEY POINTS

- Cognitive psychologists study processes such as memory, attention and perception.
- Models are constructed based on computer analogies of information processing.
- Most cognitive processes involve an interaction between bottom-up (stimulus-driven) and top-down (knowledge-driven) information.
- Schemas are mental structures that contain knowledge about objects and people derived from experience.
- Schemas play an important role in reconstructive memory.
- Cognitive neuroscientists use brain scanning techniques to study the physical base of cognitive processes in the brain.
- The cognitive approach provides a convincing explanation for depression and an effective treatment in the form of CBT.

The biological approach

History and context

In 1840 a Frenchman, Louis Leborgne, suddenly lost the power of speech. For the next 21 years, until his death in 1861, the only word he could say was 'Tan'. Despite his inability to produce words, Tan, as he became known, could understand speech and could follow instructions easily. About a week before he died, Tan came to the attention of Paul Broca, a doctor and pathologist with an interest in the brain. Broca studied Tan's symptoms and confirmed his severe problem with speech production. After Tan died, Broca performed an autopsy on his brain and identified an area of obvious damage in the left frontal lobe.

Broca reported on these findings in 1861, and then again in 1865 when he had studied a further 25 cases of patients with similar symptoms to Tan – loss of speech production. Broca concluded that

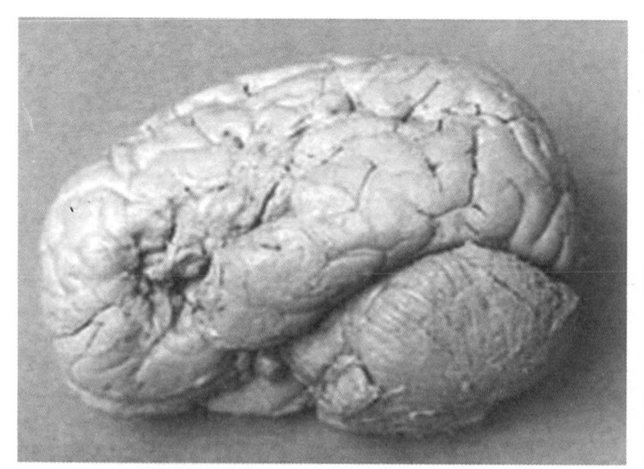

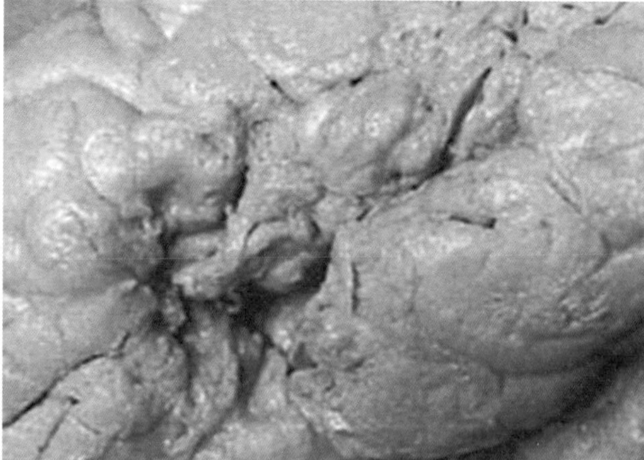

Fig. 5.10 Tan's brain

the patients had damage to the same area in the left frontal lobe, and that this area (now named Broca's area, see page 269) was responsible for speech production. Broca's findings had further implications – in particular, that certain aspects of behaviour were clearly controlled by different areas within the brain, so that brain damage could have very specific effects on behaviour.

Broca was one of the early pioneers of the biological approach in psychology, the systematic search for the biological bases of behaviour. All of our behaviour emerges from our biology, in particular the brain, so everything we do has a biological basis that can be explored. Biologist Francis Crick takes the hard-line view that every aspect of human behaviour and experience can be explained at a biological level:

> *'You, your joys and your sorrows, your memories and your ambitions, your sense of personal identity and free will, are in fact no more than the behaviour of a vast assembly of nerve cells and their associated molecules.'* (Crick, 1994)

Evolution and behaviour

150,000 years ago, our ancestors were hunter-gatherers struggling to survive in hostile environments. Although separated by thousands of generations, modern humans have retained some of these behavioural patterns from the hunter-gatherer era. Examples can be found in aggressive behaviour and in patterns of human courtship, mating and parenting.

Key term

Evolution: the gradual change within a species in response to environmental pressures.

The naturalist Charles Darwin identified the mechanisms of **evolution** in the mid-19th century. During his travels to the Galapagos Islands, Darwin noticed the different shapes of beaks in the finches on two of the islands. He wondered if the finches were variations of the same species, with the beak shapes reflecting the different food supplies in the two environments.

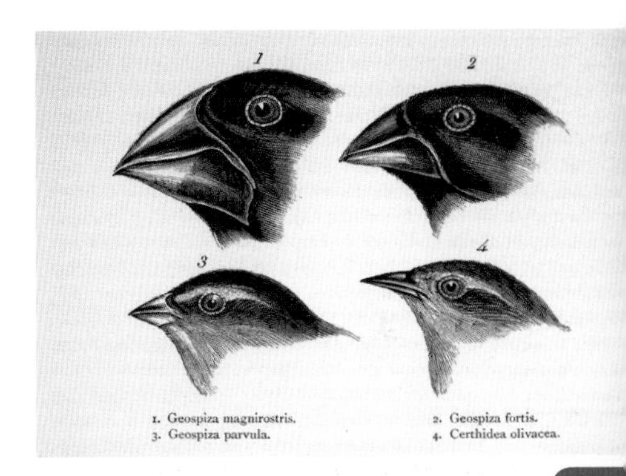

Fig. 5.11 An 1845 illustration showing the contrasting beaks of four Galapagos finches

Darwin identified two mechanisms by which gradual changes to species could take place. Environmental resources are limited, and animals/humans compete for food, mates and shelter. Members of species vary and those who are better equipped to find food or escape from predators (for example, being able to run faster or outwit predators) are more likely to survive and pass on their genes to the next generation. This idea is captured in the well-known phrase 'the survival of the fittest', the term 'fittest' referring to those most suited (fitted) to a specific environment. Offspring inherit the characteristics that lead to the survival advantage and, over time, most members of the species come to possess the adaptive characteristic. Darwin referred to this process as natural selection.

Darwin was initially puzzled by structures such as the peacock's long tail, which appeared to convey little by way of survival advantage. However, he noticed that females of the species, the peahens, seek peacocks with long tails as mates. Darwin proposed the concept of sexual selection – a specific type of natural selection – to account for this. Characteristics that are attractive to the opposite sex will lead to increased access to mates and/or better quality offspring. These qualities increase reproductive success and are also passed on to offspring. This is the mechanism of sexual selection.

Genotype and phenotype

Genotype

In relation to evolution, biological psychology makes the assumption that the biological structures and behaviours shown by modern humans exist because they brought advantages to our ancestors. These structures and behaviours are embedded in our genetic makeup.

Each individual possesses unique genetic characteristics from the moment of conception. At fertilization, two sets of chromosomes – 23 from the mother and 23 from the father – unite to form the zygote. The genetic makeup of each zygote (and therefore each individual) is made of a unique combination of genes coded in 46 chromosomes. Siblings share roughly 50 per cent of their genes. Monozygotic (identical) twins are the exception, as they are genetically identical to each other.

The zygote divides into two and the two cells divide further, a process called replication. The **genotype**, the collection of all the genes, is copied in the nucleus of every cell of the body.

Key terms

Genotype: the collection of all the genes with each cell of an individual.

Phenotype: the behaviour and physical structure of an individual arising from an interaction between their genotype and their environment.

Phenotype

From conception, genes begin to interact with the environment. The immediate environment is internal, consisting of the fluid surrounding the nucleus within the cell and the adjacent cells. The internal environment can be affected by maternal exposure to disease or toxins such as cigarettes, drugs or alcohol passed through the placenta. Once an infant is born, exposure to different kinds of environments will also have effects on the individual – for example, if the child works out in the gym when it is older, this will lead to increased muscular development. The observable structure and behaviour of each individual is made up of the genotype interacting with the environment, and is referred to as the **phenotype**.

The influence of genes on behaviour

Genes influence the structure of the body, for example height and eye colour, and the function of the nervous system. The impact of genes on behaviour is a matter of ongoing debate (the nature–nurture debate), but there is substantial evidence that genes play a role in many aspects of psychology including personality, intelligence, and susceptibility to psychological disorders.

Biological psychologists carry out family history studies in order to assess the influence of genes. The previous chapter, on psychopathology, discusses the evidence indicating that obsessive-compulsive disorder (OCD) has a genetic component. First-degree relatives (i.e. siblings, children) of OCD sufferers have an 11.7 per cent chance of developing the disorder, compared to a 2.7 per cent risk in the general population (Nestadt et al., 2000).

Twin studies provide a more precise way than family history studies of assessing the extent of genetic influences on behaviours. In these studies, scientists look at the concordance rates of these influences – the correlation between the scores of a pair of twins on a specified variable. Since monozygotic (identical) twins are genetically identical there should be a higher concordance rate than dizygotic (non-identical) twins, who share 50 per cent of their genes. Miguel et al. (1997) found a 53 to 87 per cent concordance rate for OCD in monozygotic twins compared with 22 to 47 per cent in dizygotic twins. In relation to depression, McGuffin et al. (1996) found a concordance rate of 46 per cent in monozygotic twins compared with 20 per cent in dizygotic twins. However, the fact that monozygotic twins do not show a concordance rate of 100 per cent for either psychological disorder indicates that environmental factors still also play an important role.

Neurochemistry and behaviour

If a psychological disorder has a genetic basis, something must be inherited. The main focus for the study of **neurochemistry** and behaviour is on synaptic neurotransmitters. Neurotransmitters such as dopamine and serotonin are essential for transmission of nerve impulses across the synapse and are therefore involved in all aspects of behaviour (see page 251). Serotonin has wide-ranging effects and has been implicated in a range of behaviours, such as sleep, memory, emotions, appetite, and social and sexual behaviour.

Key term

Neurochemistry: the study of chemical processes which take place in the nervous system.

Psychoactive drugs such as cocaine affect neurotransmitters. Cocaine acts at synapses, blocking the reuptake of dopamine back into the presynaptic neuron. This temporarily makes more dopamine available in the synaptic gap, which leads to the characteristic 'rush' of euphoria felt by cocaine users. However, the presynaptic neuron cannot synthesize sufficient dopamine to replace the dopamine that has not been reabsorbed. After a short period of time, dopamine becomes depleted and insufficient amounts are released. This leads to the characteristic low mood or 'crash' felt by drug users as the effects of the drug wear off (Toates, 2007).

Disruption to neurochemistry is implicated in OCD and depression. OCD is characterized by obsessive thoughts that create anxiety and compulsions, behaviours that reduce the anxiety produced by obsessive thoughts. Serotonin appears to be the most important neurotransmitter in OCD, although dopamine probably also plays a role. Serotonin has a role in preventing repetition of tasks, and a lack of serotonin therefore results in the loss of a mechanism that helps to suppress task repetition. One treatment for OCD is the prescription of selective serotonin uptake inhibitors (SSRIs) such as Prozac. SSRIs reduce the symptoms of OCD in children and adults (Rauch and Jenike, 1998).

Depression is characterized by symptoms such as loss of motivation and lack of pleasure in everyday activities. Imbalances in serotonin, dopamine and noradrenalin are implicated in depression. Treatments for depression include monoamine oxidase inhibitors (MAOIs) and SSRIs, which balance levels of neurotransmitters.

Biological structures and behaviour

An important focus for the biological perspective is to map the relationship between various parts of the brain and their functions. Early work in this field progressed via the investigation of case studies of brain injury, such as Tan from earlier in this chapter. Another case study that progressed understanding in this area was that of Phineas Gage. Gage was working on an American railroad in 1848. A gunpowder accident occurred and a metal bar 3cm in diameter passed though Gage's skull and brain. Despite the severity of the accident, Gage survived, and showed little intellectual impairment, continuing to function relatively normally. However, he showed marked changes to his personality, becoming quick-tempered and foul-mouthed. A modern examination of Gage's skull showed that damage occurred to the frontal lobes, implying that these structures are implicated in control of behaviour (Damasio, 1996).

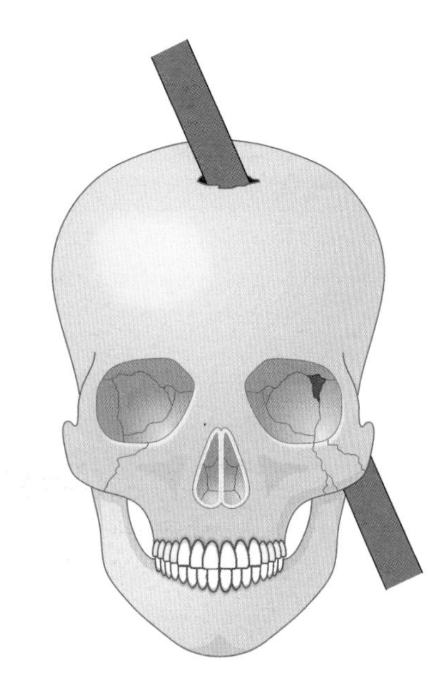

Fig. 5.12 Phineas Gage and the injurious iron bar

Modern scanning methods provide further insights into localization of function. A study by Raine, Buchsbaum and LaCasse (1997) examined the PET scans of violent criminals, comparing these with matched controls. The scans indicated reduced activity in the frontal lobes, supporting the conclusion, from the case study of Gage, that this area is important in the control of impulsive behaviours.

Case studies have also identified the brain structures implicated in memory. Henry Molaison (known as HM), born in 1926, developed epilepsy at an early age. Epilepsy is an uncontrolled electrical discharge in the brain and can be a disabling and dangerous condition. In 1953, an operation was performed to remove the area of damage causing HM's epilepsy, within the temporal lobe. This operation helped reduce the severity of the epileptic attacks but left HM with severe amnesia. He was unable to remember anything encountered after the operation to the day he died in 2008. Medical staff he met day after day were always greeted as strangers. However, he could remember and recognize his family, friends and events from before the operation. HM had anterograde amnesia (failure to learn new material after a traumatic event), but did not have significant retrograde amnesia (failure to recall material from before the traumatic event). The operation had removed a significant part of HM's hippocampus, and the resulting impairments imply that the hippocampus also plays a part in the registration of memories, in particular the transfer of memories from a short-term store into long-term memory.

The idea that some aspects of memory are localized to the hippocampus is supported by the work of Woollett and Maguire (2011) on London taxi drivers. To qualify as a taxi driver in London, applicants have to memorize routes covering around 25,000 London streets (known as 'The Knowledge'), an incredible task that takes between three and four years. Using brain scans, Woollett and

Maguire were able to show that participants who successfully completed this memory task had an enlarged hippocampus compared to control participants. They concluded that the hippocampus is a key part of our memory system.

These examples illustrate how behavioural functions can be localized to brain structures. However, memory systems are complicated and while particular aspects may be localized to specific structures, overall memory must involve interacting circuits in the brain.

Contribution of the biological approach

The biological approach has made dramatic contributions to our understanding of almost every field of psychology across the twentieth century. All of our behaviours – from basic functions such as eating and sleeping to cognitive processes such as memory – begin with biology. Modern brain-scanning methods are helping to map the brain and to identify the functions of the various structures and their role in a multitude of behaviours. The recent development of cognitive neuroscience brings together the brain imaging techniques used by biological psychologists and the study of cognitive functioning.

Insights from genetics and biochemistry provide important explanations of the causes of psychological problems, including OCD, depression, phobias and schizophrenia. Drug treatments based on our understanding of biochemistry are effective and quick-acting for many disorders. Antisocial behaviours such as aggression and violence are at least partially explained by biological factors.

EXAMPLE EXAM QUESTION

Complete the following sentence. Choose one answer only.
The genotype refers to:

A the chance of inheriting OCD through genes.
B the correlation between scores of twins.
C the collection of genes within each cell of an individual.
D the structure and behaviour of an individual.

Exam hint

Make sure you understand the difference between genotype and phenotype.

KEY POINTS

- Many behaviour patterns seen today have their roots in our hunter-gatherer past.
- Gradual changes in species take place through the mechanisms of natural and sexual selection.
- Genes play a role in intelligence and personality and in psychological disorders such as depression and OCD.
- Disruptions to neurochemicals including serotonin are implicated in depression and OCD.
- Case studies provide information on the localisation of function within brain structures.
- Case studies are complemented by modern scanning methods which are helping to map the functions of the brain.

The humanistic approach

History and context

Humanistic psychology started in the late 1950s and early 60s. The 1960s were a period of rapid social change in which long-established social norms were questioned and challenged. A group of American psychologists, including Abraham Maslow, Carl Rogers and George Kelly, had become increasingly dissatisfied with the two major approaches in explaining human behaviour, psychodynamics and behaviourism. Both perspectives held negative views of human nature: psychodynamic psychology, with the emphasis on the conflicted person, driven by unconscious instincts, and behaviourism, which viewed people as puppets controlled by the strings of the environment.

In 1961, the Association for Humanistic Psychology (AHP) was launched and the first issue of the Journal of Humanistic Psychology was published in December 1963. The founding psychologists of the AHP were interested in creating a professional organization that would explore a meaningful vision of human nature, focused on the self, health, personal growth, and creativity as central concerns.

Maslow's hierarchy of needs

Key term

Hierarchy of needs: Maslow's organisation of human needs into a tier, starting with basic survival needs and moving onto higher order needs for self-esteem and self-actualization.

Self-actualization: the highest of Maslow's human needs, which involves becoming all that we are capable of.

Abraham Maslow was one of the founders of the AHP. In 1954 he published his 'theory of motivation', which he later reworked and updated as the **hierarchy of needs** (Maslow, 1987). Maslow argued that human needs exist in a hierarchy, with basic needs at the bottom and higher order needs at the top (see Fig. 5.13).

The base of Maslow's hierarchy is physiological needs – those required for human survival, including food, water, and sleep. These needs are fundamental and if they are not met, it is unlikely that anything above this in the hierarchy will be pursued. (This is the reason sleep deprivation is such an effective form of torture.) The second level in the hierarchy refers to safety needs. This includes physical safety from environmental disasters such as earthquakes, as well as psychological safety. An individual who believes that they are being stalked may feel unsafe much of the time. The third level is the need for love and belongingness, in the form of acceptance from family, friends or partners. The fourth level of the hierarchy is esteem needs: Maslow conceptualized this as the need to feel good about oneself, and to establish a sense of competence and achievement – at work, at school or as a parent perhaps. A worker who is made redundant or who has recently retired may experience a threat to his or her self-esteem needs.

The bottom four levels of the hierarchy were referred to as 'deficiency needs' by Maslow. If these were not met, Maslow believed that we would experience this as having something important missing in our lives. The top level of the hierarchy is different to the others and is referred to as a 'being' need. Maslow believed that each individual has the desire for personal fulfilment, which he called **self-actualization**.

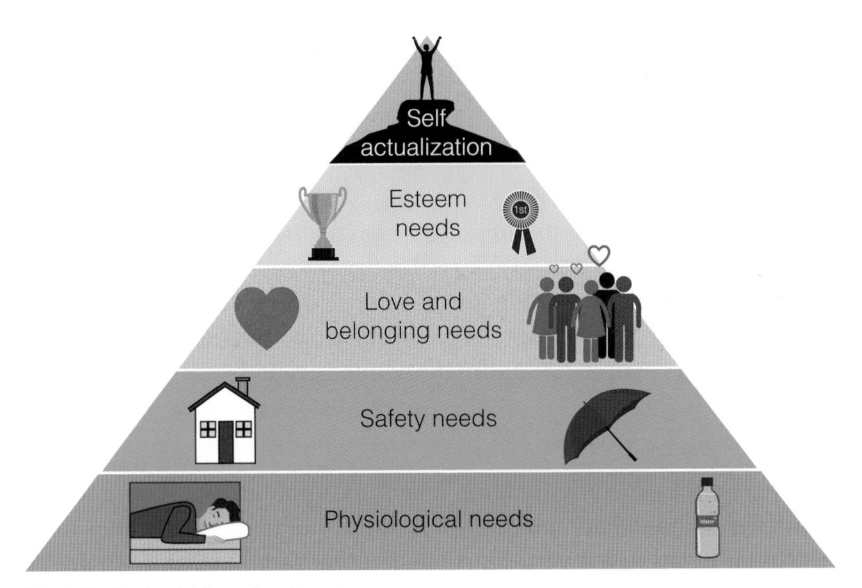

Fig. 5.13 Maslow's hierarchy of needs

Self-actualization is defined personally and can be pursued in many different ways – for example, through work, sport, and artistic or musical achievement.

Maslow developed his ideas from reading the biographies of famous people, such as scientists (Albert Einstein) and American presidents (Thomas Jefferson), who he believed demonstrated self-actualization. From these biographies, Maslow listed the characteristics of these high-achieving people, which included creativity, spontaneity and often an ability to see the world in quite an original way – to 'think outside the box'. Maslow concluded that the most important characteristic of self-actualizers 'is being involved in a cause outside themselves. They are working at something which they love so that the work–joy dichotomy in them disappears' (Maslow, 1973).

THINKING SCIENTIFICALLY: A SUBJECTIVE SAMPLE

It is worth stopping to think about Maslow's method. He personally identified those whom he believed demonstrated self-actualization, making the choice extremely subjective. His sample was limited and predominantly made up of personal acquaintances and famous people – it was also mainly white and male, reflecting the dominance of men in public life at the time. However, Maslow's hierarchy has been extremely influential in the psychology of motivation and within the work environment. It is widely accepted that people have different needs at different levels.

The self, conditions of worth, and free will

Carl Rogers (1902–1987) was another founder member of the AHP. Rogers' background was varied. He worked in teaching, counselling and psychotherapy, and was also a religious minister. Like Maslow, Rogers strongly believed in the capacity for personal growth and development. Rogers often recounted a story about his boyhood in which he had gone to the potato store located in the basement of his parent's house.

Despite the unfavourable conditions, the lack of light, soil and moisture, the potatoes were sending out spindly shoots and attempting to grow (Dryden, 2007). Rogers believed there is an innate human tendency for personal growth even when conditions are strongly unfavourable.

Key terms

The self: our concept of ourselves, which comes from our own experiences and evaluations from other people. The self includes an evaluative component, self esteem

Conditions of worth: conditions imposed by significant people (parents, partners, friends) in order for them to approve of us or love us.

Free will: the capacity to make changes to our lives and pursue goals.

An important element of Rogers's theory was the concept of **the self**. Each of us develops a sense of self during childhood – a model of who we are and what we are capable of. The self includes an important evaluative concept referred to as self-esteem – how good we feel about ourselves. According to Rogers, we construct the self during childhood from two main sources of information: our personal experiences of the world and the evaluations of other significant people, such as parents and teachers. An example will help to explore this idea.

Ten-year-old Sam enjoys reading, playing computer games, and constructing model aeroplanes. He is happy doing these activities in his room. Sam's dad is very sporty and wants Sam to excel at rugby. Sam is very frightened of getting hurt in rugby and of letting the team down. He dreads sports practice, but he wants to please his father and to win his approval. Sam's dad says he will be so proud of Sam when he scores his first try.

In this example, Sam enjoys activities such as playing computer games. However, Sam's dad has a strong idea of how he wants his son to be that contradicts Sam's own values (referred to by Rogers as the 'organismic valuing process'). Sam's feelings of self-worth and self-esteem are dependent on his father valuing him positively and feeling that his father approves of him. As Sam's father imposes **conditions of worth** ('I will be proud of you when you score your first try'), Sam experiences his father's love as conditional on him being good at sport. This leads to an unpleasant state caused by the contradiction between Sam's values based on his experiences, and the desire for his father's approval.

In contrast, if parents accept their children for who and what they are, offering them unconditional positive regard rather than conditions of worth, the child is more likely to grow into a fully functioning person who trusts their own judgement (Rogers, 1961). They are more likely to be open to experience and able to live in the moment rather than being stuck in the past or preoccupied with the future. Personal-centred counselling (PCC) aims to provide these optimum conditions for personal growth.

An important concept for both Rogers and Maslow was the idea of personal autonomy or **free will**. In contrast to psychodynamic theory, Rogers emphasized the ability of people to reflect on their feelings and experiences, and to initiate personal change and growth in themselves and their lives. Rogers' found through his work in counselling and therapy that people had the desire and ability to make changes to themselves and their lives.

The influence on counselling psychology

Rogers' ideas have been particularly influential in counselling and in psychotherapy. Person-centred counselling (originally called 'client centred') is strongly non-directive, and is based on Rogers' view that each person is the best expert on himself or herself, and should therefore be helped to find their own solution. The person-centred counsellor encourages the individual to talk as openly as they can, with the counsellor listening carefully and reflecting back what they think is being said ('What I think you are saying is …') to check their understanding. The aim is for the counsellor to enter into the client's world and see it 'as if it were their own'. The counsellor accepts the client's feelings and offers them unconditional positive regard, accepting and prizing them for who they are without imposing conditions of worth. This acceptance means that the client is able to clarify and accept their own feelings, so that feelings of harmony and acceptance of the self can replace inner conflict.

Rogers argued that three 'core' conditions are essential for a therapeutic relationship between a therapist and client:

- Empathic understanding: the therapist should aim to understand the reality of experience for the client and enter into their world, with the aim of seeing it 'as if it were their own'.
- Unconditional positive regard: acceptance and prizing of the client by the therapist for who they are without conditions of worth.
- A **congruent** therapist who is in touch with their own feelings.

PCC was adopted by the Marriage Guidance Council (now called Relate) in the 1950s in the UK and rapidly spread to other organizations. The British Association for Counselling and Psychotherapy (BACP) identifies PCC as their core approach (Dryden, 2007).

Key term

Congruence: a key quality of a person-centred therapy that refers to being genuine and authentic, rather than putting on a front of some kind.

EXAMPLE EXAM QUESTION

Liam is in his first year at university. He is not enjoying his business studies course very much. Liam's dad put pressure on Liam to choose the course because he wants Liam to follow him in the family business in the future. Liam thinks he might have been better off doing history, which he really enjoyed at school.

How would the humanistic approach explain Liam's feelings about his university course? Refer to the self and conditions of worth in your answer. (6 marks)

Exam hint

The focus of this question is on Carl Rogers' work. Whilst there are links to Maslow's ideas, you should focus your answer on Rogers' work.

KEY POINTS

- Humanistic psychology developed in the 1950s and 60s as a reaction against behaviourism and psychodynamic psychology.
- Both Maslow and Rogers stressed the importance of free will in their work.
- Maslow constructed a hierarchy of needs, starting with basic survival needs and working up to higher order needs for self-esteem and self-actualization.
- Rogers emphasized the importance of unconditional positive regard in the development of the self.
- Rogers' ideas are incorporated into person-centred counselling, which emphasizes the importance of a congruent therapist who empathizes with the client and provides unconditional positive regard and acceptance.
- Person-centred counselling is the core approach of many counselling organizations.

Comparison of approaches

	Model of the person	Focus of study	Methods	Types of data
Psychodynamic	The conflicted individual driven by unconscious processes	Unconscious processes, repressed memories, and fantasies	In-depth case studies, clinical interviews, free association, and dream analysis to access the unconscious	Qualitative data
Learning	The learning individual: stimulus-response learning and reinforcement	Behaviour in non-human and human animals	Tightly controlled experiment – e.g. the Skinner box, animal experiments	Behavioural data which is observable, rejection of inner mental states
Cognitive	The thinking individual	Cognitive processes such as memory and attention	Computer models of processes such as memory, experiments	Quantitative data derived from experiments
Biological	The embodied individual	Biological processes, brain structures, hormones, and nervous system	Brain scanning, invasive and non-invasive methods	Material (Bodily) data
Humanistic	The feeling, experiencing individual	Conscious experience	Case studies, interviews, biographies of famous people, clinical (counseling) work	Qualitative data

Text shaded in the above table represents cognitive neuroscience, an approach which overlaps with both cognitive and biological approaches.

ACTIVITY 5.3

Use the above table to identify similarities and differences between the approaches. For example, a similarity between psychodynamic and humanistic psychology is the use of case studies. A difference is the focus on conscious versus unconscious experience.

Exam focus

Read through the following example exam question, example student answer, and examiner comments. Then, have a go at answering the question yourself!

EXAMPLE EXAM QUESTION, TAKEN FROM PAGE 225

Discuss the contribution of behaviourist psychologists such as Pavlov and Skinner to our understanding of human behaviour. (16 marks)

Carly's answer

Pavlov and Skinner are both associated with the behaviourist approach. This approach was dominant in the early part of the twentieth century but has made lasting contributions to psychology today. The contributions include explaining psychological problems such as a phobias and providing effective treatments and therapies. The behaviourist approach has also helped us to understand other topics and has practical applications to changing behaviour through rewards. This essay will discuss the contribution of the learning approach to understanding human behaviour.

Examiner comment: This answer begins with a clear focus on the question, and accurate reference to the historical development of psychology.

Examiner comment: An example could be given here, for instance aggressive behaviour.

Pavlov and Skinner both started out studying animals. The behaviourist approach took the view that behaviours are learned and animals and people learn in the same ways; so it is easier to investigate learning using animals, as their environment can be controlled. Pavlov showed how dogs could associate food with a neutral stimulus (a bell) so that over time, the sound of the bell alone would produce a salivation response. This process is classical conditioning. Classical conditioning helps to explain how some people develop phobias of objects or situations such as a fear of dogs or of flying. A bad flight is associated with fear and avoided. Classical conditioning also provides the basis for systematic desensitization; in this approach the phobic is taught how to relax and then is presented with a hierarchy of images of the phobic object (e.g. pictures of planes). The response of fear is replaced by the response of relaxation as the two are incompatible. One problem with systematic desensitization and behaviourism overall is that that it ignores cognitive processes (in this case what phobic tell themselves about flying) – this is one reason why CBT can be more helpful for phobic treatment than desensitization. It also shows one of the reasons why behaviourism was followed by the cognitive approach.

Examiner comment: Succinct coverage of methods used, and principles of the behaviourist approach.

Examiner comment: Clear identification of a contribution here, with a useful example drawn from Unit 2.

Examiner comment: Thoughtful, critical points about the limitations of behaviourism here. Once again, Carly links this to the historical development of psychology.

Skinner also used animals and devised a method of studying them called the Skinner box. This was a controlled environment where environmental stimuli could be manipulated. Skinner found that the reward of a food pellet would lead to increased lever pressing in rats and rats would also press the lever to switch off unpleasant noises or electric shocks (negative reinforcement). Skinner identified the importance of rewards in shaping human and animal behaviour. Parents and teachers use rewards to 'condition' children to behave in certain ways.

Examiner comment: This is a well-focused response with a good selection of material to address the question. Specialist terms (e.g. negative reinforcement) are used effectively. In one or two places, minor details are omitted or the argument could be expanded a little further. This is a Level 4 response, at the bottom of the band **(13/16 marks)**.

Despite these important contributions there are some topics where behaviourists such as Pavlov and Skinner have had less impact. For example, attachments appear to be driven by instincts (Bowlby's theory), not rewards. Harlow showed how baby monkeys would cling to a cloth mother rather than a wire mother who supplied food, showing that feeding (reward) is not the basis of attachment. Despite this, behaviourism's contribution is substantial.

Examiner comment: This is a good example of one topic which cannot be explained using this approach.

Chapter summary

Key dates for approaches in psychology

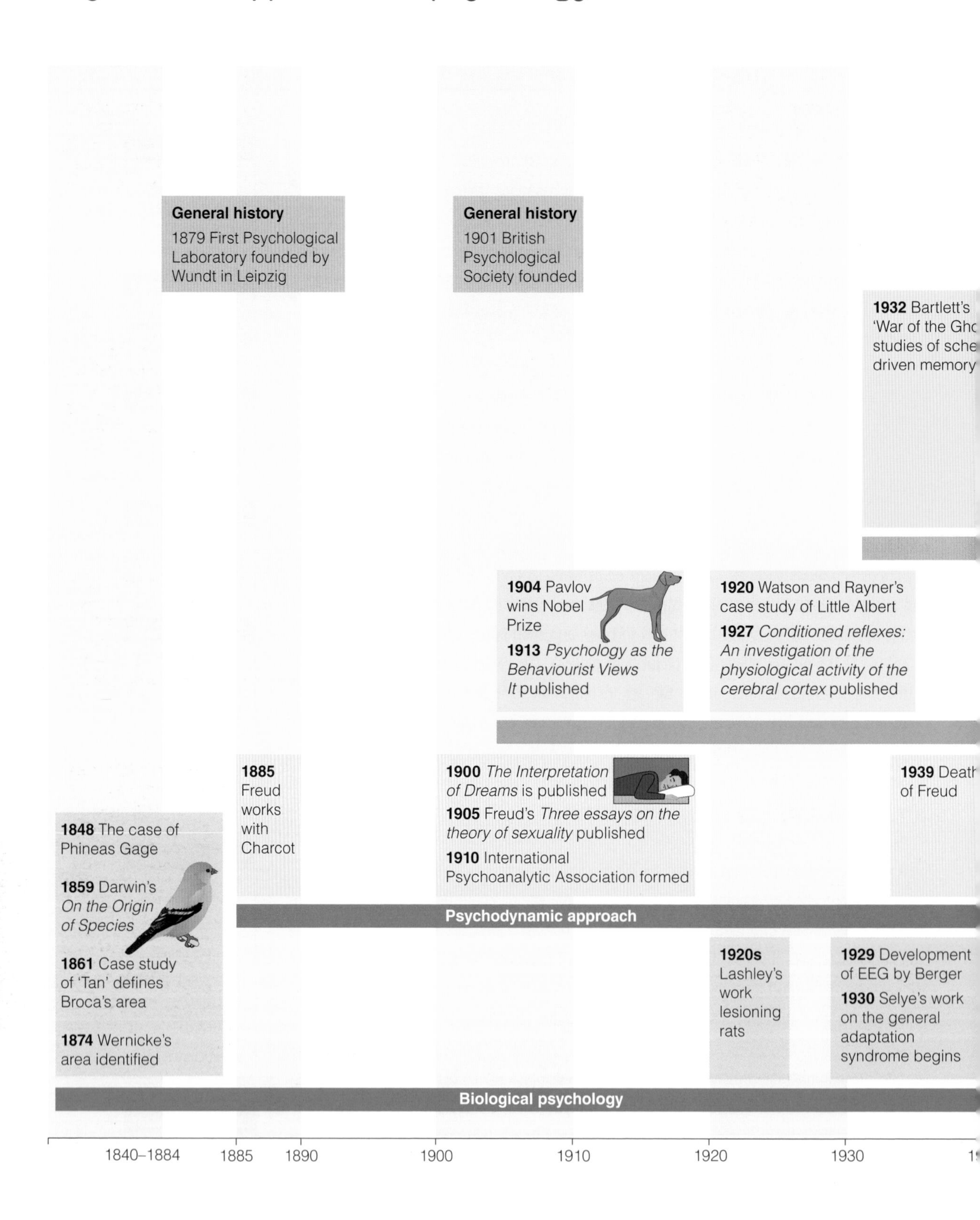

General history
1879 First Psychological Laboratory founded by Wundt in Leipzig
General history
1901 British Psychological Society founded
1932 Bartlett's 'War of the Ghc studies of sche driven memory
1904 Pavlov wins Nobel Prize
1913 Psychology as the Behaviourist Views It published
1920 Watson and Rayner's case study of Little Albert
1927 Conditioned reflexes: An investigation of the physiological activity of the cerebral cortex published
1885 Freud works with Charcot
1900 The Interpretation of Dreams is published
1905 Freud's Three essays on the theory of sexuality published
1910 International Psychoanalytic Association formed
1939 Death of Freud
Psychodynamic approach
1848 The case of Phineas Gage
1859 Darwin's On the Origin of Species
1861 Case study of 'Tan' defines Broca's area
1874 Wernicke's area identified
1920s Lashley's work lesioning rats
1929 Development of EEG by Berger
1930 Selye's work on the general adaptation syndrome begins
Biological psychology
1840–1884
1885
1890
1900
1910
1920
1930

1954 **Maslow publishes 'Theory of Motivation',** putting forward the idea of a hierarchy of needs

1957 Rogers' core conditions

1961 American Association for Humanistic Psychology founded

1971 Humanistic psychology recognized by the American Psychological Association and given its own division

Humanistic psychology

1950 The Turing Test devised by mathematician Alan Turing as a test of artificial intelligence

1957 Scoville and Milner's case study of HM

1958 Broadbent publishes filter theory of attention

1969 Warrington and Shallice's case study of KF

1968 The multi-store model of memory: Atkinson and Shiffrin

1974 Baddeley and Hitch's working memory model

1981 McClelland and Rumelhart's interactive activation model

Cognitive approach

1953 Skinner's operant conditioning

1958 Systematic desensitization developed by Wolpe

1961/63 Bandura, Ross and Ross Bobo doll studies

Behavioural approach

1950 Adorno's authoritarian personality defined

1951 Bowlby's maternal deprivation theory published

1960 Bowlby's attachment theory published

Psychodynamic approach

1950–65 Sperry's work on split-brain patients

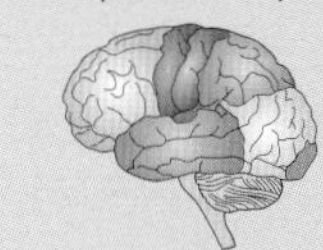

1970s and 80s Development of first fMRI and PET scans

1990s Development of neuronal transplants for Parkinson's Disease

Biological psychology

1950 | 1960 | 1970 | 1980 | 1990 | 2000s

Applications in therapy today

Person-centred therapy based on humanism underpins non-directive counseling. It underlies the positive psychology movement.

Cognitive therapies are widely used for anxiety and depression and focus on identifying and altering maladaptive thoughts.

Behaviour therapy is used today for anxiety disorders. Systematic desensitization is a treatment for problems such as fear of flying.

Psychodynamic therapy is used today and focuses on bringing unconscious material into conscious awareness.

Biological therapies such as drug treatments are effective today. Electro convulsive therapy is still used to treat severe depression.

Part 2: Psychology in context

Chapter 6: Biopsychology

Introduction

Biopsychology is the study of the biological aspects of behaviour. We are biological animals and our biology is basic for the range and types of behaviour we produce. You may not be aware of this as we take most of it for granted: you learn at school and college, you play sports, have emotional relationships, solve life's many problems, and develop career ambitions. All of these rely on your biology.

The biological approach in general was outlined on page 234. Although this is a broad approach, covering structures in the brain, neurochemistry, genetics and evolution, the focus of biopsychology is on the nervous system and, in particular, the brain.

In this chapter we will be looking at a number of different aspects of biopsychology. The foundations lie in the structure and function of neurons, followed by the organization and general functions of the nervous system and the endocrine system. The fight or flight response is used to illustrate the interaction between the brain and the endocrine system in behaviour, and the important role that hormones play in some behaviours. Biopsychology is not all about the brain.

A Level students then move on to some more detailed aspects of brain function and cognitive processes. These include localization of function in the brain, language and other aspects of hemispheric lateralization, and Sperry's important work with split-brain patients. After a consideration of brain plasticity, we review some of the key ways of studying the brain. This is followed by a final section on biological rhythms, which emphasizes our links to the rest of the animal kingdom and the environment around us.

Biopsychology does involve a good deal of new terminology and can seem very complicated. However, the study of brain function in particular has revealed fascinating findings that have helped develop our psychological models of human behaviour. In this way biopsychology provides a vital background to the study of behaviour.

What is covered in Biopsychology?

The structure and function of sensory, relay, and motor neurons

What is a neuron?

Key term

Neurons: the cells making up the nervous system, which conduct electrical impulses.

The body is made up of billions of cells organized into tissues and systems. Tissues include muscles, glands, skin, liver, and the nervous system. All these different tissues are made up of cells specialized to perform particular functions: for example, muscle tissue cells are specialized to contract, glandular cells for secretion of hormones, and fatty tissue cells for storage of fat molecules. The cells making up the nervous system are called **neurons**. They are specialized to conduct electrical impulses.

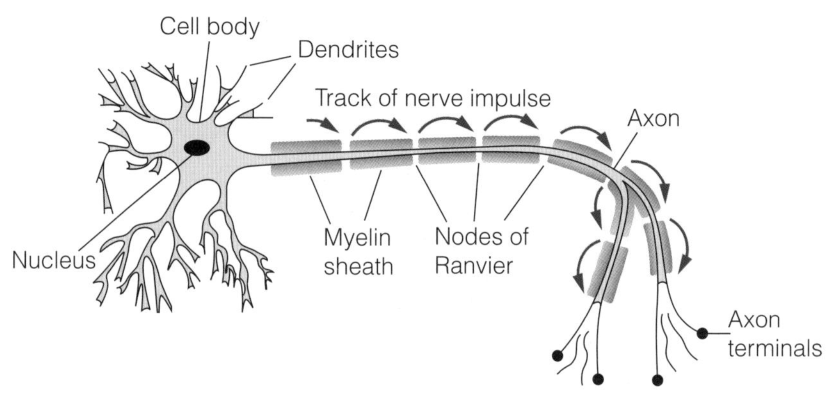

Fig. 6.1 The neuron

Neurons are elongated, with the cell body extending into a long branching axon on one side and into a number of short processes (dendrites) on the other. Neurons can come in a variety of shapes and sizes. Those in the brain, which contains billions of neurons, are obviously tiny; in contrast, the neuronal axon connecting the spinal cord to leg muscles can be a metre long. However, regardless of shape and size, all neurons operate in the same way.

Neurons are covered in a complex cell membrane made up of several layers. The biochemical structure of this membrane allows it to conduct or transmit pulses of electrical activity known as action potentials or nerve impulses. Nerve impulses begin on the dendrites and then travel across the cell body and along the axon. It is possible to use very thin wire electrodes positioned close to an axon to record nerve impulses. As a sequence of impulses travels down the axon they appear as a series of blips of electrical activity.

All action potentials have the same electrical properties and look identical wherever they are recorded in the nervous system. What does vary is their frequency and pattern. Because of the molecular make-up of the neuronal cell membrane, the maximum rate at which action potentials can be conducted along the neuron is around 250–400 impulses per second. However, the actual frequency and pattern of impulses (that is, whether they come in rapid bursts of activity or in steady trains of impulses) varies from neuron to neuron.

These action potentials or nerve impulses are the unit of information processing in the nervous system. All aspects of human behaviour (for example perception, memory, language, movement, thought, emotion, personality) are coded by the frequency and patterning of nerve impulses in different parts of the brain. Activity in the visual areas of the brain represents visual sensation, while when we move our legs there is electrical activity in the brain's movement centres. However, although this sounds relatively simple, do not forget there are around a 100 billion neurons in the brain, and this is where the complexity comes from.

Saltatory conduction

In advanced animals such as us and other mammals, many of the neurons making up the nervous system are covered in a fatty cover called the myelin sheath, which is not found in the nervous system of more primitive animals. There are gaps in this sheath, known as the nodes of Ranvier, where the neuronal cell membrane is exposed. Action potentials have the fascinating property of being able to jump from gap to gap; this is known as saltatory conduction, and is many times faster than the standard continuous conduction along the neuronal axon. Faster transmission means faster information processing, and has led to the development of complex human cognitive abilities.

Synaptic transmission

Looking at Figure 6.1 you might wonder what happens when the nerve impulse reaches the end of the axon – the axon terminal. Neurons are not physically connected to one another. Between the axon terminal and the next neuron is a tiny gap, the **synapse**, visible only under the electron microscope. Although tiny, this gap presents an obstacle to the nerve impulse as it cannot automatically jump across.

Transmission of nerve impulses across the synapse is chemical. Stored within the axon or presynaptic terminal are packets of chemicals known as **neurotransmitters**. As nerve impulses travelling down the axon reach the axon terminal, they stimulate the release of neurotransmitter molecules into the synapse. The synaptic gap is so small that the molecules can diffuse over to the postsynaptic membrane of the following neuron. Located on this membrane are synaptic receptors.

Key terms

Synapse: a tiny gap between two neurons, across which nerve impulses are passed.

Neurotransmitters: packets of chemicals stored within the axon; they enable nerve impulses to pass across the synapse to the postsynaptic neuron.

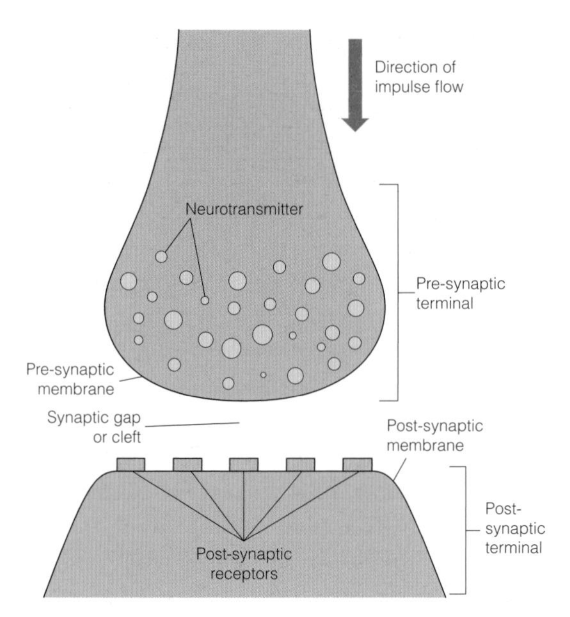

Fig. 6.2 The synapse

Synaptic receptors

Synaptic receptors are molecules with a particular structure that matches the structure of the neurotransmitter molecule, in the same way that a key matches a lock. As the neurotransmitter molecule reaches the postsynaptic membrane it binds to the receptor for a brief period of time. This combination of neurotransmitter with receptor alters the biochemical nature of the postsynaptic membrane, making a nerve impulse more likely to be triggered at that point on the membrane.

It is a feature of the nerve impulse that it is 'all or nothing'; either it crosses the synapse or it does not. For a nerve impulse to be triggered on the postsynaptic membrane, sufficient neurotransmitter molecules must be released from the presynaptic terminal. When they combine with postsynaptic receptors, changes in the postsynaptic membrane will cross a threshold and a nerve impulse will be triggered. Once triggered, the nerve impulse will be conducted along the postsynaptic neuron, along the axon to the axon terminals, where the process is repeated at the next set of synapses.

The purpose of the synapse

The purpose of the synapse is to allow for information processing. To cross the synapse, enough nerve impulses must arrive at the presynaptic terminal in a short space of time to release sufficient neurotransmitter molecules, to fire the postsynaptic membrane. If only a few impulses arrive, the amount of neurotransmitter released will not be sufficient, and the postsynaptic membrane will not fire. The information coded by those impulses will be lost. As each neuron in the brain can have axons with up to 1000 branches, they can make up to 1000 synaptic connections with other neurons. This complexity means that the synapse is a crucial component of information processing in the nervous system.

There are a limited number of neurotransmitters and associated receptors (e.g. dopamine, serotonin, noradrenaline and acetylcholine receptors). Synapses can in fact be defined by the neurotransmitter they release, so we have synapses using dopamine, serotonin, etc. We meet examples of these later in the A Level course. Knowing the chemical nature of the synapse enables us to explain the action of drugs on behaviour; many drugs have specific actions at the synapse, increasing or decreasing neurotransmitter release and/or combining with postsynaptic receptors.

Excitation and inhibition

The synapse can look quite straightforward but in fact, like the brain in general, it is extremely complicated. One immediate complication is that synaptic connections can be **excitatory** or **inhibitory**. The difference lies in the action of the neurotransmitter at the postsynaptic receptor. If the combination of neurotransmitter and postsynaptic receptor makes a nerve impulse or action potential *more* likely to be triggered, the synapse is excitatory. Neurotransmitters such as dopamine, serotonin and acetylcholine are excitatory neurotransmitters. However others, in particular GABA (gamma aminobutyric acid), are inhibitory.

Inhibitory means that when GABA is released from the presynaptic axon terminal and combines with postsynaptic GABA receptors, it stabilizes the postsynaptic membrane and makes an action potential *less* likely to occur. This means that the more active the presynaptic neuron is, the more the postsynaptic neuron is inhibited. For instance, a major role for GABA neurons in the brain is to inhibit activity in other neurotransmitter systems, such as serotonin. Therefore, an indirect effect of drugs increasing GABA activity in the brain is to reduce activity in serotonin pathways, and generally to produce a sedative or calming effect. It was discovered in the 1980s that the most popular class of anti-anxiety drugs, the benzodiazepines, act by stimulating the release of GABA in the brain.

When we talk about brain activity and behaviour we usually emphasize excitation and activation. But it is important to remember that normal brain function relies on a careful balance between excitatory and inhibitory influences. Some forms of epilepsy, for instance, may be caused by an imbalance between these excitatory and inhibitory influences.

Key terms

Excitation: synapses in the nervous system can be excitatory or inhibitory; excitatory synapses activate the postsynaptic neuron increasing neural activation in the central nervous system

Inhibition: synapses in the nervous system can be excitatory or inhibitory; inhibitory synapses inhibit activity in the postsynaptic neuron, decreasing neural activation in the central nervous system; inhibitory circuits are vital to the balance between excitation and inhibition in the nervous system

ACTIVITY 6.1

Relay neurons lie within the brain and spinal cord, connecting areas within the central nervous system. In Google Images, search for 'spinal reflex arc'. From the diagrams, see how quickly you can spot the sensory neuron, the motor neuron, and the relay neuron (interneuron). What is the role of the relay neuron in the spinal reflex arc?

Exam hint

This question is about the *functions* of relay neurons and not about their structure. There are two marks available, so you will need to make at least two points relevant to function.

EXAMPLE EXAM QUESTION

Outline the function of relay neurons. [2 marks]

KEY POINTS

- The basic unit of the nervous system is the neuron. The neuron is usually elongated and specialized to conduct electrical impulses from one end to the other.
- The nerve impulses represent information being processed by the nervous system.
- The axon of most neurons is covered by a fatty myelin sheath. Nerve impulses can jump from gap to gap in this myelin sheath. This increases the speed at which nerve impulses travel along the axon, and is known as saltatory conduction.
- Between the axon terminal and the following neuron there is a tiny gap, the synapse. Transmission of impulses across the synapse is chemical. Neurotransmitters released from the presynaptic terminal combine with receptors on the postsynaptic membrane to trigger a nerve impulse in the postsynaptic neuron.
- The best-known neurotransmitters include dopamine, serotonin, and acetylcholine.
- Synaptic connections may be excitatory or inhibitory. Many inhibitory synapses in the brain use GABA as a neurotransmitter. Therefore the role of GABA is to inhibit or damp down activity in brain circuits. Normal brain function depends upon a regulated balance between excitatory and inhibitory influences. When this goes wrong, problems such as epilepsy may arise.

The divisions of the nervous system

The nervous system is made up of billions of neurons. The brain alone has been called the most complicated structure in the universe. Nonetheless, the nervous system is organized in a very systematic way.

Key term

Sensory neuron: neuron carrying sensory information into the central nervous system from the body's sensory receptors

The brain is our key information processor, but it does not have direct connections with the outside world. To do its job effectively, it needs to receive sensory input from the body's sensory receptors, such as eyes, ears, touch and pain receptors on the skin, smell, and taste. Sensory information is carried in sensory (or 'afferent') pathways that run from the sensory receptors through the spinal nerves to the spinal cord and onwards to the brain. (One exception to this is the specialized senses, vision and hearing. Visual and auditory sensory pathways do not involve the spinal cord, but are contained within the brain.) Neurons making up these sensory pathways are called **sensory neurons**.

The brain also needs to be connected to the muscles of the skeleton, so that it can control movement. It also controls internal organs such as the heart, circulatory system, glands, and digestive system. Pathways allowing the brain to control movement and responses of internal systems are referred to as motor (or 'efferent') pathways. Neurons making up these motor pathways are called **motor neurons**.

Besides sensory and motor neurons we also have **relay neurons**, also known as interneurons. These are neither sensory nor motor, but lie entirely within the central nervous system, and their function is to interconnect different parts of the **central nervous system (CNS)**. The majority of neurons in the brain are relay neurons.

Our main interest is in the brain. This, along with the spinal cord, makes up the CNS. Radiating from the spinal cord are the spinal nerves, containing sensory and motor pathways connecting the CNS with the organs of the body. The spinal nerves are referred to as the **peripheral nervous system (PNS)**. Before looking at the PNS, we will consider the brain; how it functions as the final destination for sensory input, and how it controls our motor responses.

Key terms

Motor neuron: neuron carrying motor commands out from the central nervous system to the skeletal muscles of the body, allowing for movement

Relay neuron: neuron within the central nervous system that interconnects different parts of the CNS

The central nervous system (CNS): major part of the nervous system, made up of the brain and the spinal cord

The peripheral nervous system (PNS): consists of the 31 pairs of spinal nerves, which carry sensory and motor pathways of the somatic nervous system, and motor pathways of the autonomic nervous system; connects the CNS with the body and with the outside world

The brain

The billions of neurons in the brain can be divided into hundreds of separate structures. However, an outline of its major components brings this number down to a more manageable level, with an initial division into hindbrain, midbrain, and forebrain.

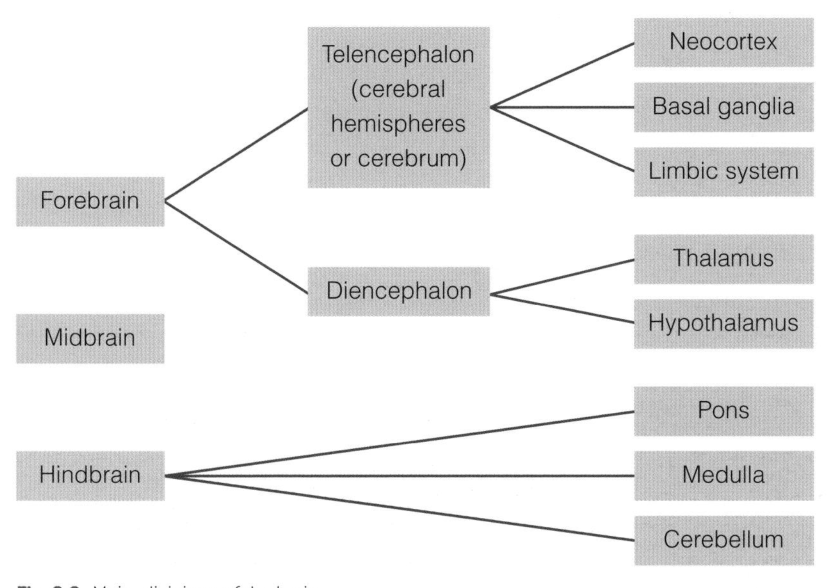

Fig. 6.3 Major divisions of the brain

Hindbrain and midbrain

The hindbrain is made up of the medulla, pons, and cerebellum. The medulla, pons and midbrain (see Fig. 6.4) together are classified as the brainstem. The brainstem is essentially a continuation of the spinal cord within the brain, with sensory and motor pathways carrying information to and from higher brain centres. Also buried within the brainstem is the ascending reticular formation, a network of neurons vital to sleep and arousal functions of the brain. The brainstem also contains the major autonomic centres (see page 258); autonomic pathways travel down from these centres through the spinal cord and are distributed throughout the body by the spinal nerves.

The cerebellum is a large structure located on the back surface of the brainstem. Its major functions relate to the control of movement, and damage results in a loss of motor coordination.

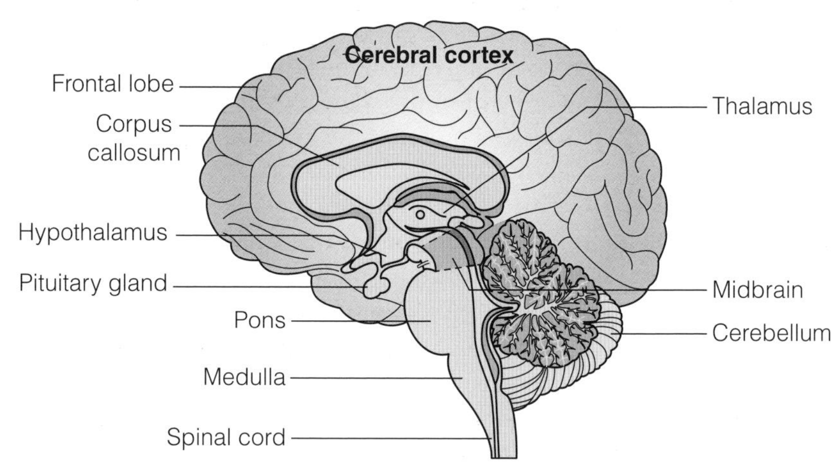

Fig. 6.4 Cross-section of the brain

Forebrain

This is the largest division of the brain, and is subdivided into two major components, the diencephalon and the telencephalon (also known as the cerebral hemispheres or cerebrum).

Diencephalon

This subdivision of the forebrain contains two main structures, the thalamus and the hypothalamus.

- The thalamus is an important sensory structure, relaying sensory information from pathways ascending up through the spinal cord and the brainstem on to the cortex.
- The hypothalamus lies at the base of the brain. Through its control over the pituitary gland (see page 260), which lies just below it, and the autonomic centres in the brainstem, the hypothalamus is involved in many of the body's physiological functions. These include stress-related arousal, hunger, thirst, and sexual and reproductive behaviours.

Telencephalon or cerebral hemispheres

The cerebral hemispheres contain the systems and structures of most interest to psychologists. High-level cognitive and emotional processes are controlled from these areas, although it must be remembered that all parts of the brain are heavily interconnected, especially the subsystems of the hemispheres. Three major systems make up the cerebral hemispheres: the limbic system, the basal ganglia and the cerebral cortex.

- **Limbic system:** This consists of a set of interconnected structures, including the hippocampus, amygdala, septum and cingulate gyrus. They are involved in functions such as learning, memory, and especially emotions.
- **Basal ganglia:** The basal ganglia have important functions in relation to movement and motor control. They include the caudate nucleus, the putamen, and the globus pallidus. Damage to the basal ganglia results in movement disorders such as Parkinson's disease.
- **Cerebral cortex:** This is the most recently evolved part of the brain, and the amount of cortex distinguishes humans from other species. It contains within it the highest cognitive functions, such as planning and problem-solving, language, consciousness, and personality, as well as perception and control of movement.

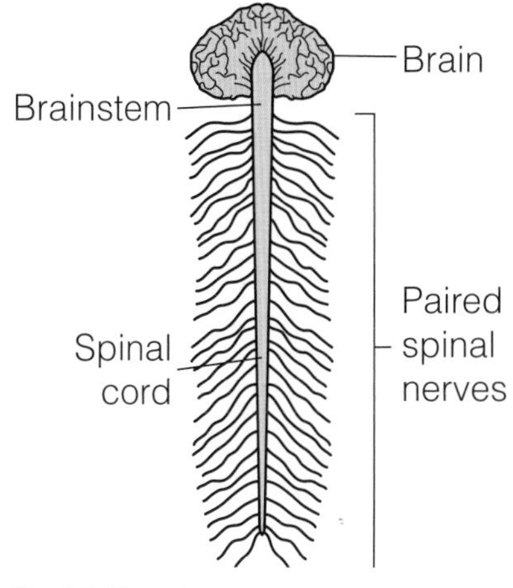

Fig. 6.5 The spinal nerves

Peripheral nervous system (PNS)

The PNS is made up of the 31 spinal nerves (see Fig. 6.5). These contain millions of sensory (afferent) and motor (efferent) pathways allowing the brain to be aware of what is going on in the body and outside world, and to control our various response systems. Although highly complicated, the millions of pathways making up the spinal nerves can conveniently be divided into the somatic and autonomic nervous systems.

The somatic nervous system (SNS)

The **somatic nervous system (SNS)** is made up of two components. The first is made up of sensory or afferent pathways from the sensory receptors of the body – touch, pain, pressure, temperature. These systems have specialized sensory receptors in the skin that respond to the various stimuli by triggering action potentials (nerve impulses) in sensory neurons. These neurons carry the sensory information into the spinal cord via the spinal nerves. In the spinal cord they make synaptic connections onto neurons that carry the information up the spinal cord to the brain, where it is processed.

Key term

Somatic nervous system (SNS): part of the PNS, the SNS is made up of sensory pathways from the sensory receptors on the body surface, and motor pathways controlling skeletal muscle; maintains communication between the CNS and the outside world

The second component of the SNS is made up of motor or efferent pathways. The axons of motor neurons travel in spinal nerves out to the skeletal muscles of the body, allowing the brain to control bodily movement. Commands to move our muscles are formulated in the cerebral cortex of the forebrain (see Figure 6.4 on page 256), and then travel down through the brain and spinal cord to the spinal nerves.

We can see the two components of the SNS as integrating the brain with the outside world. Sensory pathways carry information from the environment to the brain, and motor pathways allow for responses (movement) to environmental stimuli. But we also have an internal environment to regulate, and for this we have another division of the spinal nerves.

The autonomic nervous system (ANS)

> **Key terms**
>
> **Autonomic nervous system (ANS):** part of the PNS, the ANS is made up of motor pathways controlling the activity of internal body systems such as the heart and circulatory system, the intestines, and various glands; it has two branches, the sympathetic and the parasympathetic

The **autonomic nervous system (ANS)** plays a central role in states of bodily arousal. ANS centres are located in the brainstem. From here, ANS pathways run down through the spinal cord and are distributed throughout the body by the spinal nerves. The ANS is concerned with the regulation of our internal environment, controlling such vital functions as body temperature, heart rate, and blood pressure. The ANS is central to homeostasis, the maintenance of a constant internal environment. An example of this is the way mammals such as humans keep a constant body temperature. This means that we can be active when it is either very hot or very cold outside. Without homeostasis, snakes and other reptiles, for instance, become inactive in the cold; therefore, they spend as much time as possible basking in the sunshine to increase their body temperature. Homeostasis allows an animal to become independent of the environment and consequently more successful as a species. The ANS is vital to homeostasis as it constantly monitors and controls the internal environment.

To carry out its functions the ANS has two separate branches, the sympathetic and the parasympathetic. Nerve fibres from both branches connect with internal structures such as various glands (e.g. the adrenal medulla, pancreas, salivary glands), the heart and circulatory system, and the digestive system.

- Sympathetic arousal or dominance leads to a pattern of bodily arousal, with increases in heart rate and blood pressure and a decrease in activity in the digestive system.
- Parasympathetic dominance leads to the opposite pattern, one of physiological calm, with lower heart rate and blood pressure and increased digestive activity.

Usually the two branches are in balance, but under certain circumstances the balance shifts and one branch becomes dominant. These shifts are determined by the body's physiological requirements. Physical exercise needs energy, and this is provided by sympathetic arousal. Similarly, if a dangerous or threatening situation is perceived, higher brain centres signal the hypothalamus, a key structure buried deep in the brain (see page 256), to activate the sympathetic branch of the ANS. This provides energy in case we need to respond physically to the situation. So, as we see later, sympathetic arousal is an important part of the body's response to stress – the fight or flight response (see page 262).

ACTIVITY 6.2

Look at the boxes on the right-hand side of Figure 6.3. For 'neocortex', write down three functions without looking at the text. For the other boxes write down one function associated with that structure.

EXAMPLE EXAM QUESTION

Outline the organization of the autonomic nervous system. [4 marks]

Exam hint

The ANS is a complicated system. However, it does break down into sympathetic and parasympathetic branches. With four marks available, a sensible approach would be to make two points about each of the branches; for example, their overall effect, plus their particular actions on specific structures such as the heart.

See page 299 for example student answers to this question, and examiner feedback.

KEY POINTS

- The brain consists of three major components: the hindbrain, the midbrain and the forebrain.
- The forebrain is divided into the diencephalon and the telencephalon or cerebral hemispheres. The main structures of the diencephalon are the thalamus and hypothalamus.
- The cerebral hemispheres consist of the limbic system, the basal ganglia, and cerebral cortex.
- The cerebral cortex is the most recently evolved part of the brain.
- Sensory and motor pathways make up the peripheral nervous system (PNS). The PNS consists of the 31 spinal nerves that contain sensory and motor pathways of the somatic nervous system (SNS) and motor pathways of the autonomic nervous system (ANS).
- The SNS contains sensory pathways from receptors in the skin. Information from these receptors is conducted to the spinal cord and the brain.
- Motor pathways of the SNS carry commands from the motor cortex of the brain out to the muscles of the skeleton to enable movement.
- The ANS controls internal organs of the body. It is vital to homeostasis, the maintenance of a constant internal environment.
- Activity in the sympathetic branch of the ANS leads to bodily arousal, with increases in heart rate and blood pressure. Activity in the parasympathetic branch produces the opposite pattern, one of relaxation.

The function of the endocrine system

Someone you have fancied for some time comes up during lunchtime and asks you out. You feel your heart flutter and your mouth goes dry. You may have a similar reaction riding the Oblivion rollercoaster at Alton Towers. If you have experienced these reactions, you are familiar with the effects of the hormone **adrenaline**.

Hormones are chemical messages or substances, usually released from structures called **glands**, which can control or regulate the activity of particular cells or organs in the body. The network of glands is called **the endocrine system**. Glands making up the endocrine system secrete their hormones directly into the bloodstream or circulatory system. The arousal produced by adrenaline is one of the most obvious hormonal effects, but in fact the range of hormones and their effects is enormous, and they play an important part in many areas of behaviour.

Key terms

Adrenaline: hormone released from the adrenal medulla, acts on heart and circulatory system to increase heart rate and blood pressure; important part of the fight or flight response

Hormone: chemical released from endocrine glands into the bloodstream that acts on target structures to alter their function or to release other hormones

Gland: body organ that releases hormones into the bloodstream

The endocrine system: network of glands throughout the body releasing hormones to affect and organize the body's physiological systems; the pituitary gland is the 'master' gland in the endocrine system

The endocrine system contains a large number of glands and an even larger number of hormones, with a variety of effects on the body. Table 6.1 gives some examples of endocrine glands and the hormones they release.

Endocrine gland	Main hormone(s) released	Effects
Thyroid	Thyroxine	Regulates the body's metabolic rate and protein synthesis.
Adrenal medulla	Adrenaline and noradrenaline	Fight or flight response. Increased heart rate and blood flow to brain and muscles, release of stored glucose and fats for use in fight or flight responses.
Adrenal cortex	Glucocorticoids, such as cortisone, cortisol and corticosterone	Further release of stored glucose and fats for energy expenditure. Suppression of the immune system and the inflammatory response.
	Mineralocorticoids	These regulate the water balance of the body through water and sodium reabsorption in the kidneys.
Testes	Androgens, main one testosterone	Development of male secondary sexual characteristics at puberty. Promotes muscle mass and muscle growth.
Ovaries	Oestrogens, main one oestradiol	Regulation of female reproductive system, menstrual cycle and pregnancy.
Pineal	Melatonin	Regulation of arousal, biological rhythms and the sleep–wake cycle.

Table 6.1

The so-called 'master gland' of the body is the pituitary (see Figure 6.4, page 256). It is known as the master gland because many of the hormones released by the pituitary gland control the secretions of other endocrine glands, rather than having direct effects on cells and tissues of the body. The pituitary is located in the cranial cavity, just below the hypothalamus, to which it is directly connected.

The pituitary is divided into an anterior and a posterior portion or lobe. These are distinguished by the hormones they release (see Table 6.2).

The posterior pituitary releases oxytocin and vasopressin (also known as antidiuretic hormone, ADH). Release of pituitary hormones into the bloodstream is directly controlled by the hypothalamus.

Note that the hypothalamus controls the release of hormones from the pituitary gland, and can therefore be seen to control and regulate the endocrine system in general.

Anterior pituitary	Target organs and/or effects
Adrenocortical trophic hormone (ACTH)	Adrenal cortex, stimulating release of glucocorticoids such as cortisone and corticosterone. Key component in the stress response.
Thyroid stimulating hormone (TSH)	Thyroid gland, stimulating release of thyroxine.
Prolactin	Mammary glands, stimulating milk production and release.
Follicle stimulating hormone (FSH)	Ovaries and testes, stimulating release of ovarian follicles and promoting spermatogenesis.
Growth hormone	General promotion of cell growth and multiplication in the body.
Melanocyte stimulating hormone (MSH)	Stimulates the production and release of the pigment melatonin in the skin and the hair.
Posterior pituitary	**Target organs and/or effects**
Vasopressin or antidiuretic hormone (ADH)	Involved in regulating the water balance of the body; stimulates water reabsorption by kidney and increases blood volume.
Oxytocin	Important in promoting uterine contractions in childbirth and lactation after birth.

Table 6.2

You can see how complex the endocrine system is. It has a vital role in the internal physiological regulation of the body. It works closely with the autonomic nervous system (ANS) in this regard.

Although the contribution of the endocrine system is essentially to regulate the internal physiological processes of the body, some aspects do become important to psychologists when we look at situations such as threat and stress.

ACTIVITY 6.3

There are many hormones associated with the endocrine system. Copy and complete the following table. In the first column, write down three hormones. Then fill in the rest of the row with the name of the endocrine gland releasing that hormone, and one function of that hormone in the body.

Hormone	Endocrine gland	Function in the body
1.		
2.		
3.		

Exam hint

With four marks available, each example is worth two marks. For each example, you will need to name an accurate example (e.g. adrenaline released from the adrenal medulla, or thyroxine released from the thyroid gland) and outline the effects on the body.

EXAMPLE EXAM QUESTION

Give two examples of the effects of hormones released by glands of the endocrine system. (4 marks)

KEY POINTS

- The endocrine system consists of a network of glands throughout the body. These glands release hormones, chemical messengers, into the bloodstream.
- Key glands include the thyroid, the adrenal cortex and the adrenal medulla, testes, and ovaries. Between them, hormones released by these glands are vital to most of the physiological functions of the body.
- The pituitary gland has been called the master gland of the body. Hormones released by the pituitary gland regulate other glands.
- The release of hormones from the pituitary gland is in turn controlled by the hypothalamus in the brain. The hypothalamus can therefore be seen as a controlling centre for the end of a complex system.

The fight or flight response

Key term

Fight or flight response: the body's physiological reactions to threat or danger; involves activation of the hypothalamic-pituitary-adrenal cortex pathway and the sympathetic-adrenal medullary system; designed to provide energy and arousal for rapid responses to threat and danger

In his classic book, *Why Zebra's Don't Get Ulcers*, Robert M. Sapolsky outlines the evolution of the **fight or flight response** and why it is so important to our lives today. When a zebra spots a lion in the distance it knows that fighting is not an option (who would you bet on?). It has to flee, and to do that it needs huge amounts of energy. This energy is provided by the activation of two major pathways, the hypothalamic–pituitary–adrenal axis (HPA), and the sympathetic adrenomedullary system (SAM). Sometimes, though, the animal is cornered and has to fight. But again it needs energy, provided by the HPA and SMS.

In outline (for detail, see page 263), HPA and SAM activation results in high blood levels of glucose and fats such as triglycerides, along with raised heart rate and blood pressure. In the case of the zebra, these energy reserves are burnt up in muscle activity and, once it has escaped, blood levels return to normal and blood pressure and heart rate fall. This simple pattern would also apply to our earliest human ancestors.

The problem for modern humans is that we do not often come across lions or sabre-toothed tigers. But we do have major life stressors, for example exams, relationships, redundancy and bereavement. These stressors are equally as effective in activating the HPA and SAM system as the lion was to our ancestors. Unfortunately the response to such stressors does not usually require huge energy expenditure, even though our bloodstream is flooded with glucose and fats. It is the negative effects of this high level of bodily arousal that have been associated with stress-related illnesses.

The body's fight or flight response begins with appraisal of the situation, followed by activation of the two key pathways.

Appraisal

Appraisal or evaluation of the situation depends upon the sensory processing systems, such as vision and hearing, and stored memories of previous encounters with the situation. Key structures in the brain include higher cortical centres and parts of the limbic system, especially those involved with emotional memory such as the amygdala and hippocampus.

If the situation is appraised as potentially dangerous, the hypothalamus at the base of the brain is alerted. As we have seen, the hypothalamus controls two major systems that have central roles in bodily arousal, the hypothalamic–pituitary–adrenal axis (HPA), and the sympathetic adrenomedullary (SAM) pathway.

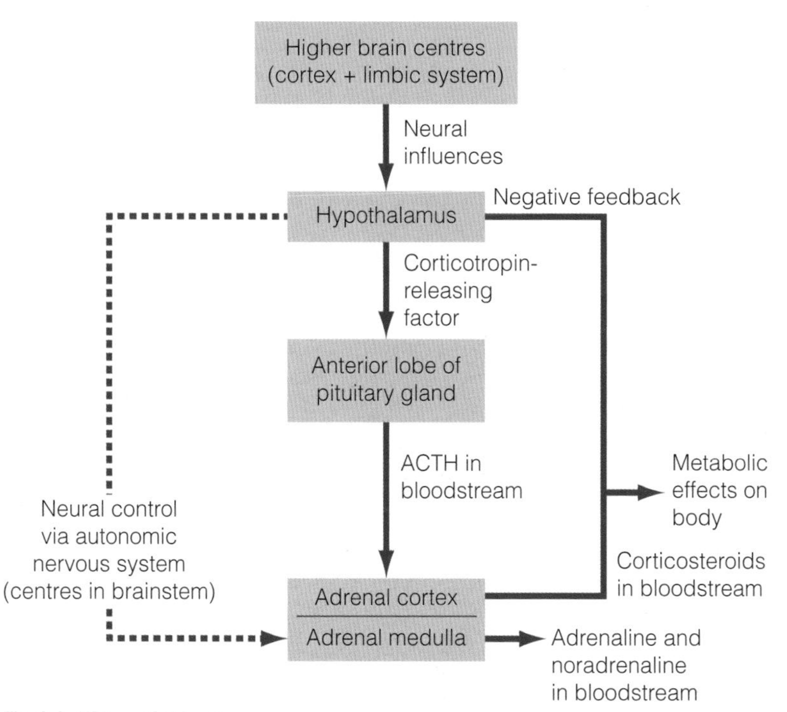

Fig. 6.6 HPA and SAM pathways

The hypothalamic–pituitary–adrenal axis (HPA)

The pituitary gland sits just beneath the brain, connected to the hypothalamus by a short stalk. The pituitary is the master gland of the body, releasing a number of hormones into the bloodstream.

The key pituitary stress hormone is adrenocorticotrophic hormone (ACTH). The hypothalamus stimulates the release of ACTH from the anterior pituitary into the bloodstream. The hormone travels to the adrenal cortex, part of the adrenal gland (we have two adrenal glands, located close to the kidney on each side of the body). When ACTH reaches the adrenal cortex, it stimulates the release of glucocorticoids, especially corticosteroids such as cortisol and corticosterone, into the bloodstream. These hormones in turn have major effects on the body, which we will review shortly.

The sympathetic adrenomedullary pathway (SAM)

The sympathetic nervous system (SNS) is one part of the autonomic nervous system (described on page 258) that controls our internal organs. Nerve pathways of the SNS originate in the brainstem (part of the brain just above the spinal cord; see Figure 6.4, page 256) and travel via the spinal cord and spinal nerves to the various body organs. One of these pathways runs to the adrenal medulla, which along with the adrenal cortex makes up the adrenal gland.

When appraisal processes in higher brain centres detect a stressful situation, the hypothalamus is instructed to stimulate ACTH release from the pituitary. In addition, the hypothalamus also activates the SNS centres in the brainstem and the pathways running to the adrenal medulla (SAM pathway). This results in the increased release of adrenaline and noradrenaline into the bloodstream.

The role of hormones in the fight or flight response

The perception of a dangerous and stressful situation therefore produces activation of the HPA axis and the SAM pathway, and a number of hormones flood into the bloodstream. These hormones have a number of effects on the body, mainly designed to provide for energy expenditure used in responses to stress, for instance confrontation (fight) or escape (flight).

- The SNS itself has direct connections to the heart and activation speeds up heart rate and raises blood pressure. These effects are increased and sustained by the release of adrenaline and noradrenaline from the adrenal medulla via the SAM pathway; these act on the heart muscles to increase the heart rate, and also on blood vessels to constrict them and so raise blood pressure. The end result is that oxygen is rapidly pumped to the muscles of the skeleton, allowing for increased physical activity.
- The body's energy reserves are largely in the form of glycogen stored in the liver and fat reserves in fatty tissue. A major effect of circulating adrenaline and corticosteroids released in response to SMS and HPA activation is the increased release or mobilization of these energy reserves; this is in the form of raised blood levels of glucose (from glycogen) and fatty acids such as triglycerides (from our fat reserves).
- Raised levels of corticosteroids, if sustained over a long period, also have the interesting effect of suppressing the body's immune system. This system is the body's defence against infection, and consists of a variety of complex subsystems vital in keeping the person healthy.

Stress-related illness

It was once thought that long periods of stress exhausted the HPA and SAM pathways, and that this led to stress-related illness. It is now thought that stress-related illnesses are not caused by exhaustion of the body's physiological stress responses. Rather, it is the effect of chronic or long-term raised levels of stress hormones that eventually can lead to illness. Examples of these effects include:

- Long-term raised levels of sugars and fats in the bloodstream. These can contribute to the furring-up and narrowing of blood vessels, known as atherosclerosis.
- The effects of adrenaline and noradrenaline in raising heart rate and blood pressure. This can physically damage blood vessels in the long term, by eroding the lining of blood vessels and causing haemorrhages (bleeding) where the lining of blood vessels is weakened.
- Long-term raised levels of corticosteroids. These suppress the body's immune system. This leaves us vulnerable to infections and disease.

ACTIVITY 6.4

There are many components to the fight or flight response. Adrenaline is one of these. List two effects of adrenaline that are central to the fight or flight response. In what ways might these effects also contribute to stress-related illness?

EXAMPLE EXAM QUESTION

On A Level results day, Martha goes into college to be with her friends. She is desperate to go to university but needs at least three Bs to be certain of a place. She is about to check the results. Her heart is pounding, her mouth is dry, and she has butterflies in her stomach.

Use your knowledge of the fight or flight response to explain the symptoms experienced by Martha. [4 marks]

Exam hint

This question is asking you to apply your knowledge. It would not be enough to provide an outline of the fight or flight response, however detailed. For four marks you must refer specifically to Martha, her situation and her symptoms.

KEY POINTS

- The fight or flight response evolved to provide energy for animals in situations of danger. In humans, the response has become less adaptive and has been linked to stress-related illnesses.
- There are two key pathways in the fight or flight response, the hypothalamic–pituitary–adrenal axis (HPA) and the sympathetic adrenomedullary pathway (SAM).
- Activation of the HPA results in release of ACTH from the pituitary gland – this hormone stimulates the release of corticosteroids from the adrenal cortex.
- Activation of the SAM results in the secretion of adrenaline and noradrenaline from the adrenal medulla.
- Circulating adrenaline and corticosteroids increase the release or mobilization of our energy reserves so that circulating levels of glucose and fatty acids rise.
- Adrenaline also acts directly on the heart and circulation system to speed up the heart rate and to raise blood pressure.
- If the fight or flight response is maintained for long periods, the increases in heart rate and blood pressure may physically damage the circulatory system.
- Corticosteroids suppress the immune system, leaving the body vulnerable to illness and infections.

Localization of function in the brain and hemispheric lateralization

Localization of function in the brain

Franz Gall, a German physician, accidentally began the debate over localization of function in the human brain in the early 1800s. He proposed that a person's personality was reflected in bumps on the skull that in turn reflected functions of the brain lying underneath the bump; this theory was called phrenology. Although fanciful (some of the personality characteristics mentioned by Gall included criminality, religiosity, love of property and a sense of humour), Gall's idea that functions were localized to specific regions of the brain eventually became extremely influential. The opposing view was that the brain functions in a more holistic manner, with all or large parts of the brain involved in all behaviours.

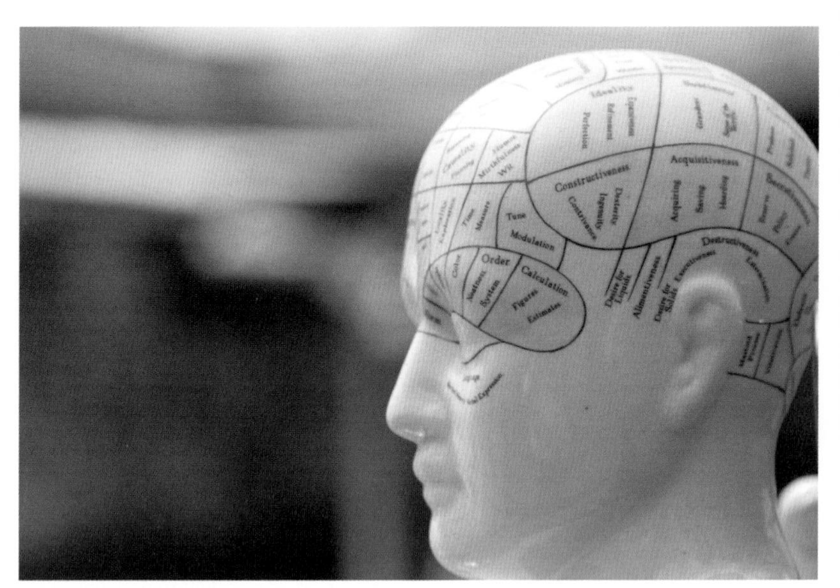

Fig. 6.7 A phrenology head

In 1861 Broca (see page 269), on the basis of his case studies of brain-damaged patients, had concluded that speech production was localized to an area in the frontal lobe, now known as 'Broca's area'. Wernicke (1874) had followed this up by showing that damage localized to a small area of the temporal lobe resulted in a loss of speech comprehension.

By the end of the 19th century, other researchers had shown in cats, dogs and monkeys that small lesions (damage) could have highly specific effects on movement and perception. Overall, these studies seem to show conclusively that the brain is organized in a highly systematic way, with functions localized to specific areas. In fact, by the middle of the 20th century, we could map out a number of functions localized in the cortex of the brain.

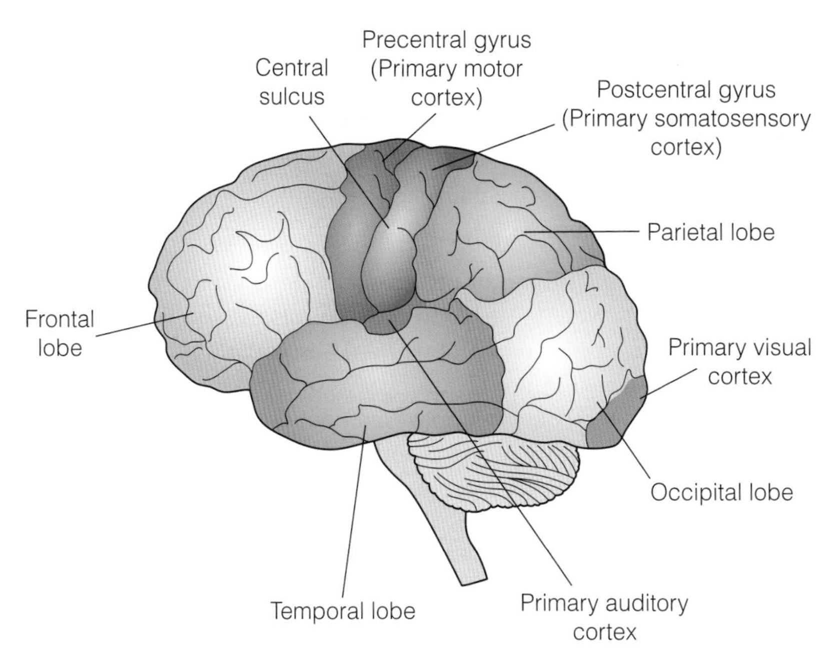

Fig. 6.8 Cortical functions

Motor, somatosensory, visual and auditory areas of the cortex

Figure 6.8 shows the key visual, auditory, somatosensory and motor areas of the cortex. Electrical stimulation of these areas can produce the appropriate sensation: visual images from the visual cortex, sound sensation from the auditory cortex, the sensation of touch or pressure from stimulation of the somatosensory cortex, and movement of skeletal muscles from stimulation of the motor cortex.

- The somatosensory cortex receives sensory input from receptors in the skin, including touch, pain, pressure, and temperature from all areas of the body surface. Interestingly, the body surface is represented systematically in the somatosensory cortex. Head areas are represented at the bottom of the postcentral gyrus, and legs and feet at the top; that is, it is a map of the body surface, though upside down.
- The motor cortex in the precentral gyrus is also organized systematically, with the muscles of the legs and feet at the top and the complicated musculature of our vocal apparatus (muscles of the mouth and tongue, larynx and pharynx) at the bottom. Stimulation of tiny areas of the motor cortex can produce movement of individual muscle fibres in the appropriate part of the body.

Figure 6.8 also shows the visual and auditory cortical areas. The visual area receives input directly from eyes and the auditory area from the ears; damage to them can lead to blindness and deafness respectively. They are known as the primary visual and auditory cortex, but visual perception, for example, requires additional processing in neighbouring cortical areas (secondary visual areas). It is in these areas that sensation is converted into perception. We know this because damage to these secondary visual areas does not lead to blindness, but can lead to loss of specific aspects of visual perception. Examples include:

- Prosopagnosia: loss of the ability to recognise familiar faces, or to identify faces at all.
- Achromatopsia: loss of the ability to see in colour – the world is perceived in black and white.

Research on sensory and motor processes supports Gall's original idea that functions were localized in the brain. However, the debate on localization was revived by the work of Lashley in the 1920s. Lashley was interested in how learning was organized in the brain, and he studied how rats learned mazes, a popular area of research at the time. He found that large lesions on visual areas impaired maze learning, but that smaller lesions covering the same brain areas had no effect. It seemed that the size of the lesion was critical. Lashley put together the results of these and many other experiments in the form of two laws:

- Law of mass action: as effects on learning were proportional to the amount of cortex damaged, Lashley concluded that behavioural functions such as learning were spread widely across cortical areas. They were not localized to specific regions.
- Law of equipotentiality: related to the law of mass action, this law states that different areas of cortex have similar capacities to process learning, so that one area can take over functions if another area is damaged. Therefore only large lesions affect learning.

Note that Lashley was interested in the brain foundations of learning and memory. He would have accepted that sensory and motor functions were localized in the brain, but he proposed that complex cognitive processes such as language were widely distributed. This view is widely accepted today.

Language and hemispheric lateralization

Sensory and motor processes are organized in an extremely orderly way. Somatosensory and motor pathways are crossed, connecting the left hemisphere to the right side of the body and the right hemisphere to the left side of the body. However, the cortical organization is the same in each hemisphere. Visual and auditory systems are more complicated. Again, however, the organization is perfectly orderly, and visual and auditory areas in the left hemisphere are matched by visual and auditory areas in the right hemisphere.

Another way of putting this is that a description of sensory and motor cortical areas in the left hemisphere can be applied equally to the right hemisphere. So the hemispheres are symmetrical, or mirror images of each other, with respect to sensory and motor cortical functions.

Language

We briefly referred to the work of Broca and Wernicke earlier in this topic. Besides localising speech production and speech comprehension to particular cortical areas, they also made a profound contribution to our understanding of **hemispheric lateralization** of function. This is the idea that some functions might be found in only one hemisphere rather than in both, i.e. lateralized (meaning 'to one side') to that hemisphere.

Key terms

Hemispheric lateralization: the idea that some functions are found only in one hemisphere; e.g. language is usually lateralized to the left hemisphere, and Sperry demonstrated that some visuo-spatial functions are lateralized to the right hemisphere

Broca's area: area at the base of the left frontal lobe involved in speech production, thought to contain the motor plans for words; first identified by Paul Broca in the 19th century

Wernicke's area: area in the temporal lobe thought to contain our store of words; Wernicke showed in the 19th century that damage to Wernicke's area resulted in receptive aphasia

KEY STUDY: BROCA AND 'TAN'

Broca, a French physician, was interested in the brain areas involved in language. In 1861 he heard about a patient with a particularly striking language impairment. This patient had suffered brain damage many years earlier that resulted in him being only able to speak one word, 'tan'. He could easily understand speech, following instructions and clearly understanding what was spoken to him. Tan, as he has become known (his real name was Leborgne), unfortunately died a week or so after Broca first met him, though this did mean that Broca could perform an autopsy on Tan's brain. He found substantial damage to an area towards the base of the frontal lobe (see Fig. 6.9). Over the next four years, Broca accumulated a dozen or so cases where the symptoms were the same as in Tan, namely a lack of speech production but intact speech comprehension. In all cases, autopsies revealed damage to the same area at the base of the frontal lobe. Importantly, the damage in all cases was only in the left hemisphere.

Broca concluded that this area of the left hemisphere, now known as **Broca's area** (see Figure 6.10), was responsible for speech production. The syndrome where speech production is lost but comprehension is intact became known as 'Broca's aphasia' or 'expressive aphasia'.

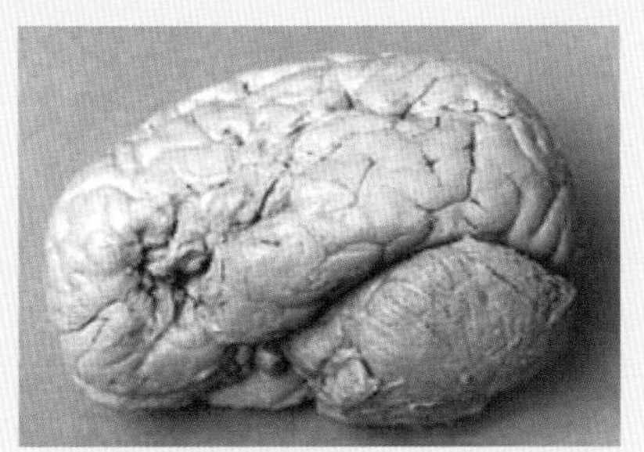

Fig. 6.9 Tan's damaged brain

Wernicke

At around the same time as Broca, Wernicke was studying patients with the opposite syndrome to Tan's – they could not understand speech, failing to follow instructions, but could produce some fluent speech (note that this was often bizarre and disconnected from their surroundings). Autopsy findings were that these patients all had damage in an area of the left hemisphere at the top of the temporal lobe, near to the auditory cortex, now known as **Wernicke's area** (see Figure 6.10). The syndrome of intact speech production but loss of speech comprehension became known as Wernicke's aphasia or receptive aphasia.

An early simple model of speech saw Wernicke's area as containing our store of words (the lexicon). When we want to speak, the word is located and activated in Wernicke's area and the information is transmitted to Broca's area. This contains the motor plans for words; that is, patterns of muscle activation that allow us to speak a particular word. This pattern is transmitted to the motor cortex, where the muscles of our vocal apparatus are activated and the word is spoken.

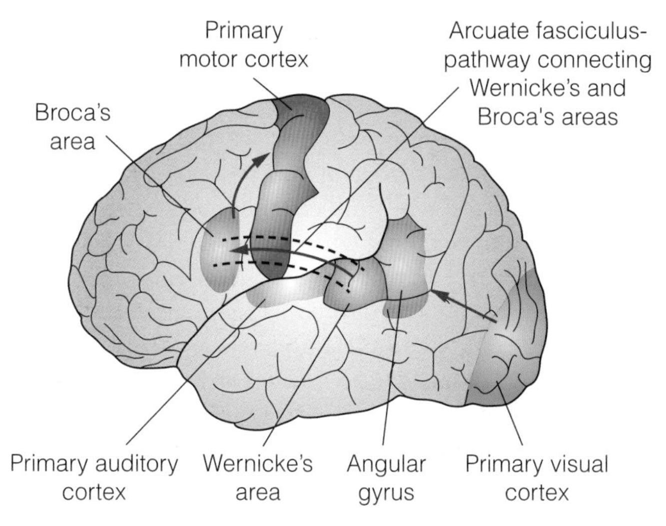

Fig. 6.10 Language areas

Later research investigated reading and writing. Reading in particular involves the visual system. The word we read is transmitted to the visual cortex for initial processing, then passed to the angular gyrus. This structure then passes the information to Wernicke's area and our internal lexicon where the word can be recognised. For writing, the word is activated in Wernicke's area, then passed to Broca's area where the motor plans for writing the word can be transmitted to the motor cortex.

Research methods link

Case studies are discussed on page 29. They have disadvantages as well as advantages, but you can see from the number referred to in this book that they have played a major role in the development of psychology.

On rare occasions the angular gyrus is damaged. As it is part of our reading system, this means that the person cannot read; this is called alexia. However Wernicke's area and Broca's area are intact, so the person can write. This produces an unusual syndrome where the person can write, but then cannot read what they have just written. This is called alexia without agraphia (agraphia is the inability to write), or pure word blindness.

THINKING SCIENTIFICALLY: PUBLISHING RESULTS

Earlier we mentioned the contribution of Broca and Wernicke to our understanding of hemispheric lateralization. This was based on their consistent observation that brain damage resulting in language impairments was always in the left hemisphere. Damage to the same areas in the right hemisphere did not cause similar impairments of language.

Broca and Wernicke were not the first to realise that left hemisphere damage was more likely to cause language problems. French researchers earlier in the 19th century had made similar observations, but fatally had not formally published their findings. So the credit for locating language mechanisms in the left hemisphere was given in particular to Broca. This shows the importance of going through the full scientific procedure for making results public, either through talks at scientific conferences or publishing in academic journals.

The work of Broca and Wernicke contributed to our understanding of the brain mechanisms of language, and in particular to the lateralization of language to the left hemisphere. This led to a view of the left hemisphere as 'dominant', as it controlled language and the preferred right hand. The right hemisphere was seen as the minor partner, looking after sensory and motor processes but having no major cognitive functions lateralized to it. This view of the hemispheres remained largely unchanged until the dramatic research of Sperry in the 1950s and 1960s.

Sperry and split-brain research

Epilepsy and split-brain surgery

Brain surgery is usually carried out for purely medical reasons. However, during the 20th century the growing interest in brains and behaviour meant that psychologists were alert to the unexpected effects of brain surgery carried out for medical reasons. In fact, two of the classic research areas in biopsychology developed following the unexpected effects of brain surgery for epilepsy. One was the amnesic patient HM (see page 238), and the other was split-brain research.

Epilepsy is a medical condition characterized by uncontrolled electrical discharges in the brain. If these are severe then brain function is seriously affected, and the person may suffer violent convulsions and lose consciousness for a few seconds (these are called grand mal attacks). Often epilepsy is not so severe and/or can be controlled by drugs. In these cases the person can live a relatively normal life.

Sometimes there is no obvious cause for the epileptic condition, and it is assumed that it is produced by an imbalance between excitatory and inhibitory processes in the brain. Sometimes, however, epilepsy can be caused by areas of scar tissue in the brain, perhaps as a result of accidental brain damage or a previous operation on the brain. In these cases it is referred to as a 'focus' for the epileptic attack.

If a focus for the epilepsy can be identified, then it is sometimes possible to remove it surgically (the famous amnesic patient HM had brain surgery to remove an epileptic focus, which resulted in his profound amnesia). Such operations would only be considered where the epilepsy is severe and disabling (several attacks every day), and has not responded to drug therapy. However, if a focus cannot be identified or it is in a part of the brain that cannot safely be reached surgically, then another operation is possible.

The two hemispheres of the brain are connected by the corpus callosum, a bundle of 200–300 million fibres. Besides its normal functions, the corpus callosum also allows epileptic discharges to travel from one hemisphere to the other (most epileptic conditions begin with a discharge in one hemisphere). This means that the epilepsy can involve the whole brain. So, in the 1940s an operation was devised to cut the corpus callosum, so preventing the epileptic discharges involving both hemispheres and so reducing the severity of the attack. This operation was called a commissurotomy as it was cutting a pathway connecting the two hemispheres. Unfortunately, the operation was not very successful at reducing the symptoms of epilepsy. On the other hand, the patients did not seem to suffer ill effects from the operation, which was surprising as they had lost one of the major pathways in the brain.

Sperry and the split brain

Key terms

Split brain: an operation used in some cases of severe epilepsy; the technical term for the operation is 'commissurotomy'

Divided field: technique devised by Sperry to present visual stimuli to either left or right hemisphere in his studies of split-brain patients; can also be used with neurotypical participants

In the 1950s Sperry, a psychologist, became interested in **split-brain** patients. He had been doing work on hemisphere function in monkeys and demonstrated that the two hemispheres of the brain have similar capacities to control behaviour. For example, each hemisphere was able to learn simple choice tasks. He concluded that in monkeys the two hemispheres were equal in terms of their behavioural capacities. This was contrasted with the situation in humans, where it was known that the key function of language was usually lateralized to the left hemisphere, which also controlled the right hand. So the left hemisphere was seen as dominant and the right hemisphere was seen as the minor partner.

Sperry realized that the split-brain patients operated on for epilepsy represented an opportunity to explore hemisphere function in humans. However, there was a problem. Although the two hemispheres were separated by the commissurotomy, each eye sends projections to both hemispheres (see Fig. 6.11).

Sperry had to design a method for projecting stimuli to each hemisphere separately. Earlier in his career he had studied the visual systems of non-human animals, and he was able to apply his knowledge of visual systems to the problem of the split-brain patient. He devised an experimental procedure that became known as the **divided field**. This is shown in Figure 6.11. It is based on the organization of the

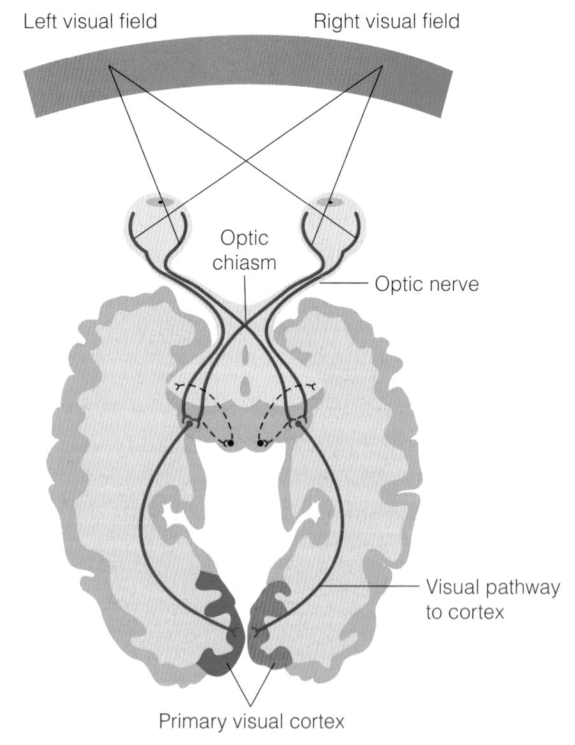

Fig. 6.11 The divided field

human visual system, and the systematic arrangement of the visual pathways from each eye to the hemispheres. Note that the right side of the right eye and the right side of the left eye both connect to the right hemisphere; similarly, the left side of the left eye and the left side of the right eye both connect to the left hemisphere.

Sperry realized that with a split-brain patient focusing their eyes straight ahead, a stimulus presented out to their right (this is called the right visual field or RVF) would be registered only by the left side of each eye. The left side of each eye projects to the left hemisphere so the stimulus would be transmitted to the left hemisphere. Similarly, a stimulus presented out to the left of the patient would be registered by the right side of each eye and projected to the right hemisphere.

In the intact human participant, a stimulus presented either to the right or the left hemisphere would immediately be conducted across the corpus callosum to the other hemisphere, so both hemispheres would be aware of the stimulus. But in the split-brain patient the corpus callosum has been cut, so a stimulus sent to the right hemisphere cannot be transmitted to the left hemisphere, and is effectively confined to the right hemisphere. In this way Sperry knew that he could present stimuli to each hemisphere separately by presenting them in either the right or the left visual field.

One limitation to the procedure was the natural tendency for the participant to move their eyes towards the stimulus. If the eyes move too much the stimulus is likely to be picked up by both hemispheres. To prevent this happening, the stimulus could only be presented for a very brief period of time, for example around 200 milliseconds. This meant in effect that Sperry could only present single words or pictures. Even so, he was able to demonstrate some dramatic effects in these early experiments (Sperry, 1965).

Research findings with the split brain – word processing

KEY STUDY: SPERRY, 1965

A split-brain patient, with eyes focused straight ahead, was asked to report any word that he or she saw. A word flashing up in the RVF was immediately reported. However, the patient seemed totally unaware of a word flashing up in their left visual field (LVF). A word in the RVF is projected to the left hemisphere. We know that the left hemisphere in most people contains the language system. Therefore, the word can be immediately recognized and spoken by the patient. A word presented in the LVF is projected to the right hemisphere. This has no language system, so the word cannot be recognized and reported.

Sperry quickly realized that the situation was not that simple. To report what they see, the split-brain patient has to use their left hemisphere language system, as this controls speech; therefore the patient can only report on what the left hemisphere has seen. Even if the right hemisphere could read the word, it could not report it as it does not have speech. What Sperry needed was some method of allowing the right hemisphere to respond to the stimulus. So, knowing that the right hemisphere controls the left hand, he placed the left hand behind a screen among a number of objects. He then flashed a word such as 'glass' to the right hemisphere, and found that the left hand would select the glass from the range of objects. What he had demonstrated was some basic language ability in the right hemisphere, in that it was able to read simple concrete nouns (a noun refers to people and physical things) (Gazzaniga, 2005). When Sperry asked the patient why their left hand was holding a glass, they could not of course explain. To answer the question they had to use speech controlled by the left hemisphere speech system, which did not know what the right hemisphere had seen.

THINKING SCIENTIFICALLY: ORIGINAL THINKING

Commissurotomized (split-brain) patients had been around since the 1940s when this operation to reduce the severity of epileptic attacks was introduced. However, it was only in the 1960s that systematic research with them began. It was Roger Sperry who first thought of the potential value of the split-brain patient to our understanding of hemisphere function. More critically, he developed methods such as the divided field to allow right hemisphere function to be investigated.

In such ways, advances in science depend upon the original thinking of individuals as well as on technological advances. Sperry's background in research with non-human animals, his awareness that split-brain patients existed, and his creative thinking came together at the right time to begin a new era of research into brain function.

Research findings with the split brain – visuospatial processing

Although Sperry's study was impressive in showing that the right hemisphere had some basic language ability, it still reinforced the idea that language was mainly a left hemisphere function. What really changed the view on lateralization of functions across the hemispheres were the findings of studies using non-verbal stimuli.

Sperry and his collaborators (Gazzaniga, 2005) repeated the divided field study with split-brain patients, but this time using faces as the stimuli rather than words. In one such study, a different face was presented to each hemisphere at the same time. Then the split brain patient was given a set of faces, including the ones presented, and asked to choose the one that they had seen earlier. They would choose the one presented to the right hemisphere. In a series of similar studies, Sperry demonstrated that the right hemisphere was better at identifying faces then the left hemisphere.

He was also able to show that the right hemisphere was better at matching shapes, and in general the right hemisphere showed a superiority over the left hemisphere in what we call visuospatial tasks (two examples of a visuospatial task would be putting together flat-pack furniture or constructing a model). So one result of the split-brain studies was a change in the way we viewed the two hemispheres. No longer did we have a dominant right hemisphere and a minor left hemisphere, but instead we have a verbal left hemisphere and a visuospatial right hemisphere.

KEY STUDY: TURK ET AL. (2002)

Split-brain research has persisted through to recent times. In the study of Turk et al., the researchers were interested in face processing after split-brain surgery, in particular whether the patient's own face was processed in a different way to the familiar face of someone else. The patient was a 48-year-old man (JW) who had had a commissurotomy for epilepsy 23 years earlier. He had been extensively tested over the years.

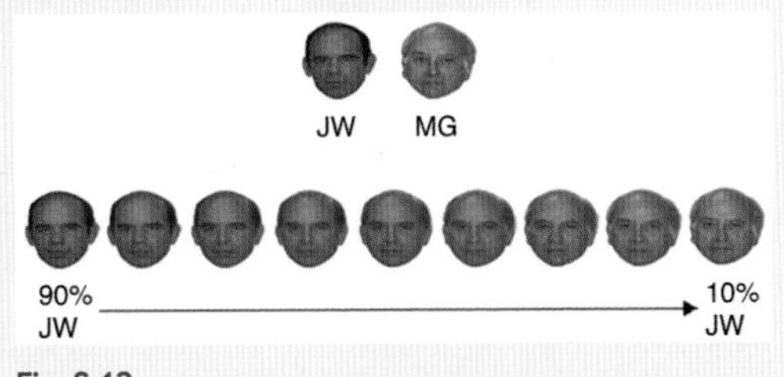

Fig. 6.12

The stimuli were morphed faces; that is, a face stimulus made up from two separate faces morphed together. One face was JW's own, the other was of one of the researchers who had worked with him for a number of years and was very familiar to him. A series of morphs was created (see Fig 6.12), from 0 per cent JW (i.e. 100 per cent familiar face), to 50/50 own/familiar, through to 100 per cent own (i.e JW's own face). Researchers used the divided field procedure to present the face stimulus to one or other hemisphere.

In one set of trials, JW was asked to press a button if the image presented was himself, and in another set of trials using the same stimuli, he was asked to press a button if the image presented was the familiar other person. Results showed that the right hemisphere showed a clear bias towards identifying the morphed faces as a familiar other. On the other hand, JW's left hemisphere showed a clear bias towards identifying the morphed faces as himself.

The researchers accepted that the right hemisphere is in general better at face-processing, but that the left hemisphere may have an important role in self-recognition. They point out that self-recognition requires personal memories and beliefs and a self-concept, and perhaps the left hemisphere has a primary role in the networks involved in self-recognition.

Evaluation of the split-brain research

The work of Sperry and others on split-brain patients was ground-breaking and changed our views on hemisphere function. However, there are considerable issues with split-brain research:

- There are very few of these patients, and only between 10 and 15 have been subjected to extensive systematic study. This is a very small sample size.
- In addition, those studied are an extremely varied group. They differ in age and sometimes gender and handedness, age

Research methods link

On page 13 you can read about the need to control extraneous and confounding variables if your study is to be valid. Sperry could not do this, as there were not many split-brain patients around. There were several possible extraneous variables that could have affected the results (i.e. become confounding variables), so it was important that his dramatic findings on hemispheric lateralization were backed up by more controlled studies in neurotypical participants.

at which they developed epilepsy, age at which they had the commissurotomy, and age at which they were tested.

- Their operations were not always comparable. Besides the corpus callosum, there are smaller pathways connecting the two hemispheres, such as the anterior commissure. In some cases this was cut along with the corpus callosum, but in other cases it was left intact, possibly allowing for some communication between hemispheres.

Given these issues we could not be confident in building a model of hemispheric lateralization using only split-brain research. We are confident with language lateralization because of the extensive case studies of language impairment after brain damage. Additionally, since Sperry's work in the 1960s and 1970s, his techniques have been modified for use with intact (neurotypical) participants.

In brief, using Sperry's divided field, the neurotypical participant is presented with two stimuli at the same time, one to each hemisphere. The stimulus in the RVF is transmitted to the left hemisphere, while the stimulus in the LVF is transmitted to the right hemisphere. With brief presentation, about 200 ms, the participant will usually report only one of the stimuli. If the stimuli are words, the one presented in the RVF is the one most likely to be reported; this is called a right visual field advantage for words. If the stimuli are faces or drawings, then the one presented in the LVF is most likely to be reported; this is called a left visual field advantage for visuospatial stimuli.

Conclusion

Stimulated by split-brain research, findings from a variety of studies have led to a general model of hemispheric specialization. The left hemisphere is seen as verbal and the right hemisphere as visuospatial. To process language we need to break down incoming speech into separate words spread out over a time interval (think of listening as a friend talks to you). It is only at the end of a sentence that we put everything together to understand what was said. Therefore the left hemisphere is also seen as analytical, working best when stimuli need to be broken down into their component parts. In contrast, the right hemisphere is better at processing faces. Faces are not taken in bit by bit, but usually as one whole stimulus. Therefore the right hemisphere is seen as a holistic or Gestalt processor.

Plasticity and functional recovery of the brain after trauma

Key terms

Plasticity: the ability of the brain to change and adapt in light of various experiences, including trauma.

Functional recovery: recovery of function lost after brain damage

Plasticity refers to the ability of the brain to change and adapt synapses, pathways, and structures in light of various experiences. These experiences are usually positive. For example, learning and memory involve brain plasticity, in that memory involves changes to brain synapses and pathways. However, plasticity can also involve the ability of the brain to adapt to damage caused by trauma. Recovery of function lost after brain damage (**functional recovery**) is currently a key area of neuroscience research.

Plasticity in the new-born brain

One of the extraordinary features of brain development is that by the end of the first postnatal year, the brain actually has more neurons and more synapses than it will have when it becomes fully mature in late adolescence/early adulthood. Why does the brain produce so many more neurons and synapses than it will eventually need? The answer to this question is also an explanation for the success of modern humans.

For the first few months and years after birth, the developing brain is exposed to a vast range of experiences, environments, and stimuli. It has to learn to recognize different people, it has to learn to recognize food that is good for it and food that is bad for it, it has to learn to avoid situations that may be dangerous, it has to learn to understand and to produce language, and in general to interact successfully with the outside world. To benefit from all of these experiences, the brain has to be maximally plastic; i.e. it has to respond to all these experiences by altering its organization and structure.

Research into plasticity in the new-born brain

One example is the work of Blakemore and Mitchell (1973) on the development of the visual cortex in cats. They were able to show convincingly that the characteristics of visual neurons could be permanently changed by exposure to specific environments soon after birth. Kittens reared in an environment with black vertical stripes did not respond to horizontal black stripes as adults, and those reared with horizontal stripes did not respond to vertical stripes as adults.

Research since those early years has confirmed these findings, and the general conclusion is that the brain is highly plastic and responsive to the environment in the first few months and years after birth. The most extreme example perhaps is the hemispherectomy. Very occasionally a baby is born with one hemisphere severely damaged either through a genetic problem, illness, or a difficult birth. It has been found that if that whole hemisphere is removed soon after birth, then as an adult that person shows few, if any, behavioural or cognitive impairments (Villablanca and Hovda, 2000).

This shows the extraordinary plasticity of the developing brain. Functions, perhaps including language, that would normally have been performed by the damaged hemisphere, have clearly been transferred to surviving brain areas (probably the healthy hemisphere). At this stage in development the brain has sufficient neurons and synapses to cope with the dramatic damage.

In the normal course of development the brain is being 'sculpted' by the environment and experience. This early plasticity helps adapt the brain to the environment the baby is developing within. So the apparent overproduction of neurons and synapses prenatally can be seen as providing the basis for this adaptation. Pathways and networks used regularly will survive, while pathways and networks that are not used will die off. As the brain finally matures and development stops around late adolescence/early adulthood, this developmental plasticity will hopefully have led to a brain well-adapted to its surroundings.

Plasticity in the adult brain

It had long been thought that the remarkable plasticity of the developing brain was lost when the brain matured at around age 20. Clearly plasticity was still present, as learning and memory functioned into old age. However the effects of brain damage on behaviour often seemed permanent, with little recovery.

Over the last 50 years the situation has changed. Although there has been no breakthrough in treatments for the behavioural effects of traumatic brain damage, we do know a great deal more about the mechanisms behind brain plasticity.

Brain trauma

Common types of brain trauma include:

- **Physical trauma**: e.g. blows and missile wounds to the skull and brain
- **Cerebral haemorrhage**: this is when a blood vessel in the brain bursts; brain areas supplied by the blood vessel begin to die, while the pressure of the blood released into brain tissue can also cause damage
- **Cerebral ischaemia**: this is when a blood vessel in the brain is blocked, for instance by a blood clot (thrombosis), or by the thickening of the blood vessel walls through fatty deposits (arteriosclerosis); brain areas supplied by the blood vessel begin to die
- **Viral or bacterial infections**: these can destroy brain tissue, e.g. meningitis.

Interruptions to the brain's blood supply through cerebral haemorrhage or ischaemia are known as strokes, and these are the major cause of traumatic brain damage in adults. Traumatic brain damage can affect virtually all areas of behaviour and cognition. It can lead to movement paralysis, language problems (aphasia), memory problems (amnesia), or difficulties in perception. Note that because the blood supply to the brain is lateralized within one hemisphere or the other, strokes are often lateralized to one hemisphere. This means that the behavioural effects are likely to be one-sided. For instance, a left hemisphere stroke may lead to a paralysis of the right side of the body. It may also affect language, as this is controlled by the left hemisphere.

Possible mechanisms of recovery

- There is often some significant recovery in the first days or weeks after traumatic brain injury. Besides destroying neurons, brain damage can cause swelling of brain tissue and this can affect behaviour. This swelling dies down over days and weeks and this is responsible for the early recovery.
- Axonal sprouting from surviving neurons. This has been observed in many animals after brain damage. The axons (see Fig. 6.1, p. 250) of surviving neurons grow new branches that make synapses in areas of the brain formerly supplied by the damaged neurons.
- Growth of new neurons. This is known as in neurogenesis. Although this is common in birds and reptiles, until recently it

was not thought to occur in the human brain. Once the brain had matured it was thought neurons could only be lost and not replaced. We now know that neurogenesis occurs in the human olfactory bulb and the hippocampus. The implications for recovery from brain trauma are not clear but this is a promising line of research.

- New behavioural strategies. This does not involve the direct recovery of functions that have been lost but the use of alternative means to the same end. It can be as simple as the person with amnesia after brain damage writing down their experiences rather than relying on memory. Kapar (1997) found that recovery after brain damage was better in doctors than in the general population. This is possibly because they have greater cognitive resources to draw on leading to better alternative strategies.
- Age at which damage occurs is still a factor in adulthood. Teuber (1975) studied soldiers with brain damage. He found that recovery from movement and visual problems over 20 years was age dependent. 60% of those under 20 showed significant improvement, while only around 20% of those over 26 showed similar recovery. Axonal sprouting and reorganization may be more extensive in the younger brains.

Possible treatments

1. Drugs: Over the last 50 years we have discovered a great deal about chemicals in the brain that help control the growth and organization of neurons in the developing brain. It is hoped that some of these chemicals, such as nerve growth factor (NGF), may eventually be used after brain damage to prevent the degeneration and death of neurons, and to increase regeneration and axonal sprouting.
2. Neuronal transplantation: As mentioned above we know that new neurons are produced in the adult brain but that the areas involved are often far from the site of brain damage. In the 1990s, it was proposed that transplants of neurons could be used to restore function in damaged brains. Early studies with Parkinson's patients (a movement disorder that involves loss of brain tissue) were promising, but later studies were less impressive. More recently the discovery of stem cells (cells that have the potential to grow into any cell type, such as neurons) has revived interest in neuronal transplantation. In theory, stem cells implanted in a damaged area have the potential to grow into neurons and make functional synaptic connections that would help to restore behavioural functions. There are huge technical problems to overcome but this is a very promising line of research.
3. Rehabilitation and brain reorganization: We know from studies on the intact brain that practising skills alters brain organization. For instance, in violin players who use the left hand for the complex fingering of the notes, the area of motor cortex dedicated to the left hand increases with practice. These observations led to the suggestion that practice of a skill affected by brain damage might lead to significant recovery. One example of this approach is constraint-induced therapy.

Research methods link

Ethical issues are discussed on page 35. Research into brain transplants as a treatment for the effects of brain damage raises several ethical issues. For example: are patients after brain damage able to give informed consent to brain surgery? Should such treatments be tried when the long-term side-effects of implanting new brain tissue into humans are largely unknown? Does the severity of the effects of brain damage justify such experimental procedures? The ethics of research and therapy are constantly under review as technical advances increase the range of potential techniques.

Constraint-induced therapy (CIT)

The first systematic studies of CIT were experiments in monkeys paralysed on one side after brain damage. The unaffected arm was constrained (i.e. the monkey could not use it) by being placed in a sling and the monkey made to use the affected arm as much as they could. Results showed that this CIT produced significant improvement in movement in the affected arm. Follow-up studies showed that the beneficial effects of CIT in monkeys were due to reorganization of neuronal networks in the motor cortex (Taub et al., 2002).

Further research (Pulvermuller et al., 2001) showed that CIT could also be effective for language impairments (aphasias) following strokes. Patients were given intensive practice in the areas of language impairment (e.g. speech) and restricted in their use of alternative communication, e.g. drawings and gestures. They showed significant improvement in the affected language skills compared to patients not given CIT. Although difficult to demonstrate in humans, it is probable that this improvement is due to reorganization of cortical networks in speech areas.

Functional recovery after brain damage in humans is often quite limited. However, we are learning more about techniques to improve recovery and the brain mechanisms of plasticity underlying any recovery. It is likely that the next ten years will see major advances in helping patients affected by brain trauma.

ACTIVITIES 6.5

Imagine a patient with memory problems after trauma-induced brain damage. They have particular problems with the names of people they know, although they can often make a reasonable guess. They try to cope by always asking people their names when they meet, even their close family. Think of a way in which constraint-induced therapy might be used to help them recover from their memory problems. Remember that the aim is to practice the affected skill and not use intact skills.

EXAMPLE EXAM QUESTION

Alena has suffered a stroke that has damaged part of her brain. Following the stroke she has severe problems with speaking and can say only a few words. However, she has no difficulty understanding what is spoken to her.

Using your knowledge of the brain mechanisms of language, explain what parts of Alena's brain may have been damaged by the stroke. [3 marks]

Exam hint

This question requires you to apply your knowledge to the scenario. Therefore, it is not sufficient simply to explain what type of aphasia Alena has, but you must refer to her particular symptoms in your answer and link them to parts of the brain. There are three marks available, so you must provide sufficient detail for full marks, e.g. where the damage is likely to have occurred, and the normal language functions of this part of the brain.

KEY POINTS

- Cortical areas specialized for processing motor and sensory information can be identified. These include motor, visual, auditory, and somatosensory areas. These functions are therefore localized in the brain.
- Lashley investigated learning and memory in rats, and concluded that these functions were not localized to specific areas but widely distributed.
- Broca concluded that speech production was located within an area of the frontal lobe now known as Broca's area. Wernicke proposed that speech comprehension was due to damage to an area in the temporal lobe, now known as Wernicke's area.

- Broca and Wernicke observed that language was only affected by damage to the left hemisphere and not by damage to the right hemisphere. This was the earliest, clear example of hemispheric lateralization of function.
- Split-brain patients have had the corpus callosum cut in order to reduce the severity of epilepsy. Sperry introduced new testing techniques to study the function of the divided hemispheres in the split-brain patient.
- Using the divided field, Sperry and other researchers were able to show that while the left hemisphere was specialized for language processing, the right hemisphere was specialized for visuospatial functions such as face recognition.
- The left hemisphere is specialized for language processing, and is seen as a sequential, analytic processor. The right hemisphere is specialized for visuospatial functions, and is seen as a parallel Gestalt processor.
- Hemispheric lateralization can vary with handedness and gender.
- The developing brain is highly plastic, absorbing huge amounts of new information and coping well with the effects of brain damage. The adult brain has limited plasticity but recovery from the effects of brain damage can occur.
- Recovery of function may be due to the reduction of brain swelling after trauma or axonal sprouting and formation of new neurons. New behavioural strategies may also be used to compensate for lost functions.
- Potential treatments to improve recovery of function after brain damage include drugs, and transplantation of new neurons or stem cells to damaged areas.
- Intensive practice of skills lost after brain damage can lead to significant recovery, even in cognitive functions such as language.

Ways of studying the brain

Scanning techniques

The introduction of scanning techniques for imaging the living human brain has been the greatest breakthrough in the long history of biopsychology. The first method, computed axial tomography or CT scanner, used x-rays to take images of brain structures. Detail was relatively poor, but major structures, or abnormalities such as tumours, could be identified.

For taking static images of brain structures, the CT scanner has been largely replaced by the magnetic resonance imaging (MRI) scanner. It is based on the magnetic properties of hydrogen atoms found in water throughout the brain. By using a strong magnetic field and then the application of radio waves, this technique can produce highly detailed images of brain structures.

Positron emission tomography (PET) scanning

In the 1980s, the positron emission tomography (PET) scanner was introduced. In this procedure, a radioactive substance such as glucose is introduced into the bloodstream. It travels to the brain where neurons use glucose as a source of energy. Therefore, the most active brain regions will accumulate more glucose, and the radioactivity emitted is picked up by the PET scanner. The scanner uses the radioactivity to construct a functional map of the brain; that is, a map showing the areas that were most active during the performance of a given task.

This was the first scanning technique to take images of the brain in action, and therefore give psychologists the opportunity to link behavioural functions to specific structures in living human participants. However, the technique was both invasive, with injections of radioactive substances into the bloodstream, and prolonged, as imaging could only take place when radioactivity had accumulated in brain structures (20–30 seconds).

To study cognitive functions in relation to brain activity, PET has been almost completely replaced by functional magnetic resonance imaging. However, it is still useful in some specialized areas. For example, using radioactive labelled drugs that bind to particular synaptic receptors, we can assess the distribution of neurotransmitter pathways in the brain.

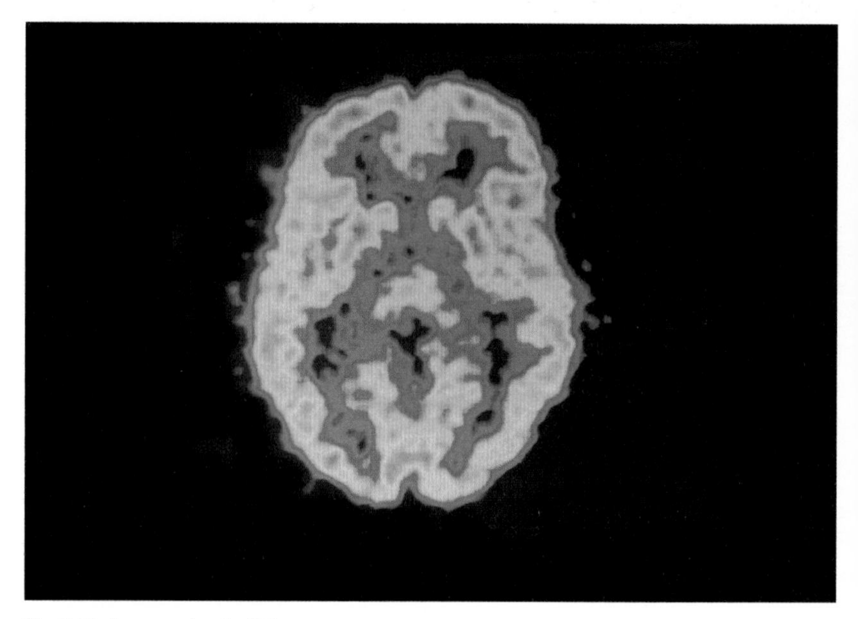

Fig. 6.13 An example of a PET scan

Functional magnetic resonance imaging (fMRI)

Functional magnetic resonance imaging was developed from the original MRI scanner. The principle behind it is that the neurons most active during a given task will be using more energy. This requires glucose and, importantly, oxygen, carried in the bloodstream. Therefore, the blood flow to active areas of the brain should increase over control levels. Oxygen is carried in the bloodstream attached to molecules of haemoglobin, found in red blood cells. After oxygen is released for use by active neurons, haemoglobin becomes deoxygenated.

Oxygenated and deoxygenated haemoglobin have different magnetic qualities. In combination with the powerful magnetic field applied in fMRI, this difference in magnetic qualities can be used to generate a signal representing blood flows in various parts of the brain. In brief, fMRI indirectly measures blood flow through the concentration of oxygen in the bloodstream. Therefore, the signal used in fMRI is called the BOLD contrast, standing for Blood Oxygen Level Dependent contrast.

The advantages of fMRI over PET are considerable. It is non-invasive, requiring only that the participant remain still and quiet in the scanner. The latency between presenting a stimulus and the BOLD signal is shorter, although at several seconds it is still long in relation to the speed of human cognitive processing. Importantly, spatial resolution (the smallest area that can be accurately imaged) is far better, being about 1 millimetre compared to about 10 millimetres for PET.

Cognitive neuroscience (see page 232) is heavily dependent upon fMRI. Virtually every cognitive process has been studied using fMRI, including attention, memory, language processing and face perception. It is also used to study problems in development such as autism, and psychological problems such as schizophrenia.

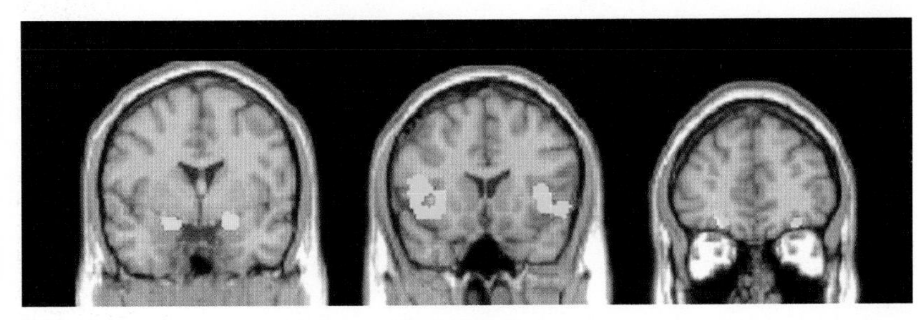

Fig. 6.14 An example of a fMRI scan

Although it should be remembered that neither PET nor fMRI measure neuronal activity directly (compared with the EEG and ERP techniques outlined below), these modern imaging techniques are revolutionizing our understanding of brain function in relation to behaviour.

Electroencephalogram (EEG)

As we saw earlier in this chapter, information in the brain is processed as electrical activity – action potentials or nerve impulses being transmitted along neurons. Therefore, measuring the electrical activity of the brain can provide an insight into information processing. There are many techniques for recording and measuring the brain's electrical activity. Some of these can only be used in non-human animals, as they involve inserting small wire electrodes into the brain to record from a small group of neurons or even a single neuron. The electroencephalogram (EEG), in contrast, provides an overall view of brain electrical activity. It was developed by Hans Berger in 1929.

A large number of small recording electrodes, for instance 24 or 32, are distributed over the surface of the skull. These pick up the electrical activity of many millions of neurons and, as you can imagine, the resulting pattern can look very messy. However, the EEG has some basic properties that can be used to characterise particular brain states:

- Amplitude: the size or intensity of the electrical activity.
- Frequency: the speed or rapidity of the electrical activity.

In addition, there are two distinctive states of the EEG:

- Synchronized pattern: this is where a recognizable waveform can be identified in the EEG recording. A waveform is a repeated pattern of electrical activity with a particular amplitude and frequency.
- Desynchronized pattern: this is where there is no recognizable waveform, although the frequency of electrical activity can still be determined.

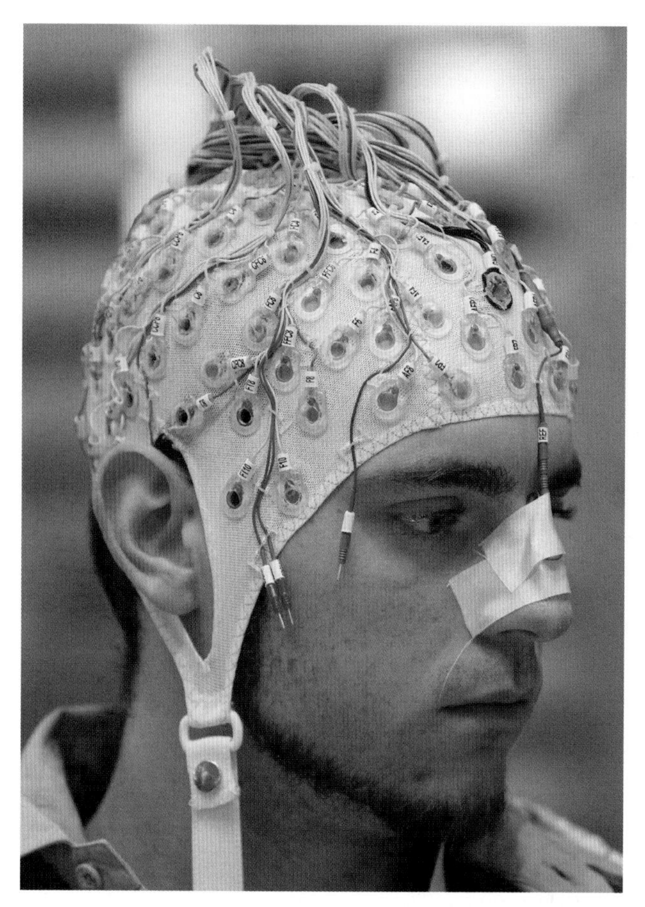

Fig. 6.15 Participant with cap holding recording electrodes for EEG or ERP

The EEG is useful for identifying the general state of the brain. For example, a fast desynchronized EEG is typical of the waking alert state. This makes sense, as many areas of the brain would be active at the same time, performing different functions, and so no overall synchronized pattern would be seen. Synchronized patterns are most typically seen in sleep. Such patterns are characterized by a particular waveform with a clear amplitude and frequency. Figure 6.16 shows the several stages of slow wave sleep. Relaxed wakefulness, just before sleep occurs, is characterized by alpha waves with a frequency of 8–12 hertz (cycles per second). Theta waves, 4–7 hertz, appear in the first stage of sleep. Later stages of this slow wave sleep are dominated by large slow delta waves, at 1–4 hertz.

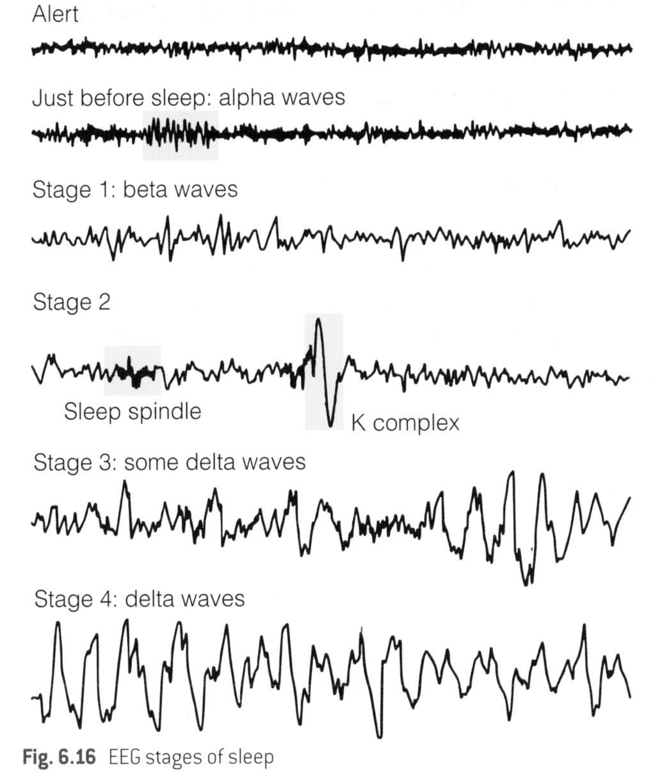

Fig. 6.16 EEG stages of sleep

One early contribution of the EEG was the finding that during sleep we have periods when the EEG shifts from a synchronized pattern of delta waves, to fast desynchronized activity similar to the alert waking state. This EEG pattern is associated with rapid eye movements (REM), so this phase of sleep is known as REM or dreaming sleep, because participants usually report dreaming activity if awakened during this phase.

The EEG is useful in the study of sleep and the different stages of sleep. In a medical setting it can also be used to identify abnormalities of brain function, for example in conditions such as epilepsy. However, the psychologist interested in cognitive functions such as attention, perception, and memory requires a more precise measure of brain activity. One example is event-related potentials.

Event-related potentials (ERPs)

This procedure uses a similar array of recording electrodes as for the EEG. However, a major difference is that a stimulus (for example, a sound or a picture) is presented to the participant, and the psychologist looks for specific electrical responses to that stimulus. This is difficult because the specific response to that stimulus may not stand out from the background electrical activity of the brain. The way around this is to present the stimulus several hundred times. The recordings for, say, five seconds after each stimulus presentation, are superimposed on each other and a computer is used to add them together. The regular specific electrical responses to the stimulus gradually add together while the background electrical noise cancels itself out. In this way an event-related potential emerges (see Figure 6.17). The procedure is called 'averaging'.

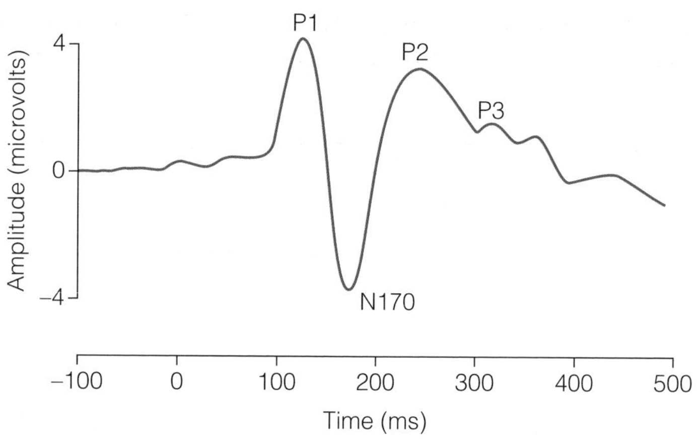

Fig. 6.17 Representative Event-Related Potential recording. Note that upwards deflections are coded as P (positive) waves (P1, P2, etc.) and downwards deflections are coded as N (negative) waves. These can be coded as N1, N2, etc. but in this figure the N170 face-processing wave is indicated.

As Figure 6.17 shows, the ERP can be a complex waveform with several components. Because of the electrical nature of the ERP, upward deviations are known as positive waves and downward deviations as negative waves. This gives a simple means of labelling the waves; P1, P2 and P3 would be the first, second and third positive waves, and N1, N2 and N3 the first, second and third negative waves.

The interval between stimulus presentation and the beginning of the ERP is known as the latency of the response. A unique feature of ERPs is their very short latency, which is measured in milliseconds (thousands of a second). Remember that with fMRI we are talking in terms of latencies of a few seconds rather than milliseconds. This means that ERPs can reflect the very early stages of cognitive processing, and in addition, by comparing ERPs to stimuli of different types, we can link components of the ERP to specific aspects of cognitive processing.

For example, a wave known as the N170 (a negative wave seen about 170 ms after stimulus onset) reflects the processing of faces, as the amplitude of this wave in response to faces is far greater than the amplitude in response to non-face stimuli. Consequently, we assume that the N170 represents the early stages of face processing. Another example is mismatch negativity, or MMN. This negative wave in the ERP at about 200 ms occurs when a succession of similar stimuli is interrupted by a different stimulus; for instance, a sequence of tones of 80 decibels is interrupted by a single tone of 70 decibels. So the MMN seems to represent novelty.

The very short latencies of ERP is their great advantage, and they can provide an insight into the earliest stages of cognitive processing. A major disadvantage, though, is their poor spatial localization. With recording electrodes spread over the scalp it is possible to localize components of the ERP to general areas of the cortex. For example, the N170 seems to have its greatest amplitude over areas of the parietal cortex. However, although technology is improving all the time, localization of ERP components to specific areas of cortex or to subcortical structures is currently impossible.

Method	Invasive or non-invasive	Temporal resolution	Spatial resolution	Advantages and disadvantages
PET	Invasive	20–30 seconds	10mm	• Uses radioactive labelled chemicals so only used once for each pp. • Long procedure, but can map neurotransmitters in the brain.
fMRI	Non-invasive	1–4 seconds	1mm	• Better temporal and spatial resolution than PET. Can record subcortical activity. • Pps can be tested repeatedly if necessary. • Does not measure neuronal activity directly. • Technology improving all the time.
ERP	Non-invasive	1–10 milliseconds	General cortical regions only	• Measures neuronal activity directly. • Excellent 'real time' temporal resolution means that cognitive processes can be analysed in detail. • Poor spatial resolution.

Table 6.3 Comparison of methods for studying the brain in action

Post-mortem examinations

We have already seen several examples of the contribution of post-mortem examinations (autopsies) to our understanding of brain function. In particular, the work of Broca and Wernicke on language processing in the brain (see page 269) was entirely dependent on the study of brain-damaged participants, followed by post-mortem examination of their brains to determine the location and extent of damage.

This tradition was maintained until the 1970s and the introduction of scanning techniques for the study of brain function. PET, MRI and fMRI scanning techniques can be used in living participants, whether brain-damaged or intact (neurotypical). They can even be used on the post-mortem brain. For example, the brain of Broca's famous patient Tan has been preserved since the 19th century, and was scanned in the 1990s to determine the precise location and extent of damage. It was these findings that led to the conclusion that Broca had underestimated the extent of the brain damage in Tan.

Modern scanning techniques have replaced the post-mortem examination in the study of brain and behaviour, but it is important to remember the vital historical contribution of this technique to our understanding of brain function.

ACTIVITY 6.6

Draw up a table with the five methods outlined in this section down the left-hand side; PET, fMRI, EEG, ERP, and post-mortem examinations. Then, alongside each one in the next column, briefly outline one way in which they have been used that is relevant to psychology. In the third column, outline one advantage of the method, and in the final column, outline one disadvantage of the method.

Exam hint

A danger with this sort of question is that you simply outline the use of ERPs in studying the brain. The question asks for an advantage over fMRI, so you need to state specifically why a particular characteristic of ERPs gives them an advantage over fMRI. Also, give sufficient detail for two marks.

EXAMPLE EXAM QUESTION

fMRI and ERPs are both methods used in studying the brain. Outline one advantage of using ERPs rather than fMRI to study brain function. (2 marks)

KEY POINTS

- The study of the brain has been revolutionized since the introduction of the first scanning techniques in the 1970s. These techniques enable us to investigate the brain in living human participants.
- Positron emission tomography (PET) scanning involves injecting a radioactively labelled substance such as glucose, which is taken up by the most active neurons. Recording the radioactivity allows a picture of the active brain to be constructed.
- Functional magnetic resonance imaging (fMRI) uses changes in blood flow to generate a picture of activity in different areas of the brain.
- The electroencephalogram (EEG) uses electrodes attached to the scalp to record the general electrical activity of the brain.
- Event-related potentials (ERPs) are recorded using a similar array of electrodes as for the EEG. They are responses to specific stimuli presented to the participant.
- Post-mortems (autopsies) were used extensively before the introduction of scanning techniques. Their use in biopsychology has now virtually disappeared in favour of modern scanning techniques.

Biological rhythms

Types of biological rhythm

The world is full of rhythms. Tides come and go daily; each year the seasons, spring, summer, autumn, and winter, follow their annual pattern, each with its own characteristics such as temperature, snow or rainfall. We have a regular pattern of day and night alternating over 24 hours. These patterns are determined by the Earth's movement around the sun and its rotation through 360 degrees every 24 hours, so the patterns have been around a very long time, well before any form of life evolved on the planet.

In the living world biological rhythms are found everywhere. Some plants open their leaves during the day and close them at night. In some regions of the world, bears and squirrels regularly hibernate during the winter months when days shorten and the temperature falls, awakening when warmer weather arrives in the early spring. Beach-dwelling algae burrow into the sand when the tide comes in, and emerge when the tide goes out again.

It looks as though these plants and animals are responding to the outside world. However, it turns out that the plants open and close their leaves regularly even when kept in the dark; squirrels prepare for hibernation by laying down fat reserves at the appropriate time of year even when kept in constant light and temperature; and the beach-dwelling algae continue to burrow into the sand at the appropriate time of day even when kept in laboratory conditions with no tides present. The study of biological rhythms aims to work out how these regular patterns are controlled, as clearly it is not just the external world that determines when and how these rhythms are observed.

In humans we can identify hundreds of different biological rhythms. The most obvious perhaps is the sleep/waking cycle, where we are active during the daylight hours and then sleep during the night when activity might be dangerous. The term for this is **diurnal** or daylight living; animals with the opposite pattern of being active at night and sleeping during the day are called **nocturnal**. We also find that body temperature in humans has a daily rhythm, peaking in the afternoon and falling to its lowest level in the early morning. Less obviously, many hormones and neurotransmitters in the body show a similar pattern of one peak and one trough every 24 hours. Even during sleep, we see a regular alternation between stages of what is called slow-wave sleep and active, or REM, sleep.

The human female menstrual cycle is an example of a biological rhythm at a much lower frequency (also known as periodicity), once every month. Biological rhythms with the lowest periodicity occur once every year. In animals this includes hibernation, and perhaps a parallel in humans is seasonal affective disorder (SAD). This is a form of depression that occurs in some people at the onset of winter, and it has been suggested that it may be an evolutionary hangover equivalent to hibernation in animals. We discuss this more later.

Rhythms such as the menstrual cycle and variations in the levels of hormones over a single day are too regular to be explained by variations in the outside world such as light and dark, or daily temperature. It was mentioned earlier that many biological rhythms persist in the absence of what we refer to as environmental cues, and overall it is clear that there must be internal mechanisms involved in the control of biological rhythms. We refer to these internal mechanisms as **endogenous pacemakers** or, more familiarly, as body clocks. Before discussing the role of endogenous pacemakers and environmental cues in the control of biological rhythms, we need a brief outline of the different types of biological rhythm found in the natural world.

Key terms

Diurnal: circadian rhythm in which the animal is active during the day and quiet or asleep at night

Nocturnal: circadian rhythm in which the animal is active at night and quiet or asleep during the day

Endogenous pacemaker: also referred to as 'body clocks'; centres in the brain that play a main role in controlling biological rhythms

Circadian rhythm: a biological rhythm that has a periodicity of 24 hours; the sleep/waking cycle and body temperature are examples of circadian rhythms

Circadian rhythms

Periodicity in relation to biological rhythms is the time between one peak or maximum value and the next peak or maximum value. **Circadian rhythms** have a periodicity of one day or 24 hours;

the name circadian actually means 'about a day'. These are certainly the most common and most studied of biological rhythms. They include the sleep–waking cycle, which has one period of sleep and one period of waking every 24 hours, and body temperature, which has one peak and one trough every 24 hours. Many hormones follow the same circadian pattern.

Key terms

Exogenous zeitgeber: environmental factors that help synchronize biological rhythms with the outside world; the best example is light onset, which resets the circadian biological clock in the suprachiasmatic nucleus

Infradian rhythm: a biological rhythm that has a periodicity of more than 24 hours; examples include the human female menstrual cycle and hibernation in squirrels and bears

We can see that these circadian rhythms are carefully synchronized with the day–night pattern in the outside world. We are diurnal animals, which means that we sleep when it is dark and too dangerous to be active. We awaken when it is light, and simultaneously our body temperature begins to rise; this rise in body temperature affects the metabolism of the body and allows us to be fully active during the daylight hours. Nocturnal animals show precisely the opposite pattern, but in both cases the behaviour is perfectly synchronized with day and night. It therefore seems obvious that light is the key to synchronizing our body clock with the outside world. Environmental cues such as light or temperature that can affect biological rhythms are called **exogenous zeitgebers** (zeitgebers for short, from the German for 'time giver'). We discuss the intricate relationship between endogenous pacemakers and zeitgebers in relation to the sleep–wake cycle later in this topic (page 291).

Infradian rhythms

Infradian means 'less than one day'. It is used to describe biological rhythms that have a periodicity of more than one day, meaning that there is less than one cycle every 24 hours. Examples include the human female menstrual cycle, seasonal affective disorder, and hibernation in bears and squirrels.

The regularity of these cycles is certainly due to endogenous pacemakers, and confirms that there must be many of these body clocks controlling the variety of biological rhythms that we can identify. The menstrual cycle in particular is under clear physiological control from hormones in the pituitary gland, whose release is in turn controlled from the hypothalamus in the brain. The regularity of the rhythm and the fact that it is largely independent of environmental cues (zeitgebers) implies that endogenous pacemakers are the key controlling factor.

KEY STUDY: RUSSELL ET AL. (1980)

Russell et al. (1980) did find evidence for an influence of zeitgebers on the menstrual cycle. They found that if sweat from one woman was rubbed on to the lips of another woman, their menstrual cycles would eventually synchronize. Russell et al. concluded that the sweat from the first woman contained pheromones, chemicals that throughout the animal kingdom serve as sexual signals. In this study pheromones were signalling phases of the menstrual cycle. The endogenous pacemaker controlling the cycle in the second woman responded to these pheromones by gradually bringing the two cycles together.

There have also been anecdotal accounts concerning groups of women living in close proximity for long periods (for example nuns) whose menstrual cycles again tend to synchronize.

In contrast to the menstrual cycle, hibernation may be another infradian rhythm, but it is clearly in tune with the outside world. The aim of hibernation is to remain as inactive and inconspicuous as possible at a time of year when food is scarce. Animals that hibernate prepare for it by laying down extra stores of fat and with a gradual slowing of their metabolic rate (the rate at which they burn up energy). We have already seen that squirrels will go through this preparation even if kept in the laboratory in constant light and temperature, implying that it is under the control of endogenous pacemakers. However, for hibernation to occur at the appropriate time, it makes sense for it to be responsive to zeitgebers such as outside temperature and day length, both associated with the onset of winter, but which can vary a few weeks either way from year to year.

Ultradian rhythms

Ultradian rhythms have a periodicity of less than one day. The best example is the rhythm of slow-wave sleep (SWS) and rapid eye movement sleep (REM) during the night; we enter a phase of REM after passing through several stages of SWS, then after 15 minutes or so in REM we move back into SWS, and the cycle begins again. The whole cycle takes about 90 minutes, so we have four to six complete cycles within a night's sleep.

Key term

Ultradian rhythm: a biological rhythm that has a periodicity of less than 24 hours; the best example is the alternation between slow wave sleep and REM sleep during a night's sleep

Other ultradian rhythms are less obvious. It has been suggested that urine production follows an ultradian pattern, while prenatal and newborn babies appear to have sleep–activity cycles of about 90 minutes throughout 24 hours.

The effect of endogenous pacemakers and exogenous zeitgebers on the sleep–wake cycle

Our sleep–wake cycle is a circadian rhythm, with one period of sleep and one period of waking every 24 hours. Humans, as diurnal animals, are awake during the daylight hours and sleep during the night time. We saw on pages 288–9 that many biological rhythms are maintained even when plants and animals are kept in constant light or darkness, with variables such as temperature also kept a constant. These studies are referred to as free-running studies, as the rhythm under investigation is allowed to run without any external interference. The common finding that rhythms are maintained under such free-running conditions implies that these rhythms are what we call endogenous, or inbuilt. The assumption is that they rely on an endogenous pacemaker or body clock, which can maintain the rhythm even when external or exogenous factors are absent.

Although not common, there have been some studies investigating the sleep–wake cycle under free-running conditions.

KEY STUDY: SIFFRE'S CAVE STUDY

In the best known of these studies, Michel Siffre, a French geologist, spent six months underground in a cave in Texas in 1972. While he was in the cave he could ask for lighting to be turned on in the morning when he awoke, and turned off in the evening when he wanted to sleep. There was no external light source. He was also wired up to a range of physiological recording equipment so that researchers could monitor how his body coped over the time he was in the cave.

Fig. 6.18 Michel Siffre at the entrance of the underground cave

Siffre was in the cave for 179 days. During this time his circadian sleep–wake cycle became longer than 24 hours. It was also inconsistent, varying between 25 and 32 hours. Compared to the 24-hour clock his days were therefore longer, and by his timing only 151 days had passed during the six months he was in the cave.

Researchers were also monitoring his body temperature, which under normal circumstances also has a 24-hour circadian rhythm. Siffre's body temperature maintained a fairly consistent cycle, but extended to 25 hours rather than 24.

Not surprisingly, Siffre suffered psychologically during his time in the cave, with bouts of depression and suicidal thoughts. These continued for some time after the study ended. Note that these were not due to sleep deprivation, as he could sleep as much as he liked. More likely they were due to the long period of isolation, or to the disturbance to his biological rhythms.

Conclusion

Siffre's study shows us that the circadian rhythm of sleep and waking is maintained under conditions where there are no exogenous zeitgebers. However, it is not perfectly regulated, as it becomes longer than 24 hours. This strongly suggests that the basic rhythm is controlled by an endogenous pacemaker or body clock, but that this needs input from the exogenous zeitgeber, light, in order to be perfectly synchronized with the day–night cycle.

The fact that the rhythm of Siffre's body temperature became uncoupled from the sleep–wake cycle also suggests that there must be at least two body clocks, one for the sleep–wake cycle and one for body temperature. In fact, it is now known that in the body there are hundreds of body clocks involved in regulating the circadian rhythms of a variety of physiological processes.

Siffre was in effect a single case study. However, similar studies (such as Aschoff et al., 1967) have found similar results. Circadian rhythms of sleep–wake and body temperature, under free-running conditions, become extended to between 25 and 30 hours. Body temperature tends to be more consistent than the sleep–wake cycle.

THINKING SCIENTIFICALLY: THE CONTROLLED CASE STUDY

Siffre's cave study has been extremely influential in the field of biological rhythms. However, it was a single case study, which might limit the generalizability of findings. But if we compare Siffre with Broca's aphasic patient Tan, we can see that even case studies can vary. Tan suffered brain damage and was only available to Broca for testing for a few days; his brain damage was not limited to the key 'Broca's area' in the frontal lobe. It was essential that other patients were studied before Broca could draw reliable conclusions.

Siffre's study, on the other hand, was carefully planned, with rigorous physiological monitoring and behavioural recording. We can be sure the results were valid and would be likely to be repeated by other free-running studies (as they were). Case studies look at individuals and will always be limited in their generalizability, but some, such as Tan, are more limited than others.

Endogenous pacemakers

The findings of free-running sleep–wake studies pointed to the existence of an endogenous pacemaker for circadian rhythms. In 1972, two groups (Moore and Eichler, 1972, Stephan and Zucker, 1972) demonstrated this conclusively. They showed that selective damage to an area of the hypothalamus called the suprachiasmatic nucleus (SCN) abolished circadian rhythms in rats. This was supported by findings in hamsters.

Unusually, there is a strain of mutant hamsters who have a 20-hour circadian rhythm rather than the usual 24-hour rhythm. When researchers transplanted the SCN from immature mutant hamsters into adult hamsters with the normal 24-hour rhythm, but whose SCN had been removed, they found that the adult hamsters regained their circadian rhythms, but they had a cycle length of 20 hours rather than 24 (Ralph et al., 1990). This means that the SCN transplant from the immature mutant hamsters had grown in place and had then imposed its 20-hour cycle on the adult hamsters. The reverse experiment also works. The circadian rhythm of mutant hamsters can be shifted from 20 hours to 24 hours by removing their own SCN and replacing it with the SCN from normal hamsters.

The clinching evidence for the role of the SCN as a key endogenous pacemaker was the finding that SCN neurons removed and kept alive outside the brain still show a circadian rhythm in their electrical activity. This demonstrates that the circadian activity of SCN neurons is intrinsic, or inbuilt; i.e. genetic. In fact, several genes have been identified as important in the control of our endogenous pacemakers. Examples include the CLOCK gene and the PER (for 'period') gene (Silver and Kriegsfeld, 2014).

The picture we have now (Silver and Kriegsfeld, 2014) is one where the 20,000 or so neurons of the SCN act as a master body clock, with regulatory control over many other body clocks in localized tissues and cells throughout the body. These individual body clocks have their own intrinsic rhythms, but the SCN acts to synchronize their activities.

Pacemakers and zeitgebers

We have seen earlier that in free-running studies the human circadian sleep–wake rhythm is regulated by our endogenous pacemaker, but that the rhythm extends slightly to between 24 and 30 hours. Under normal conditions of everyday living, this does not happen. Clearly we use endogenous zeitgebers, such as light onset in the morning, to perfectly synchronize our internal body clock with the outside world. In this way, the endogenous pacemaker and the exogenous zeitgeber work together to make sure that we are awake and alert during the day and sleep at night. To put it another way, our key endogenous pacemaker, the SCN, is reset every morning by light onset. (Note that in relation to the SCN and sleep-waking, we focus on light as the zeitgeber. There is evidence that other zeitgebers, such as body temperature, can also help reset body clocks.)

An important question concerns the pathways and mechanisms behind the interaction between SCN and light. It turns out that that there is a direct pathway from the retina of the eye (which contains our visual receptors) to the SCN, a pathway called the retinohypothalamic tract. This pathway alerts the SCN to the status of light in the outside world, especially onset of light in the morning, and in this way the SCN is tuned in to the outside world.

A further question is how the SCN exerts its regulatory role on other pacemakers in the body and on behaviours such as the sleep–wake cycle. It is certain that many hormones and neurotransmitters are involved (Silver and Kriegsfeld, 2014), but one important pathway involves the pineal gland. This gland is buried deep within the brain, but there is a direct pathway between the SCN and the pineal. In response to input from the SCN, the pineal gland releases the hormone melatonin. This hormone is circulated widely throughout the body and has a range of effects, including the control of sleep–wake behaviour. Through the pathways outlined above, daylight suppresses the release of melatonin from the pineal, while darkness leads to its gradual increase. When melatonin levels reach a certain point the animal awakes.

Endogenous pacemakers are found throughout the living world, in plants as well as animals. They provide basic circadian rhythms, most importantly the sleep–wake cycle. The interaction with endogenous zeitgebers, in particular light, ensures that under natural conditions the animal's rest–activity cycle is perfectly tuned to the outside world. The consequence of this relationship breaking down was shown in chipmunks. These are diurnal animals, normally active in the daytime and resting and inconspicuous at night. Chipmunks with damage to the SCN and released into the wild were far more vulnerable to predators, because the chipmunks were more active at night and therefore more conspicuous to predators (DeCoursey et al., 2000).

Research methods link

Even though it uses non-human animals, this type of study is completely unethical. Chipmunks suffered brain damage and were then observed to see how many died. Page 37 outlines the British Psychological Society code of ethics. Note the phrase '....shared collective duty for the welfare of human and non-human beings'. Some work with non-human animals can be justified in terms of the ultimate benefits to society, but the chipmunk study is not one of them – we already knew a great deal about the functions of the suprachiasmatic nucleus.

Pacemakers and zeitgebers: when the relationship breaks down

Further evidence regarding the relationship between endogenous pacemakers and endogenous zeitgebers can be found by looking at situations where the normal synchronized relationship breaks down. Two key examples of this in the modern world are jet lag and shift work. Say it takes about eight hours to fly from London westwards to New York. Leaving London at midday means that you arrive at 8 o'clock in the evening, according to your body clock. However, New York is five hours behind London, and so local time when you arrive will actually be 3 o'clock in the afternoon. Your endogenous pacemaker is therefore five hours ahead of local time and has to wait for local zeitgebers to catch up, a situation known as 'phase delay'.

Travelling from west to east, New York to London, the situation is reversed and your endogenous pacemaker ends up five hours behind local time and has to 'catch up', a situation known as 'phase advance'.

The symptoms of jet lag are due to this dislocation of endogenous pacemaker from local endogenous zeitgebers. For some reason jet lag is often worse travelling west to east, as though our endogenous pacemaker finds it easier to cope with phase delay rather than phase advance.

Besides the short-term symptoms of jet lag, there is some evidence that the long-term effects can be severe. Cho (2001) found that experienced female aircrew did worse on a variety of cognitive tests than less experienced aircrew, and also had some damage to the temporal lobe of the brain. Although it is difficult to control for all relevant factors, it seems likely that repeated experience of jet lag, caused by the dislocation of endogenous pacemakers from endogenous zeitgebers, can lead to serious psychological and physical consequences.

Similar findings have come from research into shift work. The invention of electric light at the beginning of the 20th century means that people can work at times when their endogenous pacemaker is trying to impose sleep. Both the Chernobyl nuclear accident in 1986 and the near-disaster at the Three Mile Island nuclear power facility in 1979 have been linked to mistakes made by workers in the early morning, between 2am and 4am. This is the time of maximum sleepiness. More controlled studies have shown that night shift work is linked to increased frequency of car accidents (Gold et al., 1992). Shift work has also been linked to an increased risk of breast cancer and heart problems (Davis et al., 2001). Milder problems include high levels of depression among workers, increased absenteeism, and lowered productivity (Czeisler et al., 1982).

It is possible to reduce some of these problems, for instance having longer periods on the same shift work pattern, so that pacemakers and zeitgebers have the opportunity to resynchronize. However, the fact remains that flying through different time zones and working at night are going against everything we know about endogenous pacemakers and endogenous zeitgebers. We evolved as diurnal animals, designed to be active during the day and quiet at night. Pacemakers and zeitgebers interact to ensure that this pattern is maintained. When our behaviour goes against these biological systems, there is inevitably a price to pay.

ACTIVITY 6.7

Keep a diary for a week that notes down when you go to sleep and when you wake up. Make sure you cover college days and the weekend. Also note down periods of alertness and extreme tiredness during the day. Does any sort of pattern emerge, such as sleep duration and daytime alertness? How might the interaction between pacemakers and zeitgebers explain your observations?

EXAMPLE EXAM QUESTION

What is the difference between ultradian and infradian rhythms? Give one example of each. (3 marks)

Exam hint

This seems a straightforward question, but make sure you don't rush it. It is all too easy to confuse ultradian and infradian rhythms.

KEY POINTS

- There are three categories of biological rhythm: circadian, infradian, and ultradian.
- Circadian rhythms have a periodicity of 24 hours Examples include the sleep–wake cycle and body temperature.
- Infradian rhythms have a periodicity of greater than one day. Examples include the human female menstrual cycle and hibernation in some animals.
- Ultradian rhythms have a periodicity of less than one day. The best example is the alternation during human sleep between slow wave and REM sleep.
- Free-running studies, such as Siffre's, show that the circadian rhythms of sleep and body temperature are controlled by endogenous pacemakers, or body clocks. However, the endogenous pacemaker for sleep on its own maintains a circadian rhythm of more than 24 hours. To maintain a 24-hour rhythm, in tune with day and night, it needs to be reset every morning by the endogenous zeitgeber, light.
- The main endogenous pacemaker in the brain is the suprachiasmatic nucleus, or SCN. The neurons making up the SCN have an inbuilt circadian rhythm that is reset every day by the zeitgeber light. To enable this, there is a pathway from the optic nerve to the SCN called the retinohypothalamic tract.
- The SCN regulates the endogenous clocks found throughout the body. An important pathway for these effects runs from the SCN to the pineal gland in the brain.
- Travel across time zones and shift work can both dislocate the relationship between endogenous pacemakers and endogenous zeitgebers. Research shows that this dislocation can cause both physical and psychological damage.

PRACTICAL ACTIVITY

It has been suggested that females are possibly less lateralized in terms of hemisphere function than males, with language spread across two hemispheres. Some results indicate that, because of this, females are better at language tasks, and males are better at visuospatial tasks.

A study to test this idea is to use a simple language test or a simple visuospatial test. After obtaining consent, ask participants to think of as many words beginning with 'L' in one minute as a simple language task, or ask them to solve simple anagrams – your teacher can advise you. Similarly, you can find visuospatial tasks on the Internet, e.g. mental rotation, and compare males and females in how long they take to complete these.

When planning and carrying out your study, you can consider the following questions:

- What type of design did you use?
- What sampling method did you use?
- What were the independent and dependent variables?
- Were there any extraneous variables you needed to control?
- What is the most appropriate measure of central tendency?
- Do the groups have similar ranges?
- Look at the mean or median, and the range. What conclusions would you draw?
- Finally, re-design the study so that the data could be analysed using the Sign test.

Exam focus

Read through the following example exam question, example student answers, and examiner comments. Then, have a go at answering the question yourself!

EXAMPLE EXAM QUESTION, TAKEN FROM PAGE 259

Outline the organization of the autonomic nervous system. (4 marks)

Thom's answer

The autonomic nervous system is divided into two branches – the sympathetic and the parasympathetic branch. These can be thought of as like the accelerator and the brake of a car. The sympathetic nervous system switches on when we are faced with a danger or a stressor. Bodily systems are activated to enable us to fight the stressor or run from it. The heart beats faster, which pumps more blood around the body, so oxygen is carried to muscles and breathing rate increases to supply oxygen. Stored energy is released and other digestive processes are halted. When the stressor has passed, the parasympathetic nervous system restores the body to a resting state. Breathing and heart rate slow down and digestion resumes, restoring the body to a state of homeostasis.

Examiner comment: Thom's answer is accurate and detailed. The two branches of the ANS are clearly identified and outlined. The answer as a whole is clear, with use of specialist terminology. This is a Level 2 answer which would score **4/4 marks**.

Karl's answer

The nervous system is highly organised, with a central nervous system made up of the brain and spinal chord and a peripheral nervous system. The nervous system communicates through the use of neurons. One part of the nervous system is the ANS. This automatic nervous system controls the body's automatic functions like breathing, digesting, and sleeping. When we need energy then the sympathetic branch makes sure we have it and when we want to relax the other branch switches on. This mechanism probably adapted a long time ago when most of our stresses were predators and we needed to fight or flight.

Examiner comment: The first two sentences of the answer, whilst accurate, are not directly relevant, so pick up no marks. These should be omitted.

Examiner comment: Karl correctly identifies the existence of two branches of the ANS, but provides little detail on the actual effects on the body. The outline lacks detail and, in places, accuracy. This is a Level 1 response, gaining **2/4 marks**.

Examination skills

Introduction

Now that the subject content is complete, your next psychological experience is the preparation and sitting of your exam – whether that is for AS, or A Level. In this section we examine the skills and knowledge you'll need. Remember, knowing your subject is one thing, but being able to revise well for it, identify what the questions require, and write concisely to the questions, are all skills that need to be developed. Preparation is the key to your success. The more opportunities you can give yourself to become familiar with the course content and the structure of the exam, the more confident you will feel on the day.

It can be helpful to think of an A Level exam in the same way as a driving test: you wouldn't dream of taking your driving test without going round the test course several times – but many students tackle A Level exams without practising writing against the clock. In this section we take a close look at the examinations you will be undertaking, illustrating the skills you will need to develop for success at AS or A Level.

How will I be assessed?

A good place to start is to ensure you know exactly what will be required of you in your exams. The Psychology examinations assess three main skills, or 'Assessment Objectives':

1. AO1: You should be able to **demonstrate knowledge and understanding** of psychological ideas, processes, techniques and procedures.
2. AO2: You should be able to **apply your knowledge** and understanding of psychological ideas, processes, techniques and procedures in different contexts and when handling data.
3. AO3: You should be able to **analyse, interpret and evaluate** psychological information and evidence, to make judgements and reach conclusions and to develop and refine designs and procedures when carrying out or planning research.

So, you can expect the exam paper to contain questions which require you to use the different kinds of cognitive skills you have developed over the course: to demonstrate knowledge of theories, research studies and methods; to apply your knowledge to novel situations; and to analyse and evaluate theories, research studies and methods. Some exam questions combine these objectives – for example, asking you to show knowledge of a topic and then apply your knowledge to a novel situation, or demonstrate knowledge of a theory and then analyse/evaluate the theory.

Later in this section, we will explore each of the assessment objectives in greater depth and provide some activities to help you construct excellent answers for each of the objectives. Throughout the book you will find examples of the different types of question, which will be used in your exam papers, along with some helpful hints about how to tackle these, and some things to avoid! We strongly advise you to write answers to these questions as part of your exam preparation: this will help you to 'hone' your writing skills for the different kinds of question.

AS Level assessment

At AS Level you will sit Paper 1 and Paper 2. These are equally weighted, so each provides 50% of your final mark for AS Level. Both exams are 90 minutes long. All three assessment objectives are assessed on both papers, but as a general rule:

- Paper 1 will contain more A01 (knowledge) marks
- Paper 2 will contain more A02 (application) marks
- Both papers will contain a similar amount of A03 (analysis and evaluation) marks.

Both question papers will include a mixture of multiple-choice questions, short questions and extended writing (essay-style) questions.

A Level assessment

At A Level you will sit Papers 1, 2 and 3. These are equally weighted, so each provides 33% of your final mark for A Level. Each exam is two hours long.

- Paper 1 will contain more A01 (knowledge) marks
- Paper 2 will contain more A02 (application) marks
- Papers 1 and 3 will contain more A03 (analysis and evaluation) marks than paper 2.

All three papers will include a mixture of multiple-choice questions, short questions and extended writing (essay-style) questions.

What about maths?

The standard of maths in the Psychology assessment is at least the standard of higher tier GCSE mathematics, and at least **10% of the marks** at AS and A Level will require you to use your mathematical skills. Questions could require you to:

- Calculate descriptive statistics (e.g. mean scores or ranges from a set of data)
- Display data in an appropriate graph
- Explain the difference between probability levels $p \leq 0.05$ and 0.01
- Use critical value tables (i.e. statistical tables) to decide whether to reject or retain the null hypothesis.

How will my answers be marked?

Your paper will be scanned and then marked online – which makes it very important to write clearly! The examiners who mark your paper will use a '**Level of response**' mark scheme. This mark scheme identifies the key characteristics of a good, reasonable, or basic answer for each question.

- Short questions (i.e. 4 marks) generally have two levels of response
- Moderate questions (i.e. 6 or 8 marks) have three levels of response
- Extended writing questions (i.e. 12 or 16 marks) have four levels of response

The descriptor for the level shows the average performance for the level. The examiner will read your response carefully and check if it fits the criteria in the lowest level before moving up the levels to see where your response fits. They will consider the overall quality of your answer to do this, rather than 'picking holes' in small and specific parts of the answer and looking for areas where you have not been as clear as you might. It's worth noting that the top level doesn't require a perfect answer.

Here is an example of a Paper 2 A02 question and the relevant mark scheme:

> A psychologist carried out a study of social learning. As part of the procedure, he showed children aged 4–5 years a film of a 4-year-old boy stroking a puppy. Whilst the children watched the film, the psychologist commented on how kind the boy was. After the children had watched the film, the psychologist brought a puppy into the room and watched to see how the children behaved with the puppy.
>
> Outline what is meant by social learning theory and explain how social learning might have occurred in the procedure described above. (6 marks)

AQA 2014

This question has two injunctions (instructions): 'outline' and 'explain how'. Two marks are awarded for the outline of social learning theory, and four marks are awarded for application of knowledge to the scenario. Here is the mark scheme for this question.

Level	Marks	Description
3	5–6	Outline of social learning is generally detailed, clear and coherent. Explanation of how social learning might have occurred in the procedure is thorough with aspects of social learning applied appropriately to the context. There is effective use of terminology.
2	3–4	Outline of social learning is mostly clear but some detail is missing. Explanation of how social learning might have occurred in the procedure is mostly sound and appropriate. There is some effective use of terminology.
1	1–2	Outline of social learning lacks detail and clarity. Explanation of how social learning might have occurred in the procedure is limited. Terminology is either minimal, absent or inappropriately used.
	0	No relevant content.

AQA 2014

ACTIVITY 1

The mark scheme identifies three levels of response. What should your answer include in order to be awarded a mark in level 3? (Answer on page 306)

So, this mark scheme provides you with goal posts, identifying exactly what you should aim for in your answers to score well.

Maximize your marks on the assessment objectives

How to gain good A01 marks

The assessment objective A01 requires you to demonstrate knowledge and understanding of theories, methods or research studies. Typical A01 terms include *outline* and *describe*. An outline is a 'sketch' of the main features without much detail. A question which asks for an *outline* is likely to have fewer marks awarded for A01. If you are asked to *describe*, more detail is required and there are likely to be more marks available. For an outline you will need to select the most important information to include. For example, if you were asked to *outline the findings* of Milgram's obedience experiment, you should say that 26/40 participants (or 65%) went to 450 volts on the shock generator, and all 40 participants went to 300 volts. These are the main findings of the experiment. If you were asked to *describe* the findings of Milgram's study, you could include information about how the participants responded; stuttering, arguing, and showing signs of stress. These are also findings.

ACTIVITY 2

Construct answers to the two following questions:

- Outline Bowlby's monotropic theory of attachment. (3 marks)
- Describe Bowlby's monotropic theory. (6 marks)

(Answers on page 307)

Your outline should provide a sketch of the key features of this approach, and for 6 marks your description should provide more detail of the key features of the theory. Compare your answers with the worked examples on page 307 at the end of this section. You might find it easier to write the 6 mark description first, then edit it down to a 3 mark outline.

How to gain good A02 marks

The assessment objective A02 requires you to apply your knowledge in different contexts. Hence the key to good A02 marks is thorough application to the scenario. How do you go about applying knowledge? Each scenario on the examination will have been carefully constructed to provide a series of clues, or 'hooks'. You should start by reading the scenario very carefully to identify the key hooks – it can help to underline these on the exam paper.

The question is about social learning theory

Opportunity for observational learning through a film

4-year-old boy is a role model

Positive reinforcement

Opportunity to see if social learning has taken place

A psychologist carried out a study of social learning. As part of the procedure, he showed children aged 4–5 years a film of a 4-year-old boy stroking a puppy. While the children watched the film, the psychologist commented on how kind the boy was. After the children had watched the film, the psychologist brought a puppy into the room and watched to see how the children behaved with the puppy.

Outline what is meant by social learning theory and explain how social learning might have occurred in the procedure described above.
[6 marks]

Once you have identified the key 'hooks', construct your answer to the scenario by referring to each hook carefully, preferably in the order they occur in the stem. You should not waste your time describing social learning theory, as no marks are available for description: remember that marks are awarded for showing your understanding through application to the example.

ACTIVITY 3

Construct an answer to the above question, making use of the underlined hooks. Remember to use appropriate terminology (language), as this is important for Level 3 marks.

How to gain good A03 marks

The assessment objective A03 requires you to analyse and evaluate theories, research studies, and methods. What do we mean by analysis and evaluation? These are critical skills which indicate that you can go further than simply describing theories and studies, and you can engage in discussion about how useful or important they are. Evaluation is literally putting a value on something – telling us how much it is worth or how useful it is.

A good start to evaluation is to identify strengths and weaknesses of a theory or a study. Many students assume that critical analysis consists only of negative points, but it is fine to be positive: all the research you have read about in the book has made a valuable contribution to psychological knowledge at some point, even though some insights may have been superseded by more recent (and possibly scientific) understanding of a topic.

If you are asked to evaluate research, you can structure your answer by examining strengths and weaknesses. Once you have identified a strength or weakness, you should aim to explore and explain it in depth, rather than barely stating it. This is referred to as *elaboration* and it will help to make your critical argument more subtle and nuanced. Have a look at the following example, relating to Loftus' experimental work on eyewitness testimony.

One criticism of Loftus' work is that it was carried out in a laboratory, so it lacks validity.

Examiner comment: This is a basic evaluation point which makes a claim.

To develop this critical point, explain *how* the experiment lacks validity:

Loftus' participants watched a video of a car accident. They were told to pay attention to it and were expecting something to happen. This is unlike real life, where accidents often happen when we aren't paying attention.

Examiner comment: Development of this point now shows that you understand the idea of validity.

You could develop this argument even further by explaining why Loftus chose to do it this way – showing that you understand that there are benefits:

However, the advantage of a lab experiment is that the researcher can control exactly what people see in the film; this means that only one variable (in this case the question asked about speed) varies, leading the researcher to be able to make conclusions about cause and effect.

Examiner comment: You have now presented a balanced argument about the strengths and weaknesses of the lab in Loftus' study. This is called a line of argument.

You could develop this critical argument further by considering ethical issues of using the lab to study eyewitness accounts.

ACTIVITY 4

Imagine that you have been asked to 'evaluate cognitive behavioural therapy as a treatment of depression' (6 marks).

You begin with a list of the strengths and weaknesses of CBT, which goes something like this:

- Strengths: as effective as drugs (Robinson), can be used by different people, can be on Internet (MoodGYM)
- Weaknesses: no more effective than a placebo (Robinson), depends upon the therapist, best when combined with drugs

Each of these points will need to be explained and elaborated in order to develop a critical argument. You may also wish to re-order them. Have a go at this and compare your answer with the example on page 307.

Evaluation of explanations (i.e. theories or models) feels more challenging than evaluation of research studies for many students. An explanation can focus on how something happens (e.g. a model of how memory operates) or why something happens (e.g. why babies form attachments, or why people develop phobias). In order to evaluate an explanation, you should examine evidence for it (i.e. theories or studies which support the claims) along with any evidence against the theory.

Let's have a look at an example using a question on memory:

Evaluate the multi-store model of memory. Refer to the findings of research in your answer. [6 marks]

Here the injunction word is 'evaluate', so you should not spend time describing the model, as you will not be awarded marks for this. You may wish to start with **a sentence**, which summarizes the MSM as conceptualizing memory as made of two stores, STM and LTM, with information transferred via rehearsal. The chapter on memory covers a range of research on the multi-store model including:

- Case studies (Milner, Shallice and Warrington) which illustrate that it is possible to lose some elements of memory whilst retaining others
- Studies of patients with Alzheimer's (Drachman and Sahakian, 1979)
- Scanning methods (Squire et al., 1992) showing a different physical basis for different types of memory.

However, there is also evidence contradicting some of the claims of the MSM:

- Kulik and Brown showed how some emotional and surprising events appear to be stored in LTM without rehearsal
- Ruckhin showed how STM tasks also involve semantic information stored in LTM, contradicting the claim that information flows in one direction through the model

In an answer of this type (A03) you will not have a great deal of space to describe research studies. Instead you should practise summarizing evidence succinctly and drawing conclusions from evidence; *'this shows that'* is an extremely useful phrase. You should also avoid the temptation to evaluate research studies in questions of this nature. Keep the focus on evaluation of the theory.

ACTIVITY 5

Have a go at the above question, then compare your answer with the example on page 307.

Checklist of skills for evaluating explanations

- Summarize research evidence succinctly with the focus on findings rather than methods
- Draw explicit conclusions from evidence (*this shows that*)
- Try to balance evidence for and against
- Structure your arguments into sections/paragraphs
- Keep the focus on the theory and don't get side-tracked into methodological evaluation

Activity answers

Activity 1

A level 3 response requires:

- An outline which is clear and coherent
- Thorough application to the example/scenario
- Effective use of language (terminology).

Activity 2

Describe Bowlby's monotropic theory. [6 marks]

Bowlby viewed attachment as an instinct, which evolved because it helped survival in the past. He thought that babies possessed social releasers (crying and smiling) to get adults to care for them, and mothers possessed instincts to protect and care for babies. Bowlby thought that infants form one attachment (monotropy) which is different to all others. This attachment needed to be formed within the first 3 years of life, otherwise lasting damage could occur. Bowlby believed that the first attachment provided the basis of later attachments – an idea called the internal working model.

Outline Bowlby's monotropic theory of attachment. [3 marks]

Bowlby viewed attachment as an instinct, which evolved because it helped survival. He believed that infants form one attachment (monotropy) which is different to all others. This attachment needs to be formed within the first 3 years of life. Bowlby argued that the first attachment provides the basis for later attachments – an idea called the internal working model.

Activity 3; AO2

Social learning theory refers to learning through observation and modelling. In the scenario, the psychologist begins by showing the children a film, providing them with an opportunity to learn through observation. He chooses the role model in the film, a 4-year-old, to be similar to the children watching the film, as role models are more likely to be copied if they are similar. The behaviour shown by the model is stroking a puppy. The psychologist includes another feature of SLT which is vicarious reinforcement: this refers to observing a model obtaining rewards, in this case praise for the boy stroking the puppy. Finally, the psychologist puts the children in a similar environment and observes to see whether they have learned the behaviour – stroking the puppy.

Activity 4: Evaluate CBT as a treatment for depression

CBT is one of the most effective treatments for depression – shown by its widespread use today. The most important strength is that CBT appears to be quite effective. Robinson et al. (1990) found that CBT was as good as drug therapy, and both were better than no therapy at all. Another strength of CBT is its versatility: it is appropriate for different ages and sexes, and newer forms can be delivered on the Internet. This makes it very attractive indeed, as it would be more accessible to more people.

However, another finding of Robinson's study was that CBT was no more effective than other forms of psychological therapy, and worryingly no more effective than a placebo. Even thinking you are being helped seems to be enough to make some people feel better. This is a wider criticism of psychological therapies: for some people, thinking that they are getting help is as good as actually getting help. This points to the fact that it might just be the relationship with a therapist that is important rather than any particular therapeutic technique. Finally CBT is most effective when it is combined with drugs – so this dual approach seems to be the best option for depression.

Activity 5

The multi-store model of memory views memory as made up of two stores, short-term memory (STM) and long-term memory (LTM) with information transferred from STM to LTM through rehearsal. There has been considerable evidence to support this model from case studies of people with injury and memory loss. Milner reported the case of HM who had surgery to reduce his epilepsy. HM could remember events from his early childhood but couldn't learn or retain new information, so he constantly thought he had just woken up. His STM was intact, suggesting that the stores might be separate.

Examiner comment: Keep any description to a minimum.

Examiner comment: Signpost your argument by identifying evidence as supporting.

Examiner comment: Keep methodological detail short.

Examiner comment: Draw a conclusion; 'this shows that'.

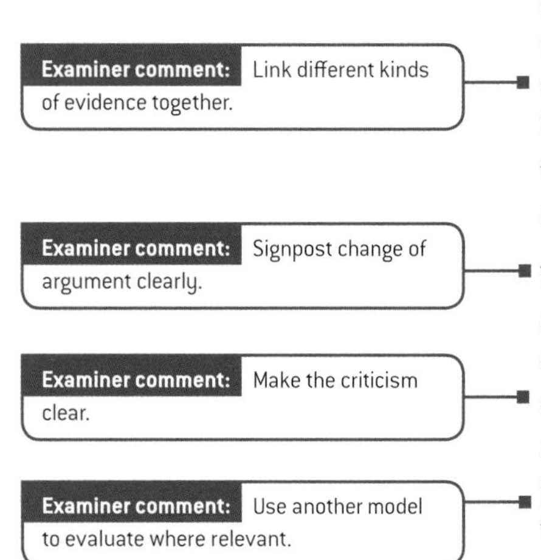

Examiner comment: Link different kinds of evidence together.
Examiner comment: Signpost change of argument clearly.
Examiner comment: Make the criticism clear.
Examiner comment: Use another model to evaluate where relevant.

Shallice and Warrington reported the case of KF who was injured in a motorbike accident. KF had a working LTM but an impaired ST with a digit span of only about 2 items (the normal is between 5 and 9). Together these two studies suggest that one part of the memory can be damaged whilst the other continues to function implying that they may be separate stores. Studies using brain-scanning (PET) and functional magnetic resonance imaging have provided biological support for the model showing that different brain areas are active when we use STM and LTM. Squire et al. (1992) found that the hippocampus is active in LTM tasks whereas areas in the pre-frontal cortex are activated for STM tasks.

But the MSM also has criticisms. One of these relates to rehearsal, which is seen as a key process in the model. Kulik and Brown found that surprising and emotional events seem to go straight into the LTM without rehearsal, implying that information doesn't have to go through the STM in the way described by the MSM. The working memory model sees STM as a more complicated and active system with different processers dealing with different kinds of information. This model has largely replaced the idea of STM put forward by the MSM.

Revising and preparing for exams

When you come to start revising, it is important to ask yourselves the following questions: Do you actually know how to revise? And do you know how you best learn? In order to find this out, you should find out whether you are primarily a **visual**, **auditory** or **kinaesthetic** learner. This will really help you to use revision strategies that play to your strengths.

Visual learning strategies: seeing is believing

If you are a visual learner, your revision strategy needs to reflect this. Activities you could use to revise include the creation of illustrations, e.g. tables, graphs, diagrams, pictures, or even video. There are freely available online applications that can be used to produce visually-rich material too, such as mind-maps. It is commonly reported that visual learners revise most effectively in a quiet environment.

Auditory learning strategies: learning by listening

Auditory learners need to hear the content they are learning. If this is you, then try recording your notes with a sound recorder and playing them back. Test yourself on small sections that you've just heard. You could also try to repeat facts out loud from your notes with your eyes closed. Word association works well when trying to remember key facts or lines from notes. You could also arrange a revision forum with friends. Hearing the ideas and discussing them strengthens your knowledge.

Kinaesthetic learning strategies: activated by action

The kinaesthetic learner likes a 'hands on' approach, and if this is you, then you should consider this when planning your revision. It is of utmost importance that your revision activities get you involved in the work, perhaps by working through a student workbook or a 'companion guide' that encourages you to read and then interact with the material. Why not create little tasks, such as a mix and match activity where the details for a topic have to be matched with its broader explanatory details? Since you learn best from participating in the learning, why not revise by carrying out studies that might have been done to support the principles of the points you are trying to learn? Kinaesthetic learners need variety, so don't just make use of one technique, but do different activities during each revision session.

'Spec check': Organizing your knowledge

Please be aware that if you are studying for AS Psychology, Psychopathology will appear in Paper 2, and not Paper 1.

Part 1: Introductory topics in psychology (*red sections are A Level only)		Have I got notes?	Revised?
1.1 Social influence	• Types of conformity: internalisation, identification and compliance. Explanations for conformity: informational social influence and normative social influence, and variables affecting conformity including group size, unanimity and task difficulty as investigated by Asch.		
	• Conformity to social roles as investigated by Zimbardo.		
	• Explanations for obedience: agentic state and legitimacy of authority, and situational variables affecting obedience including proximity, location and uniform, as investigated by Milgram. Dispositional explanation for obedience: the Authoritarian Personality.		
	• Explanations of resistance to social influence, including social support and locus of control.		
	• Minority influence including reference to consistency, commitment and flexibility.		
	• The role of social influence processes in social change.		
1.2 Memory	• The multi-store model of memory: sensory register, short-term memory and long-term memory. Features of each store: coding, capacity and duration.		
	• Types of long-term memory: episodic, semantic, procedural.		
	• The working memory model: central executive, phonological loop, visuo-spatial sketchpad and episodic buffer. Features of the model: coding and capacity.		
	• Explanations for forgetting: proactive and retroactive interference and retrieval failure due to absence of cues.		
	• Factors affecting the accuracy of eyewitness testimony: misleading information, including leading questions and post-event discussion; anxiety.		
	• Improving the accuracy of eyewitness testimony, including the use of the cognitive interview.		
1.3 Attachment	• Caregiver-infant interactions in humans: reciprocity and interactional synchrony. Stages of attachment identified by Schaffer. Multiple attachments and the role of the father.		
	• Animal studies of attachment: Lorenz and Harlow.		
	• Explanations of attachment: learning theory and Bowlby's monotropic theory. The concepts of a critical period and an internal working model.		
	• Ainsworth's 'Strange Situation'. Types of attachment: secure, insecure-avoidant and insecure-resistant. Cultural variations in attachment, including van Ijzendoorn.		
	• Bowlby's theory of maternal deprivation. Romanian orphan studies: effects of institutionalisation.		
	• The influence of early attachment on childhood and adult relationships, including the role of an internal working model.		
1.4 Psychopathology	• Definitions of abnormality, including deviation from social norms, failure to function adequately, statistical infrequency and deviation from ideal mental health.		
	• The behavioural, emotional and cognitive characteristics of phobias, depression and obsessive-compulsive disorder (OCD).		
	• The behavioural approach to explaining and treating phobias: the two-process model, including classical and operant conditioning; systematic desensitisation, including relaxation and use of hierarchy; flooding.		
	• The cognitive approach to explaining and treating depression: Beck's negative triad and Ellis's ABC model; cognitive behaviour therapy (CBT), including challenging irrational thoughts.		
	• The biological approach to explaining and treating OCD: genetic and neural explanations; drug therapy.		

Part 2: Psychology in context		Have I got notes?	Revised?
2.1 Approaches in psychology	• Origins of psychology: Wundt, introspection and the emergence of psychology as a science.		
	• Learning approaches: the behaviourist approach, including classical conditioning and Pavlov's research, operant conditioning, types of reinforcement and Skinner's research; social learning theory including imitation, identification, modelling, vicarious reinforcement, the role of mediational processes and Bandura's research.		
	• The cognitive approach: the study of internal mental processes, the role of schema, the use of theoretical and computer models to explain and make inferences about mental processes. The emergence of cognitive neuroscience.		
	• The biological approach: the influence of genes, biological structures and neurochemistry on behaviour. Genotype and phenotype, genetic basis of behaviour, evolution and behaviour.		
	• The psychodynamic approach: the role of the unconscious, the structure of personality, that is ID, ego and superego, defence mechanisms including repression, denial and displacement, psychosexual stages. • Humanistic psychology: free will, self-actualisation and Maslow's hierarchy of needs, focus on the self, congruence, the role of conditions of worth. The influence on counselling psychology. • Comparison of approaches.		
2.2 Biopsychology	• The divisions of the nervous system: central and peripheral (somatic and autonomic).		
	• The structure and function of sensory, relay and motor neurons. The process of synaptic transmission, including reference to neurotransmitters, excitation and inhibition.		
	• The function of the endocrine system: glands and hormones.		
	• The fight or flight response including the role of adrenaline.		
	• Localisation of function in the brain and hemispheric lateralisation: motor, somatosensory, visual, auditory and language centres; Broca's and Wernicke's areas, split brain research. Plasticity and functional recovery of the brain after trauma. • Ways of studying the brain: scanning techniques, including functional magnetic resonance imaging (fMRI); electroencephalogram (EEGs) and event-related potentials (ERPs); post-mortem examinations. • Biological rhythms: circadian, infradian and ultradian and the difference between these rhythms. The effect of endogenous pacemakers and exogenous zeitgebers on the sleep/wake cycle.		
2.3 Research methods	Students should demonstrate knowledge and understanding of the following research methods, scientific processes and techniques of data handling and analysis, be familiar with their use and be aware of their strengths and limitations.		
	• Experimental method. Types of experiment, laboratory and field experiments; natural and quasi-experiments.		
	• Observational techniques. Types of observation: naturalistic and controlled observation; covert and overt observation; participant and non-participant observation.		
	• Self-report techniques. Questionnaires; interviews, structured and unstructured.		
	• Correlations. Analysis of the relationship between co-variables. The difference between correlations and experiments.		
	• Content analysis. • Case studies.		
	2.3.1 Scientific processes		
	• Aims: stating aims, the difference between aims and hypotheses.		
	• Hypotheses: directional and non-directional.		
	• Sampling: the difference between population and sample; sampling techniques including: random, systematic, stratified, opportunity and volunteer; implications of sampling techniques, including bias and generalisation.		

Part 2: Psychology in context (continued)		Have I got notes?	Revised?
	• Pilot studies and the aims of piloting.		
	• Experimental designs: repeated measures, independent groups, matched pairs.		
	• Observational design: behavioural categories; event sampling; time sampling.		
	• Questionnaire construction, including use of open and closed questions; design of interviews.		
	• Variables: manipulation and control of variables, including independent, dependent, extraneous, confounding; operationalisation of variables.		
	• Control: random allocation and counterbalancing, randomisation and standardisation.		
	• Demand characteristics and investigator effects.		
	• Ethics, including the role of the British Psychological Society's code of ethics; ethical issues in the design and conduct of psychological studies; dealing with ethical issues in research.		
	• The role of peer review in the scientific process.		
	• The implications of psychological research for the economy.		
	• Reliability across all methods of investigation. Ways of assessing reliability: test-retest and inter-observer; improving reliability.		
	• Types of validity across all methods of investigation: face validity, concurrent validity, ecological validity and temporal validity. Assessment of validity. Improving validity.		
	• Features of science: objectivity and the empirical method; replicability and falsifiability; theory construction and hypothesis testing; paradigms and paradigm shifts.		
	• Reporting psychological investigations. Sections of a scientific report: abstract, introduction, method, results, discussion and referencing.		
	2.3.2 Data handling and analysis		
	• Quantitative and qualitative data; the distinction between qualitative and quantitative data collection techniques.		
	• Primary and secondary data, including meta-analysis.		
	• Descriptive statistics: measures of central tendency – mean, median, mode; calculation of mean, median and mode; measures of dispersion; range and standard deviation; calculation of range; calculation of percentages; positive, negative and zero correlations.		
	• Presentation and display of quantitative data: graphs, tables, scattergrams, bar charts, histograms.		
	• Distributions: normal and skewed distributions; characteristics of normal and skewed distributions.		
	• Analysis and interpretation of correlation, including correlation coefficients.		
	• Levels of measurement: nominal, ordinal and interval.		
	• Content analysis and coding. Thematic analysis.		
	2.3.3 Inferential testing		
	Students should demonstrate knowledge and understanding of inferential testing and be familiar with the use of inferential tests.		
	• Introduction to statistical testing; the sign test.		
	• Probability and significance: use of statistical tables and critical values in interpretation of significance; Type I and Type II errors.		
	• Factors affecting the choice of statistical test, including level of measurement and experimental design. When to use the following tests: Spearman's rho, Pearson's r, Wilcoxon, Mann-Whitney, related t-test, unrelated t-test and Chi-Squared test.		

Your calendar of action for effective exam preparation and completion

One month (plus) before the exam	• Success is built upon preparation. So ensure that you have all your notes. • Make use of the 'spec check' earlier to ensure your notes cover the whole specification. If not, speak to your teacher about getting additional notes for it. • Identify your preferred learning style (visual, auditory, kinaesthetic), and develop activities that complement this. • Bearing in mind your preferred method of learning, plan out times for revision that allow for the specification to be covered, and more than just superficially. • Develop a set of goals that are achievable as you go through your revision. Maybe reward yourself with certain numbers of rest periods that can be used how you like, e.g. time with friends.
Two weeks before	• Revision is well under way. Make sure that you complement your learning of the theory with good practice of the examination questions. • Theory is not everything – being aware of the question type, style and layout is just as important. • Make use of the exam questions and guidance throughout this book to get you started. Why not also try to use your own imagination – you can use the specification check and some of the specimen questions to create your own questions. • Remember, practice makes perfect. • Ask your teacher to look at your attempts. Note down any issues that seem to recur and ask for help in rectifying these. • Now is the time for refining your skills, and clearing up last-minute anomalies in understanding.
One week before	• In this week, focus on the issues that you might find most difficult. There is still time, but be more efficient with it! • Your mind will rest easier if you know the material well. So in a self-rewarding way, tick off on the spec check the areas that you have covered and know well. Identify the areas that need to be revisited in order to clarify understanding. • The use of highlighters is a good idea, colour coding the areas of the specification that might be well learnt (green); in need of a little more (orange); really don't understand (red).
The night before	• Should you cram until the last minute, or rest? Most teachers would say that what you don't know by the night before, you will never know. • As a general guide, however, ensure that you have plenty of rest the evening before. Go to sleep early – next morning you will need all the extra energy your body can generate. Remember, your body requires sleep, and a late night of revising may reduce your effectiveness.
The day of the exam	• If it is a morning examination, make sure you have a good breakfast. The examination will require a lot of mental energy, so slow release energy foods are often the best – for example, porridge, or bananas. • If your exam is in the afternoon, you have some more time to fine-tune your revision. Don't do this excessively. • Get to your examination location with plenty of time to spare. Try to reduce all avoidable sources of stress. • Once in the exam location, make sure you complete the necessary administration. • Start the exam – remember to enjoy it – you have worked hard and prepared for it well, now simply show the examiner what you can do. • After the exam – avoid too much unnecessary dissection of what you have done. This will worry you, and may affect future exam performance.

References

Abrahamson, L., Seligman, M.P and Teasdale, J.D. (1978) Learned helplessness in humans – critique and reformulation. *Journal of Abnormal Psychology*, 87, 49–74.

Adorno, T.W., Frenkel-Brunswik, G., Levinson, D.J. and Sanford, R.N. (1950) *The Authoritarian Personality.* New York: Harper.

Allan, K. Midjord, J.P , Martin, D & Gabbert, F. (2011) Memory conformity and the perceived accuracy of self versus other, in *Memory and Cognition* (2012) 40, 280–286.

Allen, K., Blasovich, J. and Mendes, W.B. (2002) Cardiovascular reactivity and the presence of pets, friends, and spouses: the truth about cats and dogs. *Psychosomatic Medicine*, 64, 727–39.

Asch, S.E. (1951) Effects of group pressure upon the modification and distortion of judgements. In H. Guetzkpw (ed.), *Groups, Leadership and Men.* Pittsburgh, PA: Carnegie Press.

Asch, S.E. (1956) Studies of independence and conformity: a minority of one against a unanimous majority. *Psychological Monographs*, 70.

Aschoff, J. (1967) Comparative physiology: diurnal rhythms. *Annual Review of Physiology*, 25, 581–600.

Atkinson, R.C. and Shiffrin, R.M. (1968). Chapter: Human memory: A proposed system and its control processes. In Spence, K.W. and Spence, J.T. *The psychology of learning and motivation (Volume 2)*. New York: Academic Press, 89–195.

Attanasio, V., Andrasik, F., Burke, E.J., Blake, D.D., Kabela, E. and McCarran, M.S. (1985) Clinical issues in utilizing biofeedback with children. *Clinical Biofeedback and Health*, 8, 134–41.

Avtgis, T.A. (1998) Locus of control and persuasion, social influence and conformity: a meta-analytic review. *Psychology Reports*, 83(3), 899–903.

Baddeley A, Gathercole S, and Papagno C (1998). The phonological loop as a language learning device. *Psychological Review,* 105 (1): 158–73.

Baddeley, A. and Hitch, G. (1974) Working memory. In G. Bower (ed.), *The Psychology of Learning and Motivation*. Oxford: Elsevier.

Baddeley, A. D. (1996) Exploring the central executive. *Quarterly Journal of Experimental Psychology,* 51A, 819–52.

Baddeley, A.D. (1999) *Essentials of Human Memory*. Hove: Psychology Press.

Baddeley, A.D. (2000). The episodic buffer: A new component of working memory? *Trends in Cognitive Science* 4 (11): 417–423.

Baddeley, A.D. (1966). The influence of acoustic and semantic similarities on long-term memory for word sequences. *Quarterly Journal of Experimental Psychology, 18,* 302–309.

Baddeley, A.D. and Logie, R.H. (1999) Working memory: the multiple component model. In A. Miyake and P. Shah (eds), *Models of Working Memory: mechanisms of active maintenance and executive control.* Cambridge: Cambridge University Press.

Baddeley, A.D. and Wilson, B. (2002) Prose recall and amnesia: implications for the structure of working memory. *Neuropsychologia,* 40, 1737–43.

Baddeley, A.D., Grant, S., Wight, E. and Thomson, N. (1973) Imagery and visual working memory. In P.M.A. Rabbitt and S. Dornic (eds), *Attention and Performance V* (pp205–17). London: Academic Press.

Baddeley, A.D., Thomson, N. and Buchanan, M. (1975) Word length and the structure of short-term memory. *Journal of Verbal Learning and Verbal Behaviour,* 14, 575–89.

Bahrick, H. P.; Bahrick, P. O.; Wittlinger, R. P. (1975) Journal of Experimental Psychology: General, 104(1), 54–75.

Bahrick, H.P. and Hall, L.K. (2005) The importance of retrieval failures to long-term retention: a metacognitive explanation of the spacing effect. *Journal of Memory and Language*, 52, 4, 566–77 (special issue on metamemory).

Bahrick, H.P. Phelps, E. (1987) Retention of Spanish vocabulary over eight years. *Journal of Experimental Psychology: learning, memory and cognition*, 13, 2.

Bailey, R.E. and Denstaedt, L. (2007) *Destinations: an integrated approach to writing paragraphs and essays.* McGraw-Hill.

Bandura, A. (1969) *Principles of Behavior Modification.* New York: Holt, Reinhart & Winston.

Bandura, A. (1973) *Aggression: a social learning analysis,* Upper Saddle Place, NJ, Prentice Hall.

Bandura, A. (1977) *Social Learning Theory* (2nd ed). Englewood Cliffs, NJ: Prentice Hall.

Bandura, A., and Rosenthal, T. L. (1966). Vicarious classical conditioning as a function of arousal level. *Journal of Personality and Social Psychology*, 3, 54–62.

Bandura, A. Ross, D. and Ross, S.A. (1961). Transmission of aggression through imitation of aggressive models. *Journal of Abnormal and Social Psychology*, 63, 575–582.

Bandura, A. Ross, D. and Ross, S.A. (1963) Imitation of film mediated aggressive models. *Journal of Abnormal and Social Psychology*, 66, 3–11.

Barlow, D.H., Raffa, S.D. and Cohen, E.M. (2002) Psychosocial treatments for panic disorders, phobias, and generalized anxiety disorder. In P.E. Nathan and J. M. Gorman (eds), *A Guide to Treatments that Work* (2nd edn, pp301–35). London: Oxford University Press.

Bartlett, F. (1932) Remembering: a Study in Experimental Social Psychology. Cambridge, Cambridge University Press.

Baumrind, D. (1964) Some thoughts on ethics of research: after reading Milgram's 'Behavioural study of obedience'. *American Psychologist,* 19, 421–43.

Beasley, M., Thompson, T. and Davidson, J. (2003) Resilience in response to life stress: the effects of coping style and cognitive hardiness. *Personality and Individual Differences*, 34, 77–95.

Beck, A.T. (1963) Thinking and depression. *Archives of General Psychiatry*, 9, 324–33.

Beck, A.T. (1967). Depression: Clinical, experimental, and theoretical aspects. New York: Hoeber.

Beck, A.T. (1976) *Cognitive Therapy and the Emotional Disorders*. New York: International Universities Press.

Belsky, J. and Rovine, M. (1987) Temperament and attachment security in the strange situation: a rapprochement. *Child Development*, 58, 787–95.

Bennet-Levy, J and Marteau, T (1984). Fear of Animals: What is prepared? *British Journal of Psychology*, 75, 37–42.

Berger, H. (1929) Uber das Elektrenkephalogramm des Menschen. *Archiv fur Psychiatrie und Nervenkrankheiten*, 87, 527–570.

Berger, J.A. (2000) The effect of a cognitive-behavioral stress management intervention on salivary IgA, self- reported levels of stress, and physical health complaints in an undergraduate population. *Dissertations Abstracts International*. Section B: The Sciences and Engineering, 60, 5762.

Berk, L. (1997) *Child Development* (4th edn). Boston: Allyn and Bacon.

Berkowitz, L. (1999) Evil is more than banal. Situationalism and the concept of evil. *Personality and Social Psychology Review*, 3, Special Issue – Perspectives on evil and violence, 246–53.

Berz, W.L. (1995) Working memory in music: a theoretical model. *Music Perception*, 12, 353–64.

Bickman, L. (1974a) The social power of a uniform. *Journal of Applied Social Psychology*, 4, 47–61.

Bickman, L. (1974b) Clothes make the person. *Psychology Today*, 8(4), 48–51.

Biddle, S. (2000) Emotion, mood and physical activity. In S.J.H. Biddle, K.R. Fox and S.H. Boutcher (eds), *Physical Activity and Psychological Well-being*. London: Routledge.

Blakemore, C. & Mitchell, D.E. (1973) Environmental modification of the visual cortex and the neural basis of learning and memory. *Nature*, 241, 467–468.

Blass, T. (1991) The Milgram paradigm after 35 years: some things we now know about obedience to authority. In T. Blass (ed. 2000) *Obedience to Authority: current perspectives on the Milgram paradigm*. New Jersey: Lawrence Erlbaum Associates.

Bloom, K., Russell, A. & Wassenberg, K. (1987) Turn taking affects the quality of infant vocalizations. *Journal of Child Language*, 14, 221–227.

Blum, D. (1994) *The Monkey Wars*, Oxford, Oxford University Press.

Booth-Kewley, S. and Friedman, H.S. (1987) Psychological predictors of heart disease: a quantitative review. *Psychological Bulletin*, 101, 343–62.

Bower, G.H. and Winzenz, D. (1969) Groups, structure, coding and memory for digit series. *Journal of Experimental Psychology*, Monograph 80 (No. 3, Pt 2), pp1–17.

Bowlby, J. (1944) 44 juvenile thieves: their characters and their home life. *International Journal of Psychoanalysis*, 25, 1–57.

Brandimonte, M. A., Hitch, G, & Bishop, D. V. M. (1992). Influence of short-term memory codes on visual image processing: Evidence from image transformation tasks. *Journal of Experimental Psychology: Learning, Memory, & Cognition*, I8, 157–165.

Bransford, J.D. and Johnson, M.K. (1972) Contextual prerequisites for understanding some investigators of comprehension and recall. *Journal of Verbal Learning and Verbal Behaviour.*

Brazelton, T. B., Tronick, E., Adamson, L., Als, H and Wise, S. (1975) Early mother infant reciprocity, in *Parent–infant interaction*, Ciba Foundation Symposium 33 New York.

Bretherton, I. (1992) The origins of attachment theory: John Bowlby and Mary Ainsworth. *Developmental Psychology*, 28, 759–775.

Breuer, J and Freud, S (1895/1891) *Studies in hysteria*, London, Penguin.

Brief, A.P, Dukerich, J.M. and Doran, L.I. (1991) Resolving ethical dilemmas in management: experimental investigation of values, accountability and choice. *Journal of Applied Social Psychology*, 21, 380–96.

Broca, P. (1861) Remarques sur le siege de la faculte du langage articule suivees d'une observation d'aphemie. *Bulletin de la Societe Anatomique* (Paris), 6, 330–357.

Brown, G., Neff, C. and Mangelsdorf, S. (2012) Father Involvement, Paternal Sensitivity, and Father-Child Attachment Security in the First 3 Years, *Journal of Family Psychology* 2012, 26, 3, 421–430.

Brown, R.; Kulik, J. (1977). Flashbulb Memories. *Cognition* 5 (1), 73–99.

Bunge, S.A., Klingberg, T., Jacobsen, R.B. and Gabrieli, J.D.E. (2000) A resource model of the neural basis of executive working memory. *Proceedings of the National Academy of Science USA*, 97, 3573–8.

Burger, J.M., (2009) Replicating Milgram: Would people still obey today? *American Psychologist*, 64, 1, 1–11.

Bushman, B.J. (1988) The effects of apparel on compliance: a field experiment with a female authority figure. *Personality and Social Psychology Bulletin*, 14, 459–67.

Campbell, J.D and Fairey, P.J. (1989) Informational and normative routes to conformity: The effect of faction size as a function of norm extremity and attention to the stimulus. *Journal of Personality and Social Psychology*, 57, 457–68.

Carver, C.S., Pozo, C., Harris, S.D., Noriega, V., Scheier, M.F., Robinson, D.S., Ketchan, A.S., Moffat, F.L., Jr and Clark, K.C. (1993) How coping mediates the effect of optimism on distress: a study of women with early stage breast cancer. *Journal of Personality and Social Psychology*, 65, 375–90.

Carver, C.S., Scheier, M.F. and Weintraub, J.K. (1989) Assessing coping styles: a theoretically-based approach. *Journal of Personality and Social Psychology*, 56, 267–83.

Ceraso, J. (1967). The interference theory of forgetting. *Scientific American, 317*, 117–124.

Chase, A. (2000) A lesson in hate. The *Guardian*, 22 June, pp2–3.

Cho, K. (2001) Chronic jet lag produces temporal lobe atrophy abd spatial cognitive deficits. *Nature Neuroscience*, 4, 567–568.

Choy , Y., Fyer , A. J. Lipsitz , J. D. (2007). Treatment of specific phobia in adults. *Clinical Psychology Review*, 27, 266–286.

Christensen, A., Atkins, D.C., Berns, S., Wheeler, J., Baucom, D.H. and Simpson, L.E. (2004) Traditional versus integrative behavioural couple therapy for significantly and chronically distressed married couples. *Journal of Consulting and Clinical Psychology*, 72(2), 176–191.

Christensson, K. (1996) Fathers can effectively achieve heat conservation in newborn infants. *Acta Paediatrica*, 85, 1354–1360.

Christianson and Hubinette (1993) in Kapardis, A. (2002) *Psychology and Law – a Critical Introduction* (2nd edn). Cambridge: Cambridge University Press, 42–4.

Christianson, S. A. & Hubinette, B. (1993). Hands up! A study of witnesses' emotional reactions and memories associated with bank robberies. *Applied Cognitive Psychology*, 7, 365–379.

Clark, D.M. (1986) A cognitive approach to panic. *Behavior Research and Therapy*, 24, 461–70.

Clark, R.D. (1989) Effect of number of majority defectors on minority influence. *Group Dynamics: Theory, Research and Practice*, 3(4), 303–12.

Cohen, S., Doyle, W.J., Skoner, D.P., Rabin, B.S. and Gwaltney, J.M. (1997) Social ties and susceptibility to the common cold. *Journal of the American Medical Association*, 277, 1940–4.

Cohen, S., Tyrell, D.A.J. and Smith, A.P. (1993) Negative life events, perceived stress, negative affect and susceptibility to the common cold. *Journal of Personality and Social Psychology*, 64, 131–40.

Constable, J.F. and Russell, D.W. (1986) The effect of social support and the work environment upon burnout in nurses. *Journal of Human Stress*, 12, 20–6.

Coolican, H. (1994) *Research Methods and Statistics in Psychology*. London: Hodder & Stoughton.

Cooper, C.L., Sloan, S.J. and Williams, S. (1988) *The Occupational Stress Indicator.* Windsor: NFER-Nelson.

Costall, A. (2006) Introspectionism and the mythical origins of scientific psychology, *Consciousness and cognition*, 15, 634–654.

Cowan, N. (1984). On short and long auditory stores. *Psychological Bulletin, 96*, 341–370.

Cowan, N. (1998) Visual and auditory working memory capacity. *Trends in Cognitive Sciences*, 2, 77–87.

Cowan, N. (2000) The magical number 4 in short-term-memory: a reconsideration of mental storage capacity. *Behavioural and Brain Sciences*, 24, 87–185.

Cox, T. (1978) *Stress.* London: Macmillan.

Craik, F.I.M and Tulving, E. (1975) Depth of Processing and the Retention of Words in Episodic Memory. Journal of Experimental Psychology: General, 104 (3), 268–294.

Craik and Lockhart (1972) Levels of processing: a framework for memory research. *Journal of Verbal Learning and Verbal Behaviour*, 11, 671–84.

Crick, F. (1994) The astonishing hypothesis; The scientific search for the soul, in Miell, D., Phoenix, A. and Thomas, K. (eds) *Mapping Psychology Volume 1*, Milton Keynes, The Open University.

Crutchfield, R.S. (1955) Conformity and character. *American Psychology*, 10, 191–8.

Czeisler, C.A., Moore-Ede, M.C. & Coleman, R.M. (1982) Rotating shift work schedules that disrupt sleep are improved by applying circadian principles. *Science*, 217, 460–463.

Damasio, A. R. (1996) *Descartes error: Emotion, reason and the human brain*, London, Papermac.

Darwin, C., Turvey, M. T., Crowder, RG. (1972). An auditory analogue of the Sperling partial report procedure: Evidence for brief auditory storage. *Cognitive Psychology* 3 (2): 255–67.

Davidson, J.R.T., Foa, E.B. and Huppert, J.D. (2004) Fluoxetine, comprehensive cognitive behavioural therapy, and placebo in generalised social phobia. *Archives of General Psychiatry*, 61, 1005–13.

Davies, G.M. (1993) Witnessing events. In G.M. Davies and R.H. Logie (eds), *Memory in Everyday Life*. Amsterdam: Elsevier.

Davies, G.M. (1994) Children's testimony – research findings and policy implications. *Psychology, Crime and Law*, 1, 175–80.

Davis, S., Mirick, D.K. & Stevens, R.G. (2001) Nightshift work, light at night, and risk of breast cancer. Journal of the National Cancer Institute, 93, 1557–1562.

De Bene, R. and Moe, A. (2003) Presentation modality effects in studying passages: are mental images always effective? *Applied Cognitive Psychology*, 17, 309–24.

De Boer, M.F., Ryckman, R.M., Pruyn, J.F.A. and DeCoursey, P.J., Walker, J.K. & Smith, S.A. (2000) A circadian pacemaker in free-living chipmunks: essential for survival? *Journal of Comparative Physiology*, A, 186, 169–180.

Van den Borne, H.W. (1999) Psychosocial correlates of cancer relapse and survival: a literature review. *Patient Education and Counselling*, 37, 215–30.

De Wolff, M.S. and Van Ijzendoorn, M.H. (1997) Sensitivity and attachment: a meta-analysis on parental anecdotes on infant attachment. *Child Development*, 68, 604–9.

Dekle. D.J., Beal, C.R., Elliott, R. and Huneycutt, D. (1996) Children as witnesses: a comparison of lineup versus showup identification methods. *Applied Cognitive Psychology*, 10, 1–12.

DeLongis, A., Coyne, J.C., Dakof, G., Folkman, S. and Lazarus, R.S. (1982) Relationships of daily hassles, uplifts, and major life events to health status. *Health Psychology*, 1, 119–36.

Dembroski, T.M., MacDougall, J.M., Costa, P.T. and Grandits, G.A. (1989) Components of hostility as predictors of sudden death and myocardial infarction in the Multiple Risk Factor Intervention Trial. *Psychosomatic Medicine*, 51, 514–22.

Denollet, J. (2000) Type D personality: a potential risk factor refined. *Journal of Psychosomatic Medicine*, 49, 255–66.

Denollet, J. and Van Heck, G.L. (2001) Psychological risk factors in heart disease: what Type D personality is (not) about. *Journal of Psychosomatic Research*, 51, 465–68.

Denollet, J., Sys, S.U., Stroobant, N., Rombouts, H., Gillebert, T.C. and Brutsaert, D.L. (1996) Personality as an independent predictor of long-term mortality in patients with coronary heart disease. *The Lancet*, 347, 417–21.

Deutsch, M. and Gerard, H.B. (1955) A study of normative and informational social influences upon individual judgement. *Journal of Abnormal and Social Psychology*, 51, 629–36.

Dewe, P.J. (1992) Applying the concept of appraisal to work stressors: some exploratory analysis. *Human Relations*, 45, 143–64.

DiNardo, P.A.; Guzy, L.T.; Jenkins, J.A.; Bak, R.M.; Tomasi, S.F.; and Copland, M. (1988) Etiology and maintenance of dog fears. *Behaviour Research and Therapy*, 26, 241–244.

Dollard, J. and Miller, N.E. (1951) Personality and psychotherapy: an analysis in terms of learning, thinking, culture. *American Sociological Review*, 16, 3, 414–16.

Drachman, D.A. and Sahakian, B.J. (1979) Effects of cholinergic agents on human learning and memory. In R. Barbeau (ed.), *Nutrition and the Brain* (vol. 5, pp351–66). New York: Raven Press.

Dryden, W. (2007) *The handbook of Individual therapy*, Sage, London.

Dunnett, S.B., Bjorklund, A. & Lindvall, O. (2001) Cell therapy in Parkinson's disease – stop or go? *Nature Reviews Neuroscience*, 2, 365–368.

Edgar, H. and Edgar, G. (2012) Paying Attention in Brace, N. and Byford, J. (2012) *Investigating Psychology*, Oxford, Oxford University Press.

Elkin, I., Shea, M.T. and Watkins, J.T. (1989) National Institutes of Mental Health Treatment of Depression Collaborative Research Program: general effectiveness of treatments. *Archives of General Psychiatry*, 46, 971–82.

Ellis, A. (1962) *Reason and Emotion in Psychotherapy.* New York: Lyle Stuart.

Ellis, A. (1987). Rational-emotive therapy: An update. In W. Dryden (Ed.), Current issues in rational-emotive therapy (pp. 1–45). London: Croom Helm.

Ellis, A. (1991) The revised ABC's of rational emotive therapy (RET). *Journal of Rational-Emotive and Cognitive Behavior Therapy*, 9, 139–72.

Engle, R.W., Kane, M.J. and Tuholski, S.W. (1999) Individual differences in working memory capacity and what they tell us about controlled attention, general fluid intelligence and functions of the pre-frontal cortex. In A. Miyake and P. Shah (eds), *Models of Working Memory: mechanisms of active maintenance and executive control.* Cambridge: Cambridge University Press.

Evans, P.D. and Edgerton, N. (1991) Life-events and mood as predictors of the common cold. *British Journal of Medical Psychology*, 64, 35–44.

Eysenck, H.J. (1952) The effects of psychotherapy: an evaluation. *Journal of Consulting Psychology*, 16, 319–24.

Eysenck, H.J. (1988) Personality, stress and cancer: prediction and prophylaxis. *British Journal of Medical Psychology*, 61, 57–75.

Eysenck, H.J. and Grossarth-Maticek, R. (1989) Prevention of cancer and coronary heart disease and the reduction in the cost of the National Health Service. *Journal of Social, Political and Economic Studies*, 14, 25–47.

Eysenck, W. Michael and Keane, T. Mark, (1996) *Cognitive psychology: A student's handbook*, Psychology Press, Hove.

Fava, G.A., Grandi, S., Zielezny, M., Canestrari, R. and Morphy, M.A. (1994) Cognitive behavioral treatment of residual symptoms in primary major depressive disorder. *American Journal of Psychiatry*, 151(9), 1295–1299.

Fisher, R. P. *et al.* (1987) Critical analysis of police interview techniques. *Journal of Police Science and Administration*, 15.

Flin, R., Boon, J., Knox, A. and Bull, R. (1992) The effect of a five-month delay on children's and adults' eyewitness memory. *British Journal of Psychology*, 83, 323–36.

Foa, E. B., Liebowitz, M. R., Kozak, M. J., Davies, S., Campeas, R., Franklin, M. E. et al. (2005). Randomized, placebo-controlled trial of exposure and ritual prevention, clomipramine, and their combination in the treatment of obsessive-compulsive disorder. *American Journal of Psychiatry*, 162, 151–161.

Fox, H.L., Dwyer, D.J. and Ganster, D.C. (1993) Effects of stressful job demands and control on physiological and attitudinal outcomes in a hospital setting. *Academy of Management Journal*, 36, 289–318.

Fox, N. (1977) Attachment of kibbutz infants to mother and matapelet. *Child Development*, 48, 1,288–39.

Fox, N., Kimmerley, N.L. and Schafer, W.D. (1991) Attachment to mother/attachment to father: a meta analysis. *Child Development*, 62, 210–25.

Freeman, W. (1971) Frontal lobotomy in early schizophrenia: long follow-up in 415 cases. *British Journal of Psychiatry*, 119, 621–4.

Freud, S. (1900/ 1991) *The Interpretation of Dreams*, Penguin Freud Library, 4. London, Penguin.

Freud, S. (1905/ 1991) *Three Essays on the theory of sexuality*, Penguin Freud Library, 7. London, Penguin.

Freud, S. (1909) Analysis of a phobia in a five year old boy. In J. Strachey (ed. and trans.) (1976) *The Complete Psychological Works: the standard edition*, 10. New York: Norton.

Fruzzetti, A.E., Toland, K., Teller, S.A. and Loftus, E.F. (1992) Memory and eyewitness testimony. In M. Gruneberg and P. Morris (eds), *Aspects of Memory: The Practical Aspects*. London: Routledge.

Gamson, W.A , Fireman, B. and Rytina, S. (1982) *Encounters with Unjust Authority.* Homewood IL: Dorsey Press.

Gazzaniga, M.S. (2005) Forty-five years of split-brain research and still going strong. *Nature Reviews Neuroscience*, 6, 653–659.

Geiselman, R.E., Fisher, R., MacKinnon, D. and Holland, H. (1985) Eyewitness memory enhancement in the police interview: cognitive retrieval mnemonics versus hypnosis. *Journal of Applied Psychology*, 70, 401–12.

Geiselman, R.E., Fisher, R., MacKinnon, D. and Holland, H. (1986) Enhancement of eyewitness memory with the cognitive interview. *American Journal of Psychology*, 99, 385–401.

Glanzer, M. (1972) Storage mechanisms in recall. In G.H. Bower (ed.), *The Psychology of Learning and Motivation: advances in research and theory*, V. New York: Academic Press.

Glanzer, M. and Cunitz, A.R. (1966) Two storage mechanisms in free recall. *Journal of Verbal Learning and Verbal Behaviour*, 5, 351–60.

Glanzer, M. and Razel, M. (1974) The size of the unit in short-term storage. *Journal of Verbal Learning and Behaviour*, 13, 114–31.

Gold, D.R., Rogacz, S.R. & Bock, N. (1992) Rotating shift work, sleep, and accidents relating to sleepiness in hospital nurses. *American Journal of Public Health*, 82, 1011–1014.

Gratier, M. (2003) Expressive timing and interactional synchrony between mothers and infants: cultural similarities, cultural differences, and the immigration experience, in *Cognitive Development* 18, 533–554.

Gross, R.D. (1994) *Key Studies in Psychology* (2nd edn). London: Hodder & Stoughton.

Gruneberg, M.M. and Jacobs, G.C. (1991) In defence of Linkword. *The Language Learning Journal*, 3, 25–9.

Hamilton, S. and Fagot, B.I. (1988) Chronic stress and coping style: a comparison of male and female undergraduates. *Journal of Personality and Social Psychology*, 55, 819–23.

Hammen, C. L., & Krantz, S. (1976). Effect of success and failure on depressive cognitions. *Journal of Abnormal Psychology*, 85 577–586.

Haney, C., Banks, C. and Zimbardo, P.G. (1973) Interpersonal dynamics in a simulated prison. *International Journal of Criminology and Penology*, 1, 69–97.

Harlow, H. (1958) The nature of love. *American Psychologist*, 13, 673–85.

Harlow, H. F. and Zimmerman, R. (1959) Affectional responses in the infant monkey. *Science*, 130, 421–32.

Hart, J.W., Stasson, M.F. and Karau, S.J. (1999) Effects of source expertise an physical distance on minority influence. *Group Dynamics: theory, research and practice*, 3(1), 81–92.

Hazan, C. and Shaver, P. (1987) Romantic Love Conceptualized as an Attachment Process. *Journal of Personality and Social Psychology*, 52, 511–24.

Hodges, J. and Tizard, B. (1989) Social and family relationships of ex-institutional adolescents. *Journal of Child Psychology and Psychiatry*, 30, 77–97.

Hofling, C.K., Brotzman, E., Dalrymple, S., Graves, N. and Pierce, C.N. (1966) An experimental study in nurse–physician relationships. *Journal of Nervous and Mental Disease*, 143, 171–80.

Hogg, M.A. (2003) Social identity. In M.R. Leary and J.P. Tangney (eds) *Handbook of Self and Identity* (pp479–501). New York: Guilford.

Hogg, M.A. and Abrahams, D. (1988) *Social Identifications: a social psychology of inter-group relations and group processes*. London: Routledge.

Hogg, M.A. and Turner, J.C. (1987) Social identity and conformity: a theory of referent informational influence. In W. Doise and S. Moscovici (eds), *Current Issues in European Social Psychology* (vol. 2 , pp138–82). Cambridge: Cambridge University Press.

Hogg, M.A. and Vaughan, G.M. (2005) *Social Psychology* (4th edn). Harlow: Pearson Education.

Holahan, C.J. and Moos, R.H. (1986) Personality, coping, and family resources in stress resistance: a longitudinal analysis. *Journal of Personality and Social Psychology*, 51, 389–95.

Hollander E, DeCaria CM, Nitescu A, Gully R, Suckow RF, Cooper TB, Gorman JM, Klein DF, Liebowitz MR. (1992): Serotonergic function in obsessive-compulsive disorder: Behavioral and neuroendocrine response to oral m-chlorophenylpiperazine and fenfluramine in patients and healthy volunteers. *Archives of General Psychiatry*, 49, 21–28.

Holmes, T.H. and Rahe, R.H. (1967) The social

readjustment rating scale. *Journal of Psychosomatic Research*, 11, 213–18.

Jacobs, J. (1887) Experiments in 'prehension'. *Mind*, 12, 75–9.

Jacobson, E. (1938) *Progressive Relaxation: a physiological and clinical investigation of muscle states and their significance in psychology and medical practice* (2nd edn). Chicago: University of Chicago Press.

Jahoda, M. (1958) *Current Concepts of Positive Mental Health*. New York: Basic Books.

Jandorf, L., Deblinger, E., Neale, J.M. and Stone, A.A. (1986) Daily versus major life events as predictors of symptom frequency. *Journal of General Psychology*, 113(3), 205–18.

Jerabek, I. and Standing, L. (1992) Imagined test situations produce contextual memory enhancement. *Perceptual and Motor Skills*, 75, 400.

Johansson, G., Aronsson, G. and Linstrom, B.O. (1978) Social psychological and neuroendocrine stress reactions in highly mechanised work. *Ergonomics*, 21, 583–99.

Johnson, M.H. and Morton, J. (1991) Biology and cognitive development: the case of face recognition. In Durkin, K. (1995) *Developmental Social Psychology*, Blackwell, Oxford.

Kamarck, T.W., Peterman, A.H. and Raynor, D.A. (1998) The effects of the social environment on stress-related cardiovascular activation: current findings, prospects, and implications. *Annals of Behavioral Medicine*, 20, 242–56.

Kanner, A.D., Coyne, J.C., Schaefer, C. and Lazarus, R.S. (1981) Comparison of two modes of stress measurement: Daily hassles and uplifts versus major life events. *Journal of Behavioral Medicine*, 4, 1–39.

Kapur, N. (1997) Injured brains of medical minds. Oxford: Oxford University Press.

Karasek, R.A. (1979) Job demands, job decision latitude and mental strain: implications for job design. *Administrative Science Quarterly*, 24, 285–308.

Kaye, K. Towards the origin of dialogue. In Schaffer , H. R, (1977) *Mothering*, Fontana Press.

Kebbell, M.R. and Milne, R. (1998) Police officers' perceptions of eyewitness performance in forensic investigations. *Journal of Social Psychology*, 138, 323–30.

Keller, M. B., Mccullough, J.P., Klein, D. N (2000) A comparison of nefazodone, the cognitive behavioral-analysis system of psychotherapy, and their combination for the treatment of chronic depression. *New England Journal of Medicine*, 342, 1462–1470.

Kelman, H.C. (1958) Compliance, identification and internalisation. *Journal of Conflict Resolution*, 2, 51–60. Kielcolt-Glaser, J.K., Garner, W., Speicher, G.M., Penn, G.M., Holliday, J. and Glaser, R. (1984) Psychological modifiers of immunocompetence in medical students. *Psychosomatic Medicine*, 46, 7–14.

Keppel, G., & Underwood, B. J. (1962). Proactive inhibition in short-term retention of ingle items. *Journal of Verbal Learning and Verbal Behavior, 1*, 153–161.

Kiecolt-Glaser, J.K., Dura, J.R., Speicher, C.E., Trask, O.J. and Glaser, R.S.O. (1991) Spousal caregivers of dementia victims: longitudinal changes in immunity and health. *Psychosomatic Medicine*, 53, 345–62.

Kiecolt-Glaser, J.K., Glaser, R., Cacioppo, J.T. and Malarkey, W.B. (1998) Marital stress: immunologic, neuroendocrine, and autonomic correlates. *Annals of the New York Academy of Sciences*, 840, 656–63.

Kiecolt-Glaser, J.K., Ogrocki, P., Stout, J.C., Speicher, C.E. and Glaser, R. (1987) Marital quality, marital disruption and immune function. *Psychosomatic Medicine*, 49, 13–34.

Klauer KC, and Zhao Z. (2004) Double dissociations in visual and spatial short-term memory. *Journal of Experimental Psychology: General*, 133(3), 355–81.

Kobasa, S.C. (1979) Stressful life events, personality and health: an inquiry into hardiness. *Journal of Personality and Social Psychology*, 37, 1–11.

Kobasa, S.C., Maddi, S.R. and Kahn, S. (1982) Hardiness and health: a prospective study. *Journal of Personality and Social Psychology*, 42, 168–77.

Kobasa, S.C., Maddi, S.R., Puccetti, M.C. and Zola, M.A. (1985) Effectiveness of hardiness, exercise and social support as resources against illness. *Journal of Psychosomatic Research*, 29, 525–33.

Koehnken, G., Milne, R., Memon, A. and Bull, R. (1999) The cognitive interview: a meta-analysis. *Psychology, Crime and Law*, 5, 3–27.

Kounin, J. and Gump, P. (1961) The comparative influence of punitive and non-punitive teachers upon children's concepts of school misconduct. *Journal of Educational Psychology*, 52, 44–9.

Kuyken, W. and Tsivirkos, D. (2009) Therapist competence, comorbidity and cognitive-behavioural therapy for depression. *Psychotherapy and Psychosomatics*, 78(1), 42–8.

Kyllonen, P.C. and Christal, R.E. (1990) Reasoning ability is (little more than) working-memory capacity. *Intelligence*, 14, 389–433.

Laing, R.D. and Esterson, A. (1964) *Sanity, Madness and the Family*. Middlesex: Penguin.

Lamb, M.E. (1983) Fathers: forgotten contributors to child development. *Human Development*, 18, 245–66.

Lamb, M.E and Tamis-LeMonda, C.S. (2004). The role of the father: an introduction. In M.E Lamb (Ed) *The role of the father in child development* (5th Edition) New York, Wiley.

Lashley, K.S. (1929) Brain mechanisms and intelligence. Chicago: University of Chicago Press.

Lazarus, R.S. and Folkman, S. (1984) *Stress, Appraisal and Coping*. New York: Springer.

Lazarus, R.S. and Folkman, S. (1987) Transactional theory and research on emotions and coping. *European Journal of Personality*, 1, 141–70.

Lemaine, G. (1974) Social differentiation and social originality. *European Journal of Social Psychology*, 4, 17–52.

Lesar, T.S., Briceland, L. and Stein, D.S. (1997) Factors related to errors in medication prescribing. *Journal of the American Medical Association*, 277, 312–17.

Lewis, C. and Lamb, M. (2003) Father's influence on children's development: The evidence from two parent families. *European Journal of Psychology of Education*, XVIII, 2.

Lindsay, D.S., Allen, B.P., Chan, J.C.K. and Dahl, L.C. (2004) Eyewitness suggestibility and source similarity: Intrusions of details from one event into memory reports of another event. *Journal of Memory and Language*, 50, 96–111.

List, J.A.G. (1986). Age and schematic differences in the reliability of eyewitness testimony. *Developmental Psychology*, 22, 50–57.

Littleton, K., Toates, F., and Braisby, N. (2007) Three approaches to learning in Miell, D., Phoenix, A. and Thomas, K. (eds) *Mapping Psychology Volume 1*, Milton Keynes, The Open University.

Lloyd, G. G., & Lishman, W. A. (1975). Effect of depression on the speed of recall of pleasant and unpleasant experiences. *Psychological Medicine*, 5, 173–180.

Loftus, E.F. (1992) When a lie becomes memory's truth: memory distortion after exposure to misinformation. *Current Directions in Psychology*, 1, 121–3.

Loftus, E.F. and Burns, T.E. (1982) Mental shock can produce retrograde amnesia. *Memory and Cognition*, 10, 318–23.

Loftus, E. F., & Loftus, G. (1980). On the permanence of stored information in the human brain. *American Psychologist*, 35, 409–420.

Loftus, E.F. & Palmer, J.C. (1974) Reconstruction of auto-mobile destruction: An example of the interaction between language and memory. *Journal of Verbal Learning and Verbal Behaviour*, 13, 585–589.

Loftus, E.F. (1979). *Eyewitness Testimony*. Cambridge, MA.

Loftus, E.F. (1980). *Memory.* Reading, MA: Addison-Wesley.

MacLeod, C.M. and Donnellan, A.M. (1993) Individual differences in anxiety and the restriction of working memory capacity. *Personality and Individual Differences*, 15, 163–73.

Maddi, S.R. (1987) Hardiness training at Illinois Bell Telephone. In J. P. Opatz (ed.), Health Promotion Evaluation. Wisconsin: National Wellness Institute.

Maddi, S.R., Khoshaba, D.M., Jensen, K., Carter, E., Lu, J.L. and Harvey, R.H. (2002) Hardiness training for high- risk undergraduates. *NACADA Journal*, 22, 45–55.

Main, M. and Goldwyn, R. (1984) Predicting rejection of her infant from mother's representation of her own experience: implications for the abused–abusing intergenerational cycle. *Child abuse and Neglect*, 8.

Malarkey, W.B., Kiecolt-Glaser, J.K. and Pearl, D. (1994) Hostile behaviour during marital conflict alters pituitary and adrenal hormones. *Psychosomatic Medicine*, 56, 41–51.

Manstead, A.S. R. and McCulloch, C. (1981) Sex-role stereotyping in British television advertisements. *British Journal of Social Psychology*, 20, 171–80.

Marian, V., & Fausey, C. M. (2006). Language-dependent memory in bilingual learning. *Applied Cognitive Psychology, 20,* 1025–1047.

Markus, H. and Kitayama, S. (1991) Culture and the self: implications for cognition, emotion and motivation. *Psychological Review*, 98, 224–53.

Marmot, M., Bosma, H., Hemingway, H., Brunner, E. and Stasfield, S. (1997) Contribution of job control and other factors to social variation in heart disease incidence. *The Lancet*, 350, 235–9.

Marr,D. C., (1982) *Vision: A Computational Investigation into the Human Representation and Processing of Visual Information*. New York: Freeman.

Maslow, A. H (1973) *The farther reaches of human nature*, Harmondsworth, Penguin.

Maslow, A, H (1987) *Motivation and Personality*, 3rd Edition, New York, Harper and Rowe.

Masters, J.C., Burish, T.G., Hollon, S.D. and Rimm, D.C. (1987) *Behavior Therapy: techniques and empirical* findings (3rd edn). San Diego: Harcourt Brace Jovanovich.

Matthews, K.A. and Haynes, S.G. (1986) Type A behaviour pattern and coronary risk: update and critical evaluation. *American Journal of Epidemiology*, 6, 923–60.

Max, J.E., Smith, W.L., Lindgren, S.D., Robin, D.A. Mattheis, P., Stierwalt, J. and Morrisey, M. (1995) Case study: obsessive-compulsive disorder after severe traumatic brain injury in an adolescent. *Journal of the American Academy of Child and Adolescent Psychiatry*, 34(1), 45–49.

McLelland, J.L. and Rumelhart, D. E. (1981) An interactive activation model of context effects in letter processing. Part 1: An account of basic findings. *Psychological Review*, 88, 375–407.

Mehler,J., Bertonici, J., Barriere, M., and Jassik-Gerschenfel, D. (1978) Infant recognition of mother's voice, *Perception*, 7, 491–7.

Meichenbaum, D. (1985) *Stress Inoculation Training.* New York: Pergamon.

Meichenbaum, D.H. (1972) Cognitive modification of test anxious college students. *Journal of Consulting and Clinical Psychology*, 39, 370–80.

Meltzoff , A.N. and Moore, M.K (1997) Imitation in new born infants, Exploring the range of Gestures imitated and the underlying mechanisms, *Developmental Psychology*, 25, 6, 954–962.

Memon, A., Wark. L., Bull, R. and Koehnken, G. (1997) Isolating the effects of the cognitive interview techniques. *British Journal of Psychology*, 88, 179–97.

Menges, R.J. (1973) Openness and honesty versus coercion and deception in psychological research. *American Psychologist*, 28, 1030–4.

Meuret, A.E., Wilhelm, F.H. and Roth, W.T. (1997) Respiratory feedback for treating panic disorder. *Journal of Clinical Psychology*, 60, 197–207.

Miguel, E. C., Leckman, J. F., Rauch, S., do Rosario-Campos, M. C., Hounie, A. G., Mercadante, M. T., Chacon, P., & Pauls, D. L. (2005). Obsessive–compulsive disorder phenotypes: Implications for genetic studies. *Molecular Psychiatry*, 10, 258–275.

Milgram, S. (1963) Behavioural study of obedience. *Journal of Abnormal and Social Psychology*, 67, 371–8, 467–72.

Milgram, S. (1974) *Obedience to Authority, an Experimental View.* London: Harper Collins.

Milgram, S. (1974) *Obedience to Authority: an experimental view*. New York: Harper & Row.

Milgram, S. (1974) The perils of obedience. *Harpers magazine*.

Miller, A.G. (1986) *The Obedience Experiments. A case study of controversy in social science.* New York: Praeger.

Miller, G.A. (1956) The magical number seven, plus or minus two: Some limits on our capacity for processing information. *Psychological Review*, 63, 81–97.

Miller, T.Q., Smith, T.W., Turner, C.W., Guijarro, M.L. and Hallet, A.J. (1996) A meta-analytic review of research on hostility and physical health. *Psychological Bulletin*, 119, 322–48.

Milner, B. (1966) Amnesia following operation on the temporal lobes. In C.W.M. Whitty and O.L. Zangwill (eds), *Amnesia Following Operation on the Temporal Lobes* (pp109–33). London: Butterworth.

Moniz, E. (1936) *Tentative Operatoires dans le Traitement de Certaines Psychoses*. Paris: Mason.

Moore, R.Y. & Eichler, V.B. (1972) Loss of a circadian adrenal corticosterone rhythm following suprachiasmatic lesions in the rat. *Brain Research*, 42, 201–206.

Moscovici, S., Lage, E. and Naffrenchoux, M. (1969) Influence of a consistent minority on the responses of a majority in a colour perception task. *Sociometry*, 32, 365–80.

Moscovici, S. (1980). Toward a theory of conversion behavior. In L. Berkowiyz (Ed.), *Advances in Experimental Social Psychology*, 13, 209–239.

Mugny, G. (1982) *The power of minorities*. London: Academic Press.

Murdock, B.B. (1961) The retention of individual items. *Journal of Experimental Psychology*, 62, 618–625.

Murphy, L.R. (1996) Stress management techniques: secondary prevention of stress. In M.J. Schabracq, J.A.M. Winnubst and C.L. Cooper (eds), *Handbook of Work and Health Psychology.* Chichester: Wiley.

Mutrie, N. (2000) Physical activity and clinically-defined depression. In S.J.H. Biddle, K.R. Fox and S.H. Boutcher (eds), *Physical Activity and Psychological Well-Being.* Routledge: London.

Naveh-Benjamin, M. and Ayres, T.J. (1986) Digit span, reading rate, and linguistic relativity. *Quarterly Journal of Experimental Psychology*, 38, 739–52.

Neisser, U. (1976). *Cognition and Reality*. San Francisco: W.H. Freeman.

Nestadt, G., Samuels, J., Bienvenu, O. J., et al (2000) A family study of obsessive compulsive disorder. *Archives of General Psychiatry*, 57, 358–363.

Oates, J. Learning from watching, in Brace, N. and Byford, J. (2012) *Investigating Psychology*, Oxford, Oxford University Press.

Ohman, A., Eriksson, A. and Olofsson. (1975) One-trial learning and superior resistance to extinction of autonomic responses conditioned to potentially phobic stimuli. *Journal of Comparative and Physiological Psychology*, 88(2), 619–627.

Ohman, A., Flykt, A. and Lundqvist, D. (2000) Unconscious emotion: evolutionary perspectives, psychophysiological data, and neuropsychological mechanisms. In R.D. Lane and L. Nadel (eds) *Cognitive Neuroscience of Emotion*. Oxford: Oxford University Press.

Oliner, S.P. and Oliner, P.M. (1988) *The Altruistic Personality.* New York: Free Press.

Orne, M.T. and Holland, C.C. (1968) On the ecological validity of laboratory deceptions. *International Journal of Psychology*, 6, 282–93.

Otto, M.W., Pollack, M.H. and Maki, K.M. (2000) Empirically supported treatments for panic disorder: costs, benefits, and stepped care. *Journal of Consulting and Clinical Psychology*, 68, 556–63.

Overgaard, M. (2006): Introspection in science, *Consciousness and Cognition*, 15, 629–633.

Paivio, A. (1965) Abstractness, imagery and meaningfulness in paired-associate learning. *Journal of Verbal Learning and Verbal Behaviour*, 4, 32–8.

Paquette D. (2004) Theorizing the father–child relationship: Mechanisms and developmental outcomes. *Human Development* 47:193–219 .

Pavlov, I.P. (1927) *Conditioned Reflexes.* Oxford: Oxford University Press.

Pennington, D. (1996) *Essential Social Psychology*. London: Edward Arnold.

Peterson, L.R. and Peterson, M.J. (1959) Short-term retention of individual verbal items. *Journal of Experimental Psychology*, 58, 193–8.

Pleck, J.H (2010) Paternal involvement: Revised conceptualization and theoretical linkages with child outcomes, in M.E Lamb (Ed) *The role of the father in child development* (5th Edition) New York, Wiley.

Poole, D.A. and Lindsay, D.S (2001) Children's eyewitness reports after exposure to misinformation from parents. *Journal of Experimental Psychology: Applied*, 7, 27–50.

Posner, M.I. and Keele, S.W. (1967) Decay of visual information from a single letter. *Science*, 158, 137–9. Rahe, R.H. and Lind, E. (1971) Psychosocial factors and sudden cardiac death. *Journal of Psychosomatic Research*, 8, 487–91.

Prislin, R. and Filson, F. (2009) Seeking Conversion Versus Advocating Tolerance in the Pursuit of Social Change Journal of Personality and Social Psychology, American Psychological Association 2009, 97, 5, 811–822.

Posner, M. I., & Keele, S. W. (1967). Decay of visual information from a single letter. *Science*, 158, 137–139.

Posner, M.I. and Keele, S.W. (1967) Decay of visual information from a single letter. *Science*, 158, 137–9.

Pulvermuller, F., Neininger, B., Elbert, T., Mohr, B., Rockstroh, B., Koebbel, P. & Taub, E. (2001) Constraint-induced therapy of chronic aphasia after stroke. *Stroke*, 32(7), 1621–1626.

Rahe, R.H., Mahan, J. and Arthur, R. (1970) Prediction of near-future health-change from subjects' preceding life changes. *Journal of Psychosomatic Research*, 14, 401–6.

Raine, A, Buschsbaum, M and LaCasse, L (1997) Brain abnormalities in murderers indicated by positron emission tomography, *Biological Psychiatry*, 42, 495–508.

Rank, S.G. and Jacobson, C.K. (1977) Hospital nurses' compliance with medication overdose orders: A failure to replicate. *Journal of Health and Social Behavior*, 18, 188–93.

Raphael, K.G., Cloitre, M. and Dohrenwend, B.P. (1991) Problems of recall and misclassification with checklist methods of measuring stressful life events. *Health Psychology*, 10, 62–74.

Reicher, S. and Haslam, A. (2006) Rethinking the psychology of tyranny: the BBC prison study. *British Journal of Social Psychology*, 45(1), 1–40.

Ring, H.A. and Serra-Mestres, J. (2002) Neuropsychiatry of the basal ganglia. *Advances in neuropsychiatry*, 72, 12–21.

Robinson, L. A., Berman, J. S. & Neimeyer, R. A. (1990) Psychotherapy for the treatment of depression: a comprehensive review of controlled outcome research. *Psychological Bulletin*, 108, 30–49.

Roediger, H.L. (1990). Implicit memory: Retention without remembering. *American Psychologist*, 45, 1043–1056.

Rogers, C. (1957) The necessary and sufficient conditions of therapeutic personality change, *Journal of Consulting Psychology*, 21 (2): 95–103.

Rogers, Carl (1951). *Client-Centered Therapy*, Cambridge Massachusetts: The Riverside Press.

Rogers, Carl (1961). *On Becoming a Person. A therapist's view of psychotherapy*. London, Constable.

Rohrer, J.H., Baron, S.H., Hoffman, E.L. and Schwander, D.V. (1954) The stability of auto-kinetic judgements. *Journal of Abnormal and Social Psychology*, 49, 595–7. Rosenhan, D.L. and Seligman, M.E.P. (1989) *Abnormal Psychology* (2nd edn). New York: Norton.

Roopnarine, J.L. Talukder, E., Jain, D., Joshi, P and Srivastav, P. (1993) Personal well being, kinship tie and mother infant and father infant interactions in single wage and dual wage families in New Delhi India. *Journal of Marriage and the family*, 54, 293–301.

Rosander, M. (2012) Conformity on the Internet—The role of task difficulty and gender differences. *Computers in Human Behavior*, 28, 5, 1587–1595.

Rosenhan, D.L. and Seligman, M.E.P. (1989) *Abnormal Psychology* (2nd ed). New York: Norton.

Rosenman, R.H., Brand, R.J., Sholtz, R.I. and Friedman, M. (1976) Multivariate prediction of coronary heart disease during 8.5 year follow-up in the Western Collaborative Group study. *The American Journal of Cardiology*, 37, 903–10.

Rosnow, R.L (1981) *Paradigms in Transition*. New York: Oxford University Press.

Roth, S. and Cohen, L.J. (1986) Approach avoidance and coping with stress. *American Psychologist*, 41, 813–19. Rotter, J.B. (1966) Generalized expectations for internal versus external control of reinforcement. *Psychological Monographs*, 80, 609.

Ruchkin, D.S., Berndt, R.S., Johnson, R., Grafman, J., Ritter, W. and Canoune, H.L. (1999) Lexical Contributions to Retention of Verbal Information in Working Memory: Event-Related Brain Potential Evidence. *Journal of Memory and Language* 41, 345–364.

Russell, M.J., Switz, G.M. & Thompson, K. (1980) Olfactory influences on the human menstrual cycle. *Pharmacology, Biochemistry and Behavior*, 13, 737–738.

Russell, N. (2010) The making of an infamous experiment, *The Psychologist*, 23, 9.

Rutter, M. (1972) Maternal Deprivation 1972–1978. New findings, New concepts, New approaches. *Child Development*, 1979, 50, 283–305.

Rutter, M., Colvert, E., Kreppner., J., Beckett, C., Castle, J., Groothues, C., Hawkins., A., O'Connor, T., Stevens, S. and Sonuga-Barke, E. (2007) Early adolescent outcomes for institutionally-deprived and non-deprived adoptees: I: Disinhibited attachment. *Journal of Child Psychology and Psychiatry*, 48(1), 17–30.

Rutter, M., Quinton, D. and Hill, J. (1990) Adult outcomes of institution-reared children: Males and females compared. In L. N. Robbins and M. Rutter (eds), *Straight and Devious Pathways From Childhood to Adult Life*. Cambridge: Cambridge University Press.

Sarason, I.G., Johnson, J.H. and Siegel, J.M. (1978) Assessing the impact of life changes: development of the life experiences survey. *Journal of Consulting and Clinical Psychology*, 46, 932–46.

Schaffer, H.R. and Emerson, P.E. (1964) The development of social attachments in infancy. *Monographs for the Society for Research in Child Development*, 29, 3, serial no. 94.

Schaffer, R. (1977) *Mothering*, Fontana Press.

Schaffer, R. (1996) *Social Development*. Oxford: Blackwell.

Schooler, J.W., Gerhard, D. and Loftus, E.F. (1986) Qualities of the unreal. *Journal of Experimental Psychology: Learning, Memory and Cognition*, 12, 171–81.

Schweickert, R. and Boruff, B. (1986) Short-term memory capacity: magic number or magic spell? *Journal of Experimental Psychology: Learning, Memory, and Cognition*, 12, 419–25.

Scoville, W.B., and Milner, B (1957) Loss of recent memory after bilateral hippocampal lesions, *Journal of Neurology, Neurosurgery and Psychiatry*, 20, 11–21.

Sebrechts, M.M., Mar sh, R.L., & Seamon, J.G. (1989). Secondary memory and very rapid forgetting. *Memory & Cognition*, 17, 693–700.

Segerstrom, S.C. and Miller, G.E. (2004) Psychological stress and the human immune system: a meta-analytic study of 30 years of inquiry. *Psychological Bulletin*, 130(4), 601–30.

Seligman, M.E.P. (1971) Phobias and preparedness. *Behavior Therapy*, 2, 307–20.

Selye, H.S. (1956) *The Stress of Life*. New York: McGraw-Hill.

Shah, P. and Miyake, A. (1996) The separability of working memory resources for spatial thinking and language processing: an individual differences approach. *Journal of Experimental Psychology: General*, 125, 4–27.

Shahar, G., Soffer, N. and Gilboa-Shechtman, E. (2008) Sociotropy, Autonomy, and Self-Criticism Are Three Distinguishable Dimensions of Cognitive-Personality Vulnerability. *Journal of Cognitive Psychotherapy: An International Quarterly*, 22(3), 219–227.

Shallice, T. and Warrington, E.K. (1970) Independent functioning of verbal and memory stores: a neuropsychological study. *Quarterly Journal of Experimental Psychology*, 22, 261–73.

Shekelle, R.B., Hulley, S.B. and Neaton, J.D. (1985) The MRFIT behaviour pattern study. II. Type A behaviour and incidence of coronary heart disease. *American Journal of Epidemiology*, 122, 559–70.

Shepard, R.N. and Feng, C.A. (1972) A chronometric study of mental paper folding. *Cognitive Psychology*, 3.

Shipley, R. H., & Boudewyns, P. A. (1980). Flooding and implosive therapy: are they harmful? *Behavior Therapy*, *ll*, 503–508.

Shorter, E. (1997) A *History of Psychiatry: from the Era of the Asylum to the Age of Prozac*. Chichester: John Wiley & Sons.

Shulman, H.G. (1970) Encoding and retention of semantic and phonemic information in short-term memory. *Journal of Verbal Learning and Verbal Behaviour*, 9(5), 499–508.

Siegel, S. (1984) Pavlovian conditioning and heroin overdose; reports by overdose victims, *Bulletin of the Psychonomic Society*, 22, 428–30.

Siffre, M. (1975) Six months in a cave alone. *National Geographic*, 147, 426–435.

Silver, R. & Kriegsfeld, L.J. (2014) Circadian rhythms have broad implications for understanding brain and behavior. *European Journal of neuroscience*, 39, 1866–1880.

Simon, G. E., Ornel, J., VonKoroff, M., Barlow, W. (1995) Health care costs associated with anxiety and depressive disorders in primary care. *American Journal of Psychiatry*, 152, 353–357.

Simon, H.A. (1974) How big is a chunk? *Science*, 183, 482–8.

Simpson H.B, Liebowitz M.R, Foa E.B. (2004) Post-treatment effects of exposure therapy and clomipramine in obsessive-compulsive disorder. *Depression and Anxiety*, 19(4), 225–233.

Skinner, B.F. (1938) *The Behavior of Organisms: An Experimental Analysis*. Cambridge.

Skinner, B.F. (1953) Science and human behavior, New York, NY, The Free Press.

Skinner, B.F. (1971) *Beyond freedom and dignity*, Harmondsworth, Penguin.

Skinner, B.F. (1974) *About Behaviourism*. New York: Knopf.

Slater, M., Antley, A., Davison, A., Swapp, D., Guger, C., Barker, C., Pistrang, N. and Sanchez Vives, M.V (2006) A virtual reprisal of the Stanley Milgram obedience experiments.

Sperling, G. (1960) The information available in brief visual presentations. *Psychology Monographs*, 74, 11, 498.

Sperry, R.W. (1982) Some effects of disconnecting the cerebral hemispheres. *Science*, 217, 1223–1226.

Squire LR, Knowlton B, and Musen G. (1993). The structure and organization of memory. *Annual Review of Psychology*, 44, 453– 495.

Stang, D.J. (1976) Group size effects on conformity. *Journal of Social Psychology*, 98, 175–81.

Stephan, K.K. & Zucker, I. (1972) Circadian rhythms in drinking behaviour and locomotor activity in rats eliminated by hypothalamic lesions. *Proceedings of the National Academy of Sciences*, 60, 1583–1586.

Stern, D. N. (1971) Micro analysis of mother infant interaction: behavior regulating social contact between a mother and three and a half month old twins, in Schaffer, H.R. *Mothering*, Fontana Press.

Stevens, R. (2007) Person psychology : Psychoanalytic and humanistic perspectives in Miell, D., Phoenix, A. and Thomas, K. (2007) *Mapping psychology*, 2, Milton Keynes, The Open University.

Stone, A.A. and Neale, J.M. (1984) New measure of daily coping: development and preliminary results. *Journal of Personality and Social Psychology*, 46, 892–906.

Szasz, T. (1972) *The Manufacture of Madness*. London: Routledge & Kegan Paul.

Tajfel, H., Billig, M., Bundy R.P. and Flament, C. (1971) Social categorisation and intergroup behaviour. *European Journal of Social Psychology*, 1, 149–77.

Taub, E., Uswatte, G. & Elbert, T. (2002) New treatments in neurorehabilitation founded on basic research. *Nature Reviews Neuroscience*, 3, 228–236.

Tennen, H., Affleck, G., Armeli, S. and Carney, M.A. (2000) A daily process approach to coping: linking theory, research and practice. *American Psychologist*, 55, 626–36.

Teuber, H.L. (1975) Recovery of function after brain injury in man. In 'Outcomes of severe damage to the nervous system.' *CIBA Foundation Symposium* 34. Amsterdam: Elsevier.

Thoren P, Asberg M, Bertilsson L, Mellstrom B, Sjoqvist F, Traskman L. (1980) Clomipramine treatment of obsessive–compulsive disorder. II. Biochemical aspects. *Archives of General Psychiatry* 37, 1289–1294.

Thorne, B. Person centred therapy. In Dryden, W. (2007) *Dryden's handbook of Individual therapy*, Sage, London.

Throne, L.C., Bartholomew, J.B. and Craig, J. (2000) Stress reactivity in fire fighters: an exercise intervention. *International Journal of Stress Management*, 7, 235–46.

Toates, F (2007) Biological Psychology in Miell, D., Phoenix, A. and Thomas, K. (2007) *Mapping psychology*, 1, Milton Keynes, The Open University.

Toates, F. (2012) Changing behavior in Brace, N., and Byford, J. *Investigating psychology*, Milton Keynes, the Open University.

Todd, J.J., & Marois, R. (2004). Capacity limit of visual short-term memory in human posterior parietal cortex. *Nature*, 428, 751–754.

Tolman, E.C. (1932) *Purposive behavior in Animals and Men*, New York, The Century Co.

Tolpin, M. (1993) The unmirrored self, compensatory structures, and cure: the exemplary case of Anna O. *The Annual of Psychoanalysis*, 21, 157–77.

Tomes, J.L. and Katz, A.N. (1997) Habitual susceptibility to misinformation and individual differences in eyewitness memory. *Applied Cognitive Psychology*, 11, 233–51.

Trevarthen C, Daniel, S. (2005) Disorganized rhythm and synchrony: Early signs of autism and Rett syndrome. *Brain & Development*, 27: S25–S34.

Tuckey, M.R. and Brewer, N. (2003) How schemas affect eyewitness memory over repeated retrieval attempts. *Applied Cognitive Psychology*, 7, 785–800.

Tulving, E., & Thompson, D. M. (1973). Encoding specificity and retrieval processes in episodic memory. *Psychological Review*, 80, 352–373.

Turk, D.J. (2002) Mike or me? Self-recognition in a split-brain patient. *Nature Neuroscience*, 5, 841–842.

Turner, J.C. (1991) *Social Influence*. Buckingham: Open University Press.

Turner, M. L. & Engle, R. W. (1989). Is working memory capacity task dependent? *Journal of Memory and Language*, 28, 127–154.

Uchino, B.N., Cacioppo, J.T. and Kiecolt-Glaser, J.K. (1996) The relationship between social support and physiological processes: a review with emphasis on underlying mechanisms and implications for health. *Psychological Bulletin*, 119, 488–531.

Ucros, C.G. (1989) Mood state-dependent memory: a meta-analysis. *Cognition and Emotion*, 3, 139–67.

Vaillant, G.E. (2003) Mental health. *American Journal of Psychiatry*, 160, 1373–84.

Van der Doef, M. and Maes, S. (1998) The job demand- control (-support) model and physical health outcomes: a review of the strain and buffer hypotheses. *Psychology and Health*, 13, 909–36.

Van IJzendoorn, M.H. and Kroonenberg, P.M. (1988) Cross-cultural patterns of attachment: a meta analysis of the Strange Situation. *Child Development*, 59, 147–56.

Veríssimo, M., Santos, A. J., Vaughn, B.E., Torres, N., Monteiro L., and Santos O. (2011) Quality of attachment to father and mother and number of reciprocal friends, *Early Child Development and Care*, 181(1), 27–38.

Villablanca, J.R. & Hovda, D.A. (2000) Developmental neuroplasticity in a model of cerebral hemispherectomy and stroke. *Neuroscience*, 95(3), 625–637.

Vitaliano, P.P., Maiuro, R.D. and Russo, J. (1990) Coping profiles associated with psychiatric, physical health, work and family problems. *Health Psychology*, 9, 348–76.

Vogt, T.M., Mullooly, J.P., Ernst, D., Pope, C.R. and Hollis, J.F. (1992) Social networks as predictors of ischemic heart disease, cancer, stroke and hypertension: incidence, survival and mortality. *Journal of Clinical Epidemiology*, 45, 659–66.

Warrington, E.K and Shallice, T. (1969) The selective impairment of auditory visual short term memory, *Brain*, 92, 885–96.

Waters, E., Merrick, S., Treboux, D., Crowell, J., and Albersheim, L. (2000) Attachment security in infancy and early adulthood: A twenty year longitudinal study in Hertzig, M. and Farber, E., (Eds) *Annual progress in child psychiatry and child development, 2000–2001*, Brunner Routledge, New York.

Watson, J. B. (1913) Psychology as the behaviorist views it. *Psychological Review*, 20, 158–177.

Watson, J. B. (1928) *Psychological care of infant and child*. New York, Harper and Bros.

Watson, J.B. and Rayner, R. (1920) Conditioned emotional reactions. *Journal of Experimental Psychology*, 3, 1–14.

Watson, S.L., Shiveley, C.A., Kaplan, J.R. and Line, S.W. (1998) Effects of chronic social separation on cardiovascular disease risk factors in female cynomolgus monkeys. *Atherosclerosis*, 137, 259–66.

Waugh, N.C. & Norman, D.A. (1965). Primary Memory. *Psychological Review, 72*, 89–104.

Wells, G.L., Small, M. and Penrod, S. (1998) Eyewitness identification procedures: recommendations for lineups and photospreads. *Law and Human Behaviour*, 22, 603–47.

Wernicke, C. (1874) Der aphasische Symptomenkomplex. Breslau: Cohn & Weigert.

Williams, J. and Warchal, J. (1981) Relationship between assertiveness, internal-external locus of control and overt conformity. *Journal of Psychology – Interdisciplinary and Applied*, 109(1), 93–6.

Willis, R.W. and Edwards, J.A. (1969)A study of the comparative effectiveness of systematic desensitization and implosion therapy. *Behaviour, Research and Therapy*, 7, 387–395.

Wise, S.P. and Rapoport, J.L. (1989). Obsessive-compulsive disorder: is it basal ganglia dysfunction? In Rapoport JL (ed.) *Obsessive-compulsive Disorder in Children and Adolescents*. American Psychiatric Press Inc., Bethesda, Maryland, 327–344.

Wolff, P.H. The causes, controls and organization of behavior in the neonate, in Schaffer, R. (1977) *Mothering*, Fontana Press.

Wolpe, J. (1958) *Psychotherapy by Reciprocal Inhibition*. Stanford: Stanford University Press.

Yuille, J.C., & Cutshall, J.L. (1986). A case study of eyewitness memory of a crime. *Journal of Applied Psychology*, 71(2), 291–301.

Zimbardo, P.G. (2006) On rethinking the psychology of tyranny: the BBC prison study. *British Journal of Social Psychology*, 45(1), 47–53.

Zimbardo, P.G., Banks, P.G., Haney, C. and Jaffe, D. (1973) Pirandellian Prison: the mind is a formidable jailor. *New York Times Magazine*, 8 April, 38–60.

Zimmerman, P., Becker-Stoll, F., Grossman, K., Scheurer- Englisch, H. and Wartner, U. (2000) Longitudinal attachment development from infancy through adolescence. *Psychologie in Erziehung und Unterricht*, 47(2), 99–117.

www.brin.ac.uk/figures/attitudes-towards-gay-rights

Index

C

G

H

I

J

K

L

M

N

O

P

Q

R

T

U

V

W

Y

Z